Introduction
to
Dynamic Systems

PRENTICE-HALL SERIES IN
ENGINEERING OF THE PHYSICAL SCIENCES
James B. Reswick and Warren M. Rohsenow, editors

PRENTICE-HALL INTERNATIONAL, INC., *London*
PRENTICE-HALL OF AUSTRALIA PTY., LTD., *Sydney*
PRENTICE-HALL OF CANADA, LTD., *Toronto*
PRENTICE-HALL OF INDIA PRIVATE LTD., *New Delhi*
PRENTICE-HALL OF JAPAN, INC., *Tokyo*

Introduction

to

Dynamic Systems

James B. Reswick

Professor of Engineering
and
Director of Engineering Design Center
Case Institute of Technology

Charles K. Taft

Associate Professor of
Mechanical Engineering
Case Institute of Technology

Prentice-Hall, Inc.　*Englewood Cliffs, New Jersey*

© 1967 by
PRENTICE-HALL, INC.
Englewood Cliffs, N. J.

Library of Congress Catalog Card Number 67-18929
Printed in the United States of America

Current printing (last digit):
10 9 8 7 6
 5 4 3 2 1

Preface

This text is intended to meet the needs of a one-semester course in dynamic systems and to provide a strong base from which all engineering students can move into the study of such fields as automatic control, applied mechanics, electric circuit analysis, systems engineering and process analysis. The existence of a common engineering method in these fields has long been evident, especially in mathematical modeling and analysis. The authors lean heavily on the unification which these techniques make possible but we also recognize that a thorough understanding of physical laws must come first. It is assumed that students bring some knowledge of electricity and mechanics from their first year studies. However, much space in this book is devoted to reinforcing these concepts and defining sufficient new concepts so that the student may solve real problems in mechanical, electrical and, to a limited extent, fluid systems.

The book has been written for sophomore engineering students. No professor knows how a young person really learns nor can he always gauge the most effective level and rate for presenting new material. On the assumption that authors sometimes err in the direction of an overly sophisticated treatment of their subject, we have attempted to cover important material in as simple a way as is possibly consistent with the background of second year college students.

New concepts and techniques often seem simple after they are understood and it is sometimes difficult for teachers to remember the blocks to learning which they themselves had to overcome. Recognizing that many such blocks confront the student we have attempted to call attention to those which we do remember by means of a marginal "logos" (a hand symbol) and informal footnotes. The reader is encouraged to add notes of his own.

A glance at the table of contents will show the subject matter and its organization. Suffice it to say here that we have presented mathematical model formulation and analysis of engineering systems in one of the many possible orders which seem logically consistent. Systems are viewed primarily in terms of their outputs (responses) due to their inputs (initial states and forcing functions) and they are characterized in terms of the mathematical relationships (differential equations and block diagrams) which relate those outputs to inputs. Calculations of dynamic responses are important but more important is the abstraction of a simplified model of a physical system and the evaluation of results in terms of the system design objectives. We hope the student will complete his course with an understanding of this truth, and will have developed a beginning of systems analysis capability.

Concering analytical methods let us point out that we have avoided the use of Laplace transform methods. We are sure the student will later come to learn of their effectiveness but we would have him first understand the algebraic basis of classic transient and steady-states solution techniques on which operational and computer methods are based. The use of D to replace d/dt appears as a tool to aid in block diagram formulation and algebraic manipulation of constant coefficient linear differential equations. We do admit to the use of $j\omega$ to define a complex frequency function and we add a heuristic treatment of the Fourier series. We hope this introduction will facilitate later learning.

It is difficult for us as authors to adequately acknowledge the sources of our ideas. Some may be our own but most of the thoughts stated here—and especially the attitudes with which they are expressed—come from our own teachers. Among the many deserving mention, John A. Hrones, Charles Stark Draper, George A. Philbrick, Jacob Den Hartog, and Donald P. Eckman would find something of themselves in our writing. Anthony Bartley (during his year at Case away from Newcastle-upon-Tyne) made many important contributions in writing and in addition, he transformed an errata-filled manuscript into a virtually error-free form. David Limbert carefully organized (and solved) the many problems at the ends of chapters. These problems have accrued in the authors' files over a period of many years. We have attempted to include only problems original with us, but good problems have a way of reappearing in many forms and it may be that our colleagues will find some old friends amongst them.

An early form of the manuscript was developed in conjunction with (but not supported by) NSF Grant No. G 23325.

JAMES B. RESWICK
CHARLES K. TAFT

Cleveland, Ohio

Contents

6. Approximate Transient Response 157

7. Second Order Differential Equation Transient Solution 183

1 *On Engineering and Dynamic Systems*

1.1 Introduction

Engineering is a purposeful activity. The engineer is characterized by his role in helping to bring into being something which has not existed before. He may have complete responsibility for the creation of an entire system; he may participate as a member of a team seeking to use materials and energy in the best way possible; from his own inspiration he may act as a lone inventor and create a new idea which may, by means of a patent, become real property; or he may participate in the utilization of new systems or devices by helping others to understand their use and to insure their maintenance and repair.

In many of these tasks, engineers employ the discoveries of physical science and find purpose for the methods of analysis and machine computation that are born in the mathematical sciences. To all of this, the engineer brings methodology. He is often faced with a complex task where the problem to be solved is not clear, where data necessary for a solution may be missing, and wherein the pressures of time, economic competition, and the exigencies of national defense may place constraints which force him to achieve less than optimum solutions. But he is never satisfied with a given solution, and as time and new science give deeper insight, he continues to improve past creations in a never-ending search for more optimum solutions. The task of seeking optimum results when the rules are not spelled out is perhaps the most characteristic nature of an engineer's activity.

Almost all systems with which the engineer works are dynamic. Even in the construction of bridges and buildings, the civil engineer must be concerned with the accumulation of stress and design for the effects of corrosion and other changes that occur over a long period and at the same time guard against destructive vibrations. An engineer must be concerned with variations in temperature and the effects of seasons. A search radar must rotate without error in any anticipated wind load; a bridge in the state of Washington once collapsed because of vibrations induced by the wind.

We are confronted with motion everywhere in our daily lives. The clocks which regulate our lives are inherently dynamic and provide the fundamental basis for all dynamic measurements. Our own body functions are ever changing. We drive, fly, ride, walk, are lifted by elevators and moving stairs; we read of missiles and antimissiles; we learn of the motions of molecules, atoms, and subatomic particles. All these things are dynamic systems and it is the study of such systems which enables the engineer to improve and understand those which now exist and to design new and better systems. Much of the essence of engineering is contained in the study of dynamic systems.

1.2 Modeling and Analysis

The process of moving from a real or proposed engineering system to an expression by means of which the behavior can be predicted is a major part of the engineering process. The steps by which this is usually done are as follows:

1.2–1 THEORETICAL MODELING

A system may be considered as an assembly of interacting units or components. These components and the ways in which they are affected by and act upon other components become the subject of analysis. Generally speaking, a component is characterized as a single functioning unit. This may be, for example, an electronic amplifier in one system or it may be a capacitor within an amplifier in another system. How to determine how small a system is and when a system becomes a component is one of those philosophical questions which really has no definitive answer. The situation is indicated in the following parody on the well-known poem about fleas:

> Great systems have little systems upon their backs to bite 'em,
> Little systems have lesser systems and so ad infinitum.

The engineer must bring judgment and experience to bear in

modeling systems or subsystems for analysis. His decision is usually based on how far he needs to go in order to achieve his purpose. When he deals with a very large complex system such as an air traffic control system, he may need to consider only the individual aircraft as the system components. On the other hand, if he is designing a hydraulic boost system to move the control surfaces of a large jet aircraft, he must consider each check valve, piece of pipe, cylinder, and accumulator as individual components of his system.

Whether his system is large or small, the engineer will represent it by a mathematical model. Such a model always involves approximation and assumptions which must never be lost sight of. No mathematical model can precisely represent any physical object or device. Even the simplest element requires a sophisticated mathematical equation to represent it with great accuracy. Nature is exceedingly complicated and the phenomena which may seem at the time relatively simple are usually much more difficult to represent by mathematical equations than we realize. Thus, the engineer is continually making approximations to what is happening in nature and these approximations restrict the range of validity of the equations.

The model should include all important characteristics of the system and generally should not include those which are unimportant. The decision in each case between those which are important and those which are unimportant is sometimes obvious and straightforward and other times requires great physical insight and intuition. Experience plays an important role in such decisions and it is very important that, whatever decisions are made, all assumptions, limitations, and approximations are clearly stated and not forgotten. In the process of mathematically modeling a device, it is desirable to find out what is happening inside of the device physically and to determine the important phenomena involved in its operation. From physical principles and the mathematical equations which describe these principles, a mathematical expression may be developed to describe the device. Often the degree of approximation can only be determined experimentally, and in the mathematical model there may be unknown parameters which must be evaluated through actual tests.

1.2–2 EXPERIMENTAL MODELING

Often the physical principles which govern the behavior of a system element are not completely defined and at times it is impossible to "see inside" clearly enough to formulate a mathematical model a priori. In such cases the "black box" experimental modeling process may be used. In this process the element is usually subjected to a set of known inputs and its outputs are measured. From the input-output relationships a mathematical model can sometimes be deduced. The generality of such models depends to a great extent on what is known or may be assumed about the structure of the element. When the structure is known, a few tests can suffice to characterize general equations, but when little is known of the structure a wide variety of inputs are required to determine its characteristics with any great accuracy. This technique is at present one of the core problems in the control of many physical systems. Such systems as economic systems, steam power plants, and many chemical processes can only be controlled satisfactorily if one is able to write mathematical equations describing them. However, these processes or systems are so complicated that it is difficult to write such mathematical equations. Thus, the techniques of experimental modeling are usually employed. The process is very much in its infancy and much work remains to be done before the necessary tools are available to model all types of physical systems experimentally with any degree of accuracy.

1.2–3   MATHEMATICAL ANALYSIS

Having achieved a mathematical representation or model, the system may now be analyzed. This is a purely mathematical operation and it may be done by a person with pencil and paper or it may be accomplished by means of an analogue or digital computer. While the methods of analysis may be extremely sophisticated and require a great deal of effort to learn their use, nevertheless mathematical analysis often becomes a relatively routine step in the total analytical problem.

1.2–4   ENGINEERING SYNTHESIS AND DECISION MAKING

In the fourth step, the engineer interprets and applies the results of his analysis to his basic task. The analysis may indicate that a proposed design will not work or it may indicate that it might work. Often the analysis is formulated in such a way that various parameters in the problem may be varied so that a number of solutions can be produced. The engineer may then compare these solutions and by noting the interplay of effects such as cost, safety, reliability, time for completion, size, and weight, reach a decision on the most optimum course of action. This decision making process is one of the fundamental parts of engineering and is the essence of synthesis activity. In this process, methods of analysis may be used in reaching good decisions. In fact, in some cases, it is possible to program a modern digital computer to automate such decision making. But whether the engineer says, "This looks best to me; let's do it", or whether a large scale computer prints out a course of action, it should be kept in mind that the first goal of engineering activity is to formulate a situation or problem so that an engineering analysis may be employed.

2 Formulation of Differential Equations in Mechanical Systems

2.1 Introduction

We have discussed the engineering approach to the solution of problems in the previous chapter. At the heart of this method is the formulation or construction of a model which can be analyzed by the engineer. This model may take the form of a mathematical expression or it may be contained only in a diagram of interactions which in a sense is a picture of the mathematical model. In dynamic systems the most powerful mathematical model takes the form of a differential equation which is an algebraic relationship that describes the system behavior at an instant in time. Later we shall use this equation to find the system behavior for all time.

2.2 Mass and Inertia

The concept of mass and inertia is well developed in most first year courses in physics. It is assumed that the student has completed such a course. The following material considered as background is outlined below. This work may be found in most beginning physics texts.

Particle Dynamics
    (1) Newton's First Law of Motion

(2) Force

(3) Concept of Mass: Newton's Second Law of Motion

(4) Newton's Third Law of Motion

(5) Mass Standards, Systems of Mechanical Units

(6) Weight and Mass

(7) A Static Procedure for Measuring Forces

(8) Some Applications of Newton's Laws of Motion

Conservation of Linear Momentum

(1) Center of Mass

(2) Motion of Center of Mass

Rotational Dynamics

(1) Rotational Variables

(2) Torque or Moment of a Force

(3) Kinetic Energy of Rotation and Rotational Inertia

(4) Rotational Dynamics of a Rigid Body

(5) Combined Translational and Rotational Motion of a Rigid Body

2.3   Principle of d'Alembert

We will find that a slight rearrangement of Newton's second law leads to a useful concept for formulating differential equations. This is the idea of d'Alembert—that instead of thinking of acceleration as resulting from the application of a force, one can think of the same problem as an equilibrium situation wherein the sum of all external forces is opposed by a fictitious inertia force. A total equilibrium equation results wherein all forces, including inertia forces (and in the case of rotational systems, all torques, including inertia torques), are set equal to zero. This concept becomes very useful in mechanical problems which include combined rotation and translation when the center of gravity undergoes acceleration.

We shall illustrate d'Alembert's principle by considering the plane motion of the rigid body shown in Fig. 2.1(a).

$\sum \vec{F}$ is the vector sum of all the forces acting on the body and is shown offset from the center of gravity through the perpendicular distance b.

We can replace $\sum \vec{F}$ by a force of the same magnitude and direction acting *through* the center of gravity plus a torque or couple T of magnitude $b \sum F$ as shown in Fig. 2.1(b) (i.e., the force systems shown in Fig. 2.1(a) and (b) are equivalent).

---

 d'Alembert is pronounced Dalmbear.

It is apparent from Fig. 2.1(b) that the body will suffer rotation as well as translation and we therefore define a_{cg} as the positive linear acceleration of the center of gravity and α as the positive angular acceleration of the body.

We can then write in accordance with Newton's laws,

$$\sum \vec{F} = M \vec{a}_{cg} \qquad (2.1a)$$

and

$$\sum T_{cg} = T = J_{cg} \alpha \qquad (2.1b)$$

where M is the mass of the body and J_{cg} is the moment of inertia about a perpendicular axis through the center of gravity.

Now Eq. 2.1a can be rewritten as follows:

$$\sum \vec{F} - M \vec{a}_{cg} = 0 \qquad (2.2a)$$

This tells us that the sum of the externally applied forces minus the vector $M \mathbf{a}_{cg}$ is equal to zero. If we regard $-M \mathbf{a}_{cg}$ as a force, then the equation can be interpreted to mean that the sum of *all* the forces (including $-M \mathbf{a}_{cg}$) is equal to zero, i.e., that the forces are in equilibrium.

Similarly, we can write for Eq. 2.1b that

$$T - J_{cg} \alpha = 0 \qquad (2.2b)$$

and deduce that all the torques are in equilibrium providing that we interpret $-J_{cg} \alpha$ as a torque.

This result may appear to be trivial but in fact it has a practical significance since it tells us that a body in plane motion [Fig. 2.1(b)] can be treated as a body in equilibrium providing that we add a fictitious inertia force and a fictitious inertia torque as shown in Fig. 2.1(c).

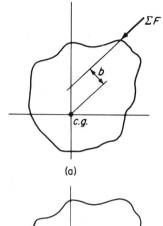

(a)

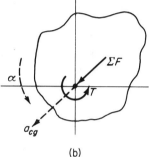

(b)

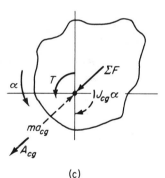

(c)

Figure 2.1

The student should verify this proposition for himself.
Try taking moments about any point. ☆

The concept presented above is d'Alembert's principle and the fictitious inertia forces and torques are sometimes called d'Alembert forces or d'Alembert torques.

The main advantage of d'Alembert's principle compared with the straightforward application of Newton's laws is that it frees us from the constraint of always having to consider the action of forces about an axis through the center of gravity. Instead, we can, if we wish, choose an axis through some other point and there are many situations in which it proves advantageous to do so.

If we do use the d'Alembert principle to enable us to consider forces about an axis other than that through the center of gravity, then the torque equilibrium equation will differ from Eq. 2.2b since it will have to include a term representing the moments of the d'Alembert inertia forces about the new axis. This can be shown as follows:

Figure 2.2 shows our rigid body subjected to an offset force as before. Let P be any point in the body with coordinates $\bar{x}$ and $\bar{y}$ relative to the center of gravity. In addition, let us assume that the perpendicular distance between point P and the line of action of the force is r.

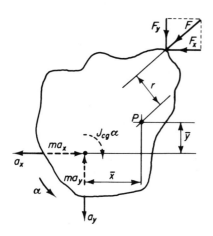

We specify that force F has components F_x and F_y and that the positive components of linear acceleration of the center of gravity in the x- and y-directions are a_x and a_y.

According to d'Alembert's principle, the inertia forces will be Ma_x and Ma_y acting in directions opposite to the assumed positive linear accelerations while the inertia torque will be $J_{cg}\alpha$ acting in a direction opposite to the assumed positive angular acceleration.

Figure 2.2

We can now write the equations of equilibrium as follows.
Equilibrium of forces in the x- and y-directions

$$F_x - Ma_x = 0 \qquad (2.3a)$$

$$F_y - Ma_y = 0 \qquad (2.3b)$$

Equilibrium of torques about point P

$$Fr + Ma_x \bar{y} - Ma_y \bar{x} - J_{cg}\alpha = 0 \qquad (2.3c)$$

Note that the moment of a couple is the same at all points in a body.

Equations 2.3a, b, and c can be expressed in a more general form as follows.

$$\sum \vec{F} + \vec{F}_{\text{inertia}} = 0 \tag{2.4a}$$

$\sum$ torques about $P = \sum T_P(\text{external}) + \sum$ moment of inertia forces

$$+\ T_{\text{inertia}} = 0 \tag{2.4b}$$

where

$$\vec{F}_{\text{inertia}} = -M\vec{a}_{cg}$$

$$T_{\text{inertia}} = -J_{cg}\alpha$$

Although the analysis above demonstrates the utility of d'Alembert's method for considering forces about an axis other than the center of gravity it does not illustrate the advantages of using such an axis. This can be shown best by considering a practical example.

Figure 2.3(a) shows the classical problem of a cylinder rolling down an inclined plane without slip. Since there is no slip there must be a friction force F_f acting up the plane. There will also be a normal force F_n acting through the point of contact and a gravitational force Mg acting vertically downward through the center of gravity.

We shall assume that the positive linear acceleration of the center of gravity parallel to the plane is a_{cg} and that the positive angular acceleration is α.

If the radius of the cylinder is R then we can write

$$a_{cg} = R\alpha$$

In order to calculate α by the conventional application of Newton's laws we have to write two equations.

(1) Linear motion parallel to the plane:

$$Mg \sin \theta - F_f = Ma_{cg}$$

(2) Rotational motion about the center of gravity:

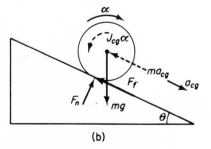

(a)

(b)

Figure 2.3

$$F_f R = J_{cg} \alpha$$

Eliminating F_f from these equations we find,

$$M a_{cg} + \frac{J_{cg} \alpha}{R} = Mg \sin \theta$$

or

$$M R \alpha + \frac{J_{cg} \alpha}{R} = Mg \sin \theta$$

i.e.,

$$\alpha = \frac{MgR \sin \theta}{MR^2 + J_{cg}}$$

Now let us attempt the same problem using d'Alembert's principle. First of all, we insert the fictitious inertia force $M a_{cg}$ and the fictitious inertia torque $J_{cg} \alpha$ insuring that these "forces" oppose the directions of the positively assumed a_{cg} and α, respectively.

We can now treat the cylinder as though it were in equilibrium under the action of all the forces and torques shown [Fig. 2.3(b)]. We are also free to sum torques about any point in the body and in this case it is advantageous to sum torques about the point of contact between cylinder and plane because this eliminates the forces F_f and F_n; i.e.,

$$MgR \sin \theta - J_{cg} \alpha - M a_{cg} R = 0$$

or

$$MgR \sin \theta = J_{cg} \alpha + MR^2 \alpha$$

hence

$$\alpha = \frac{MgR \sin \theta}{MR^2 + J_{cg}}$$

Since this is a rather simple problem, there is not much to choose from between the two methods as far as ease of solution is concerned. However, it does demonstrate that the d'Alembert approach leads more directly to the final answer since we only needed to derive one equation instead of two, using Newton's laws.

The d'Alembert approach will be used more or less exclusively from now on because it greatly facilitates the setting up of *free body diagrams* from which our mathematical models of mechanical systems will be derived. Before discussing this, however, we shall consider the mechanical elements such as springs and dampers which are used in the modeling of mechanical systems.

2.4 The Spring

While an ideal mass remains rigid when acted upon by an outside force, a spring will not remain rigid and its parts will move with respect to each other. Nearly all materials tend to resist deformation or relative motion of their constituent parts. Thus, a spring can be defined as a mechanical element which can be deformed by an external force. We shall assume further that the deformation is directly proportional to the force applied to the spring. A spring can take many geometrical forms as shown in Fig. 2.4. In all these springs the force or torque required to deflect the spring is nearly proportional to the deflection or deformation.

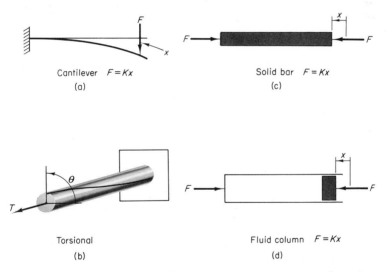

Cantilever $F = Kx$
(a)

Solid bar $F = Kx$
(c)

Torsional
(b)

Fluid column $F = Kx$
(d)

Fig. 2.4. Mechanical springs.

Consider the bar spring shown in Fig. 2.4(c). Hooke's law states that for a wide range of force there is a linear relationship between stress and unit deformation for the bar as in Eq. 2.5:

$$\frac{S}{e} = Y \tag{2.5}$$

where *stress*, S, is defined as the force on the bar divided by the area of the bar perpendicular to the force. *Strain*, e, is defined as the change in bar length divided by the unstressed bar length. The constant Y is called Young's modulus. This relationship is valid for small strains in most solid materials. If the strain becomes large, the material will either break or yield like taffy and Hooke's law no longer applies.

As the force on the bar in the direction shown in Fig. 2.4(c) is increased, the area of the bar perpendicular to the force will increase. However, if the force is kept small this increase in area with force will be small and we can write

$$AS = F \tag{2.6}$$

where A is the area of the unstressed bar perpendicular to the force. In addition, according to the definition of strain given above,

$$\epsilon = \frac{\Delta L}{L} \tag{2.7}$$

where L is the unstressed bar length and ΔL is the change in length or the amount of deformation.

Hooke's law can be rewritten in terms of the force and the deformation.

$$\frac{FL}{\Delta LA} = Y$$

or

$$F = \left(\frac{AY}{L}\right)\Delta L \tag{2.8}$$

Thus, the force F is proportional to the deformation ΔL. The constant of proportionality is called the spring constant K, so that

$$K = \frac{AY}{L} \tag{2.9}$$

This expression relates the "stiffness" of the spring as expressed by the spring constant to the bar area, the length, and the elastic properties of its material. For example, an iron bar one square inch in area and two inches long would have a spring constant of

$$K = \frac{1 \times 28.5 + 10^6}{2} = 14.25 \times 10^6 \text{ lb/in.}$$

where $Y = 28.5 \times 10^6$ psi for iron. That is, it would take a force of 14,250 lb to shorten the bar 0.001 in.

A fluid can also be used as a spring. A sketch of such a fluid spring is shown in Fig. 2.3(d). Here a fluid is confined inside a cylinder which is closed by a movable piston. It is assumed that the piston permits no fluid leakage and that there is no friction between the piston and the cylinder. The bulk modulus of a fluid can be used to relate its deformation to the stress applied to it. Unlike the bar, it is impossible to stress an unconfined fluid in a particular direction. Hence the stress acts everywhere in the fluid and is uniform within the fluid. Recognizing this difference, it is possible to write Hooke's law for a fluid, considering its change in volume with pressure. That is,

$$\frac{V \cdot \Delta P}{\Delta V} \equiv \beta \tag{2.10}$$

where ΔP is the change in pressure above atmospheric pressure in the fluid, ΔV is the change in fluid *volume* V due to this change in pressure, and β is defined as the bulk modulus of the fluid. β is nearly a constant for most fluids. Its value depends on how heat is transferred to or from the fluid as it is compressed. The change in pressure and volume of the fluid in the fluid spring can be related to the cylinder dimensions,

$$\Delta P = \frac{F}{A} \tag{2.11}$$

where F is the applied force and A is the area of the piston. The fluid volume can also be related to the cylinder dimensions.

$$V = AL \quad \text{and} \quad \Delta V = A \Delta L \tag{2.12}$$

L is the length of the fluid column constrained in the cylinder when the force is zero. The bulk modulus definition can then be rewritten.

$$\frac{FL}{A \Delta L} = \beta$$

or

$$F = \frac{A\beta}{L} \Delta L \tag{2.13}$$

This relation is of the form

$$F = K \Delta L \tag{2.14}$$

where $K = A\beta/L$ is the spring constant. If the fluid used were oil,

$$\beta = 2.7 \times 10^5 \text{ psi.}$$

Hence, an oil spring of one square inch area and two inch length would have a spring constant of

$$K = \frac{1 \times 2.7 \times 10^5}{2} = 1.35 \times 10^5 \text{ lb/in.}$$

Notice that the oil spring is about $1/100$ as stiff as the iron spring of the same dimensions.

The fluid in the spring could also be air. In this case the spring constant could be determined from the thermodynamic properties of the air. It is possible to express a relation between the pressure and density of a gas during a polytropic process which is valid for so-called perfect gases; that is, gases which are far from their critical temperatures and pressures. In this case,

$$\frac{P_a}{\rho^n} = C \tag{2.15}$$

where P_a is the absolute gas pressure assuming that the pressure is everywhere uniform in the cylinder; ρ is the gas density and n is a constant which depends on the process and how heat is transferred to the cylinder. If the gas remains at a constant temperature, then n equals one and the equation is the same as the state equation for a perfect gas. This assumes that the piston moves slowly and all heat generated inside the cylinder is transferred to the outside. If the piston moves quickly in a frictionless cylinder which is well insulated so that no heat flows in or out, n equals 1.4 for air and the process is called isentropic.

The gas pressure and density are related to the cylinder dimensions as follows:

$$AP_a = F + AP_e \tag{2.16}$$

where A is the piston area, F is the force exerted on the piston, and P_e is atmospheric pressure which acts with the external force on the piston. The density of the gas in the cylinder can be related to cylinder dimensions,

$$\rho = \frac{M}{AL} \tag{2.17}$$

where M is the mass of gas inside the cylinder. Since no leakage is assumed, M is a constant. L is the length of the gas column and A is its area.

In order to establish the relationship between the change in gas column length ΔL and force F, it is necessary to find an expression for ΔL. This can be done by substituting the relations for pressure and density into the process equation and differentiating. Hence:

$$\frac{F/A + P_e}{(M/AL)^n} = C \qquad (2.18)$$

Differentiating this expression yields

$$\frac{dF/A}{(M/AL)^n} + n\left(\frac{F}{A} + P_a\right)\left(\frac{A}{M}\right)^n L^{n-1} dL = 0$$

Then

$$dF = -\frac{An(F/A + P_e)}{L} dL \qquad (2.19)$$

If the initial force is zero, then $F = dF$ and considering small changes in L, $dL = -\Delta L$. So, $F = An/L(F/A + P_e)\Delta L$.

For forces which are small compared with $P_e A$, the relationship between force and displacement is identical in form to that derived for the bar spring and the oil spring. In this case, the spring constant is:

$$K = \frac{AnP_e}{L} \qquad (2.20)$$

If the air spring is uninsulated and moves slowly, the temperature will remain constant so that $n = 1$. Then for a spring of one square inch area and two inch length:

$$K = \frac{1 \times 1 \times 14.7}{2} = 7.3 \text{ lb/in.}$$

Note that the oil spring is about 20,000 times stiffer than the air spring.

In all these examples the change in length of the spring was shown to be nearly proportional to the applied force. Hence, if we define the positions of the end of the spring by separate coordinates, as pictured in Fig. 2.5, we obtain the following relationships:

$$F = K(x_2 - x_1) + K\delta_0 \qquad (2.21)$$

$$\Delta F = K(\Delta x_2 - \Delta x_1) \qquad (2.22)$$

Both ends of the spring move in the same direction even though the forces on each end are in opposite directions. This can really happen—think about it.

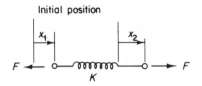

Fig. 2.5. The spring.

Note that our picture shows the spring having been deflected from its initial position by a force applied to each end. The spring is assumed to be massless and since only the two forces act at each end, according to Eq. 2.3 they must be equal. When formulating equations for a spring, it is necessary to worry about initial deflections and forces in the spring. Thus, in Eq. 2.21, x_1 and x_2 are shown as variables measured from initial positions where they are zero but where, in fact, the spring still exerts a force. That initial force is given by the term, $K\delta_0$. δ_0 is the static deflection of one end of the spring relative to the other end from its no-force condition. When we are interested only in the changes in force which result from changes in the variables, the initial force does not appear in the equation as indicated in Eq. 2.22 where the symbol Δ is used to represent a change in the force from some initial position. The proportionality between deflection and force exhibited in springs is the so-called spring constant K. The units of K are given by the defining relationships as follows:

$$\begin{array}{ccc} \textit{English} & \textit{mks} & \textit{cgs} \\ K = Fx = \text{pound/feet} & \text{or} \quad \text{newton/meter} & \text{or} \quad \text{dyne/centimeter} \end{array}$$

The assumption that a spring is linear (has a straight line force-deflection curve) is clearly arbitrary. We know that when a spring is stretched, a point is reached where the force per unit displacement begins to change. Finally, we reach a point where we can stretch it no farther or else we manage to break it. Thus, the assumption of linearity may be quite excellent for relatively small motions, but it may be very poor for rather large motions, as shown in the bar and fluid spring examples. In addition, all springs have mass. We must assume that the inertia forces due to accelerations of the spring are small compared with the spring forces. When this is not true, as sometimes occurs, a different problem results. From an analytical point of view, one must always check such an assumption against the final result to see if it is compatible. From a designing point of view, it may mean that the designer must insure that his spring is designed to remain linear over the region of its intended use; on the other hand he may want to make it intentionlly nonlinear.

2.5 The Dashpot or Damper

The dashpot or linear damper is a mechanism which dissipates energy in the form of heat rather than storing it as the mass and the spring do. There are many engineering systems where it is desirable to get rid of stored energy for improved performance. The automobile shock absorber and the pneumatic door closer are two examples.

It is in the damper that we probably must stretch our credulity the most in assuming a linear relationship (that is, its force is proportional to a variable or its derivative). We would like to assume that all dampers produce a force which is proportional to the relative velocity of their two parts. The automobile shock absorber, which looks the most like our picture, approaches this requirement only approximately and sometimes acts differently in one direction than in the other. There are many examples, however, where damping may be assumed sufficiently linear so that the model we will propose will be valid in our analysis. At this point, let us say that the equations which result from other than the assumption of linearity are many times more difficult to handle than those which result from the linear assumption. This point is illustrated in some detail in Chap. 4; Fig. 2.6 shows a schematic drawing of a damper. The force relationships are given in Eq. 2.23.

$$F = B\left(\frac{dx_2}{dt} - \frac{dx_1}{dt}\right) \qquad (2.23)$$

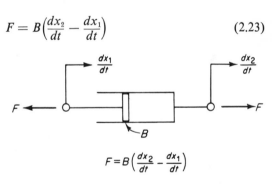

Fig. 2.6. The dashpot or damper.

Since the damper elements are assumed to be essentially massless (this is not always true), we assume as in the case of the spring that the only forces which act must be at each end and are therefore

Both ends of the dashpot move in the same direction even though the forces on each end are in opposite directions. This happens because one end (the right) moves faster than the other.

equal. Equation 2.23 implies that for the forces in the direction shown, dx_2/dt is greater than dx_1/dt. This is inherent in the concept that the dashpot dissipates the work done by the forces as they move. We note that the force acting on a damper is proportional only to the velocity difference and therefore the initial position of the elements does not appear in Eq. 2.23

The units of the damping constant B may be derived from the defining relationship as follows:

$$B = \frac{F}{v} = \left(\frac{\text{pound-second}}{\text{feet}}\right) \quad \text{or} \quad \left(\frac{\text{newton-second}}{\text{meter}}\right) \quad \text{or} \quad \left(\frac{\text{dyne-second}}{\text{centimeter}}\right)$$

One of the few cases where linear damping is clearly the major effect occurs when a flat plate is drawn slowly across a thin film of fluid in a way that insures a constant film thickness. The force is proportional to velocity and is given by Newton's law of viscous shear in Eqs. 2.24 and 2.25.

Newton's law of viscous shear:

$$\tau = \mu \frac{dv}{dy} \tag{2.24}$$

then $\tau =$ shear stress
$\mu =$ coefficient of viscosity
$dv/dy =$ velocity gradient across film

Thus

$$\frac{F}{A} = \frac{\mu}{h} \cdot v \qquad F = \frac{\mu A}{h} v = Bv \tag{2.25}$$

Figure 2.7 illustrates the flat plate linear damper and Fig. 2.8 shows the equivalent form in rotation. Dampers are often built in the form shown in Fig. 2.8 and represent one of the most reliable ways to achieve linear damping in engineering systems.

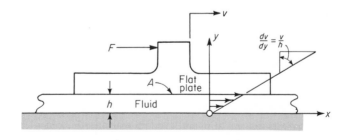

Fig. 2.7.   A flat plate linear damper.

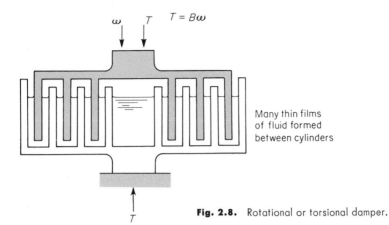

Fig. 2.8. Rotational or torsional damper.

2.6   Sources of Force and Motion in Mechanical Systems

So far the three basic elements of all mechanical systems, namely masses, springs, and dampers, have been modeled mathematically. There must also be a force which causes the motion of a mechanical system; namely, an input or a disturbing force. This force can be derived in many ways. For example, it can be exerted by a gravitational field on the body. It may be due to an electromagnetic field. It may arise from the impingement of a fluid on the body, such as wind blowing on a sail or a sign. In most cases, however, the force exerted on the system will not be independent of the motion of the system. For example, if the force on the system is exerted by a spring, then as the system moves, the end of the spring will move and, in general, will change the force upon the system. As another example, if a force is exerted by wind impinging upon a sign, a motion of the sign will tend to change the force. There are, however, many cases in which the force is nearly independent of the motion of the body and in these cases it is assumed that the force is being exerted by a force source. In other cases the motion of some part of the system is maintained nearly independent of the forces required to sustain this motion. As mentioned before, in general the force required to sustain motion will vary with the motion. However, in some cases this variation is very small compared to the forces available. For example, if one were to consider the effect upon the hand in moving a needle toward a piece of thread, the reduction in force applied to

---

For some reason the concept of sources of force and motion is difficult for
students. Just remember that most sources have *both* force and motion at the same
time. Read Sec 2.6 carefully and think about it.

the needle due to its accelerations is rather insignificant compared to the force available to move the needle.

A practical force source can be generated by means of a very weak spring as shown in Fig. 2.9. If one end of a weak spring is

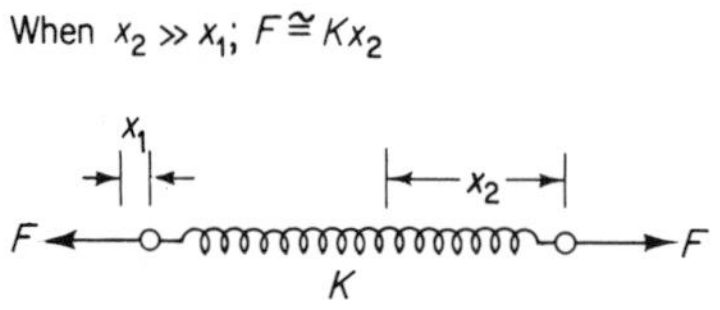

When $x_2 \gg x_1$; $F \cong K x_2$

x_1

F ◄─────o─⌇⌇⌇⌇⌇⌇⌇⌇⌇⌇⌇⌇⌇─o────►F
K

Fig. 2.9. The "weak" spring as a "force source."

moved through large prescribed amplitudes and the other end is constrained to move through small amplitudes, the force in the spring is essentially that due to the large amplitude motion. Thus, a weak spring transforms a motion source into a force source since the force F is nearly independent of x_1.

The motion source is more familiar. Cranks and connecting rods, levers, gears, etc., often comprise motion sources. A record groove acting on a needle in a hi-fi pickup is a good example of a motion source. Figure 2.10 shows a so-called "Scotch Yoke" mechanism which produces a sinusoidal or *simple harmonic* motion from a crank rotating at a constant speed.

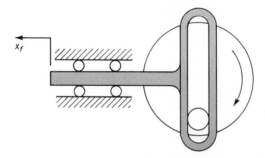

Fig. 2.10. An example of a motion source. The "Scotch Yoke" which produces a sinusoidal or simple harmonic motion.

If crank is made to move at constant speed as when driven through a great flywheel, x_f is independent and sinusoidal.

2.7 Free Body Diagrams

In the figures which show each of the mechanical elements, the element itself has been shown as if floating in space with forces acting upon it. These diagrams are *free body diagrams*. It would be difficult to overstate the importance of the free body diagram in formulating differential equations in mechanical systems. The free body diagram is a symbolic form which permits the variables and the forces to which they are related, to be shown in their proper relationships. Considerable confusion and many mistakes can result from attempting to formulate differential equations without carefully drawing free body diagrams. More will be said about this in the section which follows.

2.8　Formulation of Differential Equations in Mechanical Systems

The subject of formulating equations in mechanical systems is worthy of a course in itself when treated in its entirety. In fact, a great part of any course in mechanics is devoted to this subject. The problem of defining the reference frame and coordinates of displacement for the elements which appear in mechanical systems is often not trivial. We have seen that the forces which act between these elements may be proportional to their acceleration, velocity, or displacements, as the case may be. It is vital then that these displacements and their derivatives be defined carefully.

When combined translation and rotation in a plane is present or when the motions are more complex in three dimensions, the geometrical relationships between the variables can become very complicated and it is not within the scope of this text to deal with all these problems. We shall therefore restrict ourselves to very simple cases which are members of a class of problems which can be very complex. That is, all the problems will deal with systems which translate in one dimension and/or rotate about one axis. In general a body can translate in 3 dimensions and rotate about 3 perpendicular axes. The rules and concepts to be presented here are fundamental and will work in the most complex situations if carefully applied. We shall, however, limit our examples to relatively simple linear or rotational coordinate systems.

We shall set down a series of steps which, if followed carefully, will lead to correct formulations in all mechanical systems. The best way to elaborate on the points within these steps is through specific examples. We shall, therefore, set the steps down in brief form and then illustrate their application in several instances.

System definition:

 (1) Recognize all variables (degrees of freedom).
 (2) Define a suitable set of reference frames.

Most students *hate* to draw free body diagrams. Please take our word for it— they are worth the trouble.

We believe these steps are the most important ones in this book. Follow them carefully every time.

(3) Select a set of a minimum number of independent variables in case some are redundant.
(4) Assign sign conventions to variables and their derivatives.
(5) Make a careful scale drawing with every variable shown as not zero.
(6) Show vectors for positive conventions (show displacements, velocities, and accelerations—linear and rotational—positive in the same directions).
(7) Make definite assumptions of relative magnitudes of variables when displaced and show these on a sketch.

Isolate each rigid body:

Show *all* external forces and torques acting at and about centers of gravity including inertia forces and torques.

Inertia forces act opposite to positive total acceleration and are given by:

$$\vec{\mathbf{F}}_{\text{inertia}} = -M\vec{\mathbf{a}}_{cg} \tag{2.26}$$

Inertia torques act opposite to positive total angular acceleration and are given by:

$$T_{\text{inertia}} = -J_{cg}\alpha \tag{2.27}$$

External reaction forces should be expressed in terms of the system variables. These expressions are formed from a knowledge of the system elements.

Formulation of differential equations:

Apply the equilibrium equations of d'Alembert to each rigid body.

$$\sum \vec{\mathbf{F}}_{\text{ext}} + \vec{\mathbf{F}}_i = 0 \quad \text{(in any direction)} \tag{2.4a}$$

$$\sum T_{\text{ext}} + \sum \text{moments of inertia forces} + T_i = 0 \quad \text{(about any point)} \tag{2.4b}$$

Reduction:

(1) Group terms in differential equations so that terms containing the same variables are together.
(2) For two or more equations, write terms so that like terms form columns of a matrix. For example, if x_1, x_2, and x_3 are system variables, a set of typical equations might appear as Eq. 2.28, 2.29, and 2.30.*

---

*In Eqs. 2.28, 2.29, and 2.30, Newton's notation for differentiation with respect to time is introduced: $dx/dt = \dot{x}$; $d^2x/dt^2 = \ddot{x}$.

$$M_1\ddot{x}_1 + B_1\dot{x}_1 + K_1 x_1 \quad -K_2 x_2 \quad +0 = F(t) \tag{2.28}$$

$$-K_2 x_1 \quad +M_2\ddot{x}_2 + B_2\dot{x}_2 + K_2 x_2 \quad -K_3 x_3 = 0 \tag{2.29}$$

$$0 \quad -K_3 x_2 \quad +M_3\ddot{x}_3 + B_3\dot{x}_3 + K_3 x_3 = 0 \tag{2.30}$$

A classical dynamic system is that shown in Fig. 2.11, the so-called mass-spring-dashpot system. Figure 2.11 is intended merely to state the parameters and nature of the system.

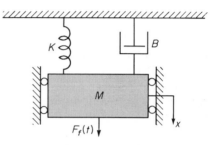

We notice that the mass is drawn so that it is constrained to move in the x direction only. Thus, one coordinate, namely x, is sufficient to define its position at any time. We may assume that all forces act through the center of gravity since rotational movements

Fig. 2.11. The mass-spring-dashpot system.

are prohibited by massless side rollers. Our next step is to show the system displaced, choose a reference frame, designate variables and coordinates, and assign positive directions to displacements, derivatives, and forces. This is done in Fig. 2.12, where we measure x from the static equilibrium point.

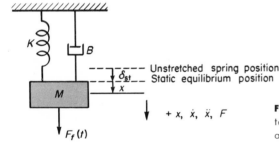

Fig. 2.12. "Displaced" diagram to show variables, coordinates, and sign conventions.

Next a figure of a rigid body (mass) is drawn with all forces acting on it, including the inertia force. Since rotary motion is prohibited, we do not need to show them acting through the center of gravity. However, the effect is the same as if they did. The free body diagram is shown in Fig. 2.13.

We now apply Eq. 2.3 to form a differential equation:

$$\Sigma\,\vec{F} + \vec{F}_i = 0$$

$$-B\dot{x} - Kx - K\delta_{st} + F_f(t) + Mg - M\ddot{x} = 0 \tag{2.31}$$

Since $Mg = K\delta_{st}$, from Fig. 2.12 we write

$$M\ddot{x} + B\dot{x} + Kx = F_f(t) \qquad (2.32)$$

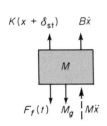

Fig. 2.13. Free body diagram.

Equation 2.32 is the desired differential equation. *Note that the gravity force or weight of the mass does not appear in the equation. This happened because we chose to measure our displacement from the position of static equilibrium.* Check by noting the effect of x, $\dot{x}$, and F_f upon acceleration. As in Fig. 2.13, a displacement x or velocity $\dot{x}$ tends to oppose $F_f(t)$ so that the acceleration $\ddot{x}$ is decreased.

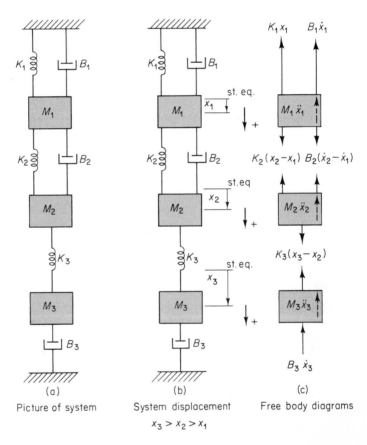

(a)

Picture of system

(b)

System displacement

$x_3 > x_2 > x_1$

(c)

Free body diagrams

(d) Differential equations

1. $M_1\ddot{x}_1 + (B_1 + B_2)\dot{x}_1 + (K_1 + K_2)x_1 - B_2\dot{x}_2 - K_2x_2 \qquad = 0$

2. $\quad -B_2\dot{x}_1 - K_2x_1 + M\ddot{x}_2 + B_2\dot{x}_2 + (K_2 + K_3)x_2 - K_3x_3 = 0$

3. $\qquad -K_3x_2 + M_3\ddot{x}_3 + B_3\dot{x}_3 + K_3x_3 = 0$

Fig. 2.14. Example 2—steps to formulate equations.

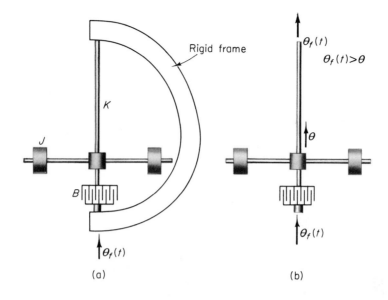

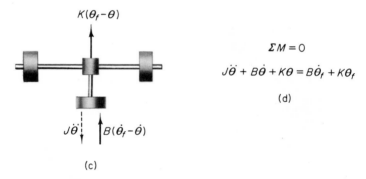

Fig. 2.15. Example 3—formulations of torsional differential equation.

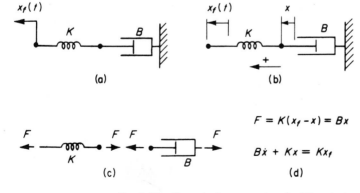

Fig. 2.16. Example 4—spring-damper differential equation.

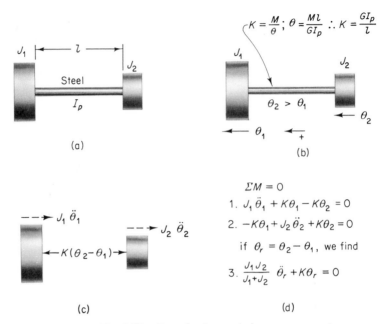

Fig. 2.17. Example 5—coupled inertias as either one or two degrees of freedom.

An increase in $F_f(t)$ increases acceleration. Equation 2.32 agrees with these conclusions.

Figures 2.14, 2.15, 2.16, and 2.17 illustrate the solution of a series of more complicated examples. Notice that the system in Fig. 2.14 has three dependent variables, x_1, x_2, and x_3, denoting the displacements of the three masses. This system is said to have three degrees of freedom, while the systems in Figs. 2.15, 2.16, and 2.17 have one, one, and two degrees of freedom, respectively.

2.9   Alternative Methods of Approach

The differential equations for mechanical systems were written by choosing position and force as the system variables. In other words, the position of each mass and its derivatives determined the forces on that mass. The sum of these forces and the external driving forces must then be zero for each mass. This led to a set of second order differential equations, one for each mass in the system. However, there are many ways in which these equations could be derived from the same basic physical principles. The potential and kinetic energies could have been used with the Lagrange equations to derive the differential equations. This is a very powerful method but it is beyond the scope of this book.

Another alternative is to represent the mechanical system as a network of two-terminal elements. This method bears some similarity to that used in electrical systems and is therefore presented in Sec. 3.12 after electrical networks have been discussed.

Problems

2-1. A 4.9 Ferrari weighing 3,850 lb can do the standing $\frac{1}{4}$ mile in 14.6 sec. Assuming constant acceleration (which isn't too far off), what is the force exerted on the car?

2-2. (a) Three blocks are connected by strings and are placed on an inclined frictionless surface as shown in Fig. P. 2.2a.

$M_1 = 1$ slug, $M_2 = 2$ slug, and $M_3 = 3$ slug. Find T_1 and T_2.

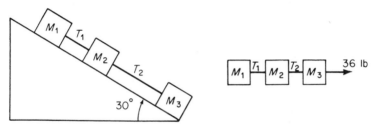

Figure P. 2.2(a)   **Figure P. 2.2(b)**

(b) If they are placed on a frictionless horizontal surface and M_3 is pulled to the right with a force of 36 lb, find T_1 and T_2.

2-3. A 100-lb crate has been designed to withstand a 10 ft fall. What is the minimum strength rope that may be used to lower the crate from 20 ft if a constant pull is exerted on the rope at all times during the lowering?

2-4. A small missile is fired from the earth at an angle of 45° with an initial velocity of 1,414 ft/sec. When it reaches its maximum altitude, it splits into two equal parts, one part falling straight down as though it were dropped from that height. Neglect air resistance.

(a) How high does the missle go?

(b) How far did each part go from the launch site?

(c) What was the terminal velocity of each piece when it hit the ground?

(d) Which part hit the ground first?

Figure P. 2.4

2-5. A yoyo of mass M and moment of inertia J is released from rest and the end of the string held still.

(a) What is the tension in the string during descent, assuming the shaft radius r is small enough to assume the string is always vertical?

(b) What is the tension in the string while the yoyo climbs the other side of the string?

(c) What is the linear acceleration of the yoyo?

2-6. A 10-lb rhesus monkey is hanging on a rope that goes over a massless frictionless pulley and down to a 10-lb bunch of bananas. Suppose this "system" starts at rest. Can the monkey reach the bananas by climbing the rope without jamming the bananas into the pulley? Show why or why not.

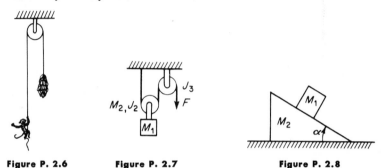

Figure P. 2.6   Figure P. 2.7   Figure P. 2.8

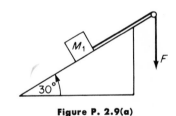

Figure P. 2.9(a)

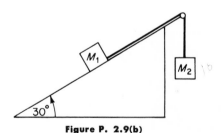

Figure P. 2.9(b)

2-7. Write the differential equations of motion for the system shown in Fig. P. 2.7.

2-8. Write the equations of motion for the two masses in Fig. P. 2.8. All surfaces are frictionless.

2-9. In part (a) of Fig. P. 2.9 determine the acceleration of block M_1. If now in part (b) we have a weight $M_2 g = 10$ lb as a source of force, what is the acceleration of M_1? Are the accelerations the same? If so, why? If not, why? $M_1 g = M_2 g = F = 10$ lb

2-10. Given the following series (a) and parallel (b) spring, the dashpot configurations with spring constants and damping coefficients as shown, find the equivalent spring constant and damping coefficient for (a) and (b). Generalize your result for n springs and n dampers.

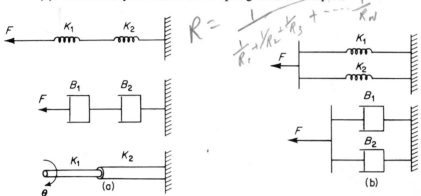

$$R = \frac{1}{\frac{1}{R_1} + \frac{1}{R_2} + \frac{1}{R_3} + \cdots \frac{1}{R_N}}$$

$$\frac{1}{\frac{1}{R_1} + \frac{1}{R_2} + \frac{1}{R_3}}$$

Figure P. 2.10

2-11. Find equivalent T versus θ "spring" constant. Does it obey Hooke's law?

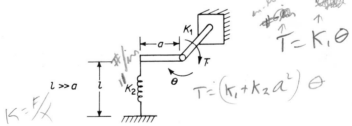

$$T = K_1 \theta$$

$$T = \left(K_1 + K_2 a^2\right) \theta$$

$$K = \frac{F}{x}$$

Figure P. 2.11

2-12. Find the equivalent damping coefficient, B_{eq}, of Fig. P. 2.12 of dashpots. The bars a, b, and c are rigid, massless, and do not rotate.

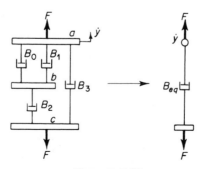

Figure P. 2.12

2-13. Find the equivalent spring constant K_{eq} of Fig. P. 2.13. Note: Bars a and b do not rotate and are massless.

$$K_2 + K_3$$

$$\frac{(K_0 + K_1) K_2}{K_0 + K_1 + K_2} + K_3 = K$$

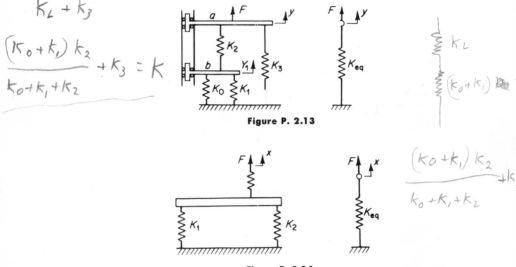

Figure P. 2.13

$$\frac{(K_0 + K_1) K_2}{K_0 + K_1 + K_2} + K_3$$

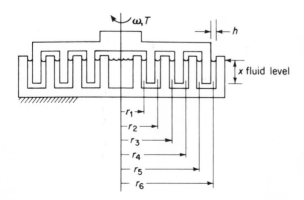

Figure P. 2.14

2-14. Find the equivalent spring constant K_{eq} of Fig. P. 2.14, assuming the springs are much longer than a and b. Note: The bar is free to rotate and is massless.

2-15. Figure P. 2.15 shows a viscous damper. The fluid between the concentric cups is a silicone fluid having a viscosity of 150 lb-sec/sq in. Using the given dimensions, find the damping coefficient B as a function of x.

$$r_1 = 1.0 \text{ in.} \qquad r_4 = 1.6 \text{ in.}$$
$$r_2 = 1.2 \text{ in.} \qquad r_5 = 1.8 \text{ in.}$$
$$r_3 = 1.4 \text{ in.} \qquad r_6 = 2.0 \text{ in.}$$

The radial clearance h between each cylinder is 0.05 in.

Figure P. 2.15

2-16. Shown in Fig. P. 2.16 is a simplification of an automobile shock absorber. The flow of oil through a hole, such as the holes in the piston, is given by $q = CA\sqrt{2(\Delta P/\rho)}$ where C is the flow coefficient (assume $C = 0.6$), A is the hole area, ΔP is the pressure drop across the hole, and ρ is the fluid density. The specific gravity of the oil is 0.85.

(a) Plot the force required to move the piston as a function of the velocity of the piston (neglect friction and mass).

(b) What is the linear approximation of the damping coefficient B about the operating points $\dot{x} = 5$ and $\dot{x} = 10$ in./sec?

(c) For $\dot{x} = 5$, by what per cent can the velocities be varied before 5% error of B is encountered, assuming the damping coefficient B constant?

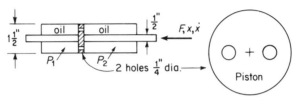

Figure P. 2.16

2-17. Figure P. 2.17 shows an amplifier and loud speaker combination. The cone of the speaker (which makes the noise) may be approximated as shown in the sketch where its mass, spring, and damping are given as separate elements, and the applied force is directly proportional to the current supplied by the amplifier.

The differential equation for the amplifier current which results when an input voltage e_0 is applied is as follows.

$$L\frac{di}{dt} + Ri + \frac{1}{C}\int i\,dt + K_2\dot{x} = K_3 e_0$$

Derive the other equation (i.e., for the mechanical system).

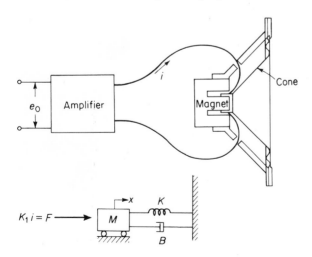

Figure P. 2.17

2-18. A physical pendulum of length l has a mass M_1, inertia J_1, and point friction B_1. At the bottom is an inertial wheel of mass M_2, inertia J_2, and bearing friction (between M_1 and M_2) of B_2. Write the differential equations for small angles of pendulum motion (collect terms). Be careful, and draw neat pictures. See Fig. 2.18

2-19. (a) Draw a free body diagram for Fig. P. 2.19.
(b) Write the equations of motion.

$$\frac{k_1 k_2}{k_1 + k_2} + k_3 + k_4 = k$$

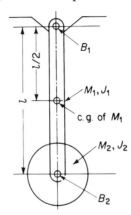

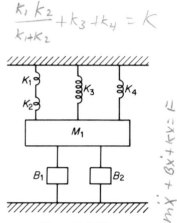

$m\ddot{x} + B\dot{x} + kx = F$

Figure P. 2.18   **Figure P. 2.19**

2-20. Perhaps as a child (or even more recently) you balanced a pole (length l, mass m) on the end of your nose (Fig. P. 2.20). Assuming motion in one plane only, with F_x and F_y in the horizontal and vertical directions respectively and coordinates X_{cg}, Y_{cg}, and θ, write the differential equations of motion.

Figure P. 2.20

2-21. An automobile power train, designed several years ago, with a hydraulic transmission may be roughly modeled as in Fig. P. 2.21. Write the equations of motion.

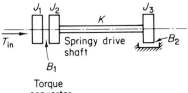

Figure P. 2.21

2-22. How many degrees of freedom are present in the system for Prob. 2-21?

2-23. Given the system in Fig. P. 2.23, for *small* motions, write the equation of motion.

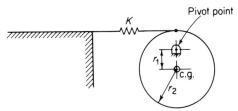

Figure P. 2.23

2-24. Write differential equations for the system in Fig. P. 2.24., Assume the ropes never go slack.

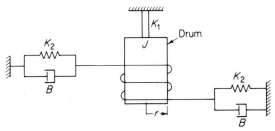

Figure P. 2.24

2-25. The two masses rest on an inclined plane in the system in Fig. P. 2.25. For a long time mass M_1 has been held in place with a pin, M_2

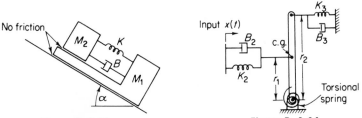

Figure P. 2.25   **Figure P. 2.26**

has been free to move but has reached equilibrium. At $t = 0$, the pin is removed. Write the equations necessary to describe the motion.

2-26. Write equations of motion for small motions for the system shown in Fig. P. 2.26.

2-27. Write equations of motion for small motions of the system shown in Fig. P. 2.27.

2-28. Write equations for small motions and big motions of the system shown in Fig. P. 2.28.

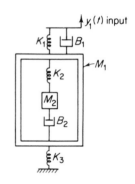

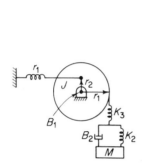

Figure P. 2.27   **Figure P. 2.28**

2-29. In the operation of rotating machinery, pronounced rotational vibrations are sometimes encountered which, in aggravated cases, may cause shaft failure. A rotational vibration damper is sometimes used to reduce this type of vibration. One such damper is shown in the figure (P. 2.29) which consists of an extra flywheel with moment of inertia J_2 which is free to turn on the shaft and is coupled to the fixed flywheel by means of a torsional spring. Write the necessary differential equations that relate torque output to torque input.

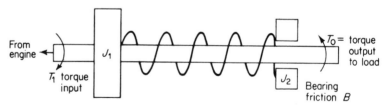

Figure P. 2.29

2-30. Two masses, M_1 and M_3, move toward each other without friction at the same velocity V_0. They are joined at the instant of impact by two

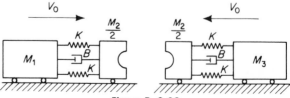

Figure P. 2.30

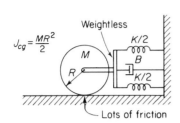

$J_{cg} = \dfrac{MR^2}{2}$

Weightless

M

R

K/2

B

K/2

Lots of friction

Figure P. 2.31

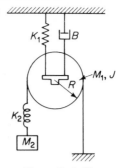

K_1

B

M_1, J

R

K_2

M_2

Figure P. 2.32

equal magnets which do not separate ever afterwards. The magnets each have mass $M_{2/2}$ See Fig. P. 2.30.

(a) Choose reference positions, draw block diagrams, and write differential equations for system.

(b) What are initial conditions for the equations?

2-31. Draw a free body diagram and obtain *the* differential equation (one) for the system in Fig. P. 2.31.

2-32. (a) How many degrees of freedom in this system in Fig. P. 2.32?
(b) How many equations are necessary?
(c) Obtain differential equations and reduce to (b) above.

2-33. Assume small motions in Fig. P. 2.33. Write the equations of motion.

2-34. (a) List the degrees of freedom in the system in Fig. P. 2.34.
(b) Write differential equation(s) necessary to describe the motion. Assume rope never goes slack.

2-35. Derive equations of motion for the system in Fig. P. 2.35.

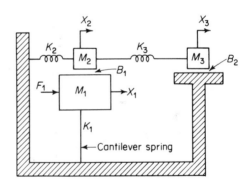

X_2

X_3

K_2

M_2

K_3

M_3

B_2

B_1

F_1

M_1

X_1

K_1

Cantilever spring

Figure P. 2.33

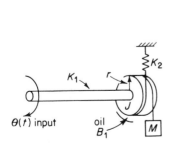

K_1

r

K_2

J

$\theta(t)$ input

oil

B_1

M

Figure P. 2.34

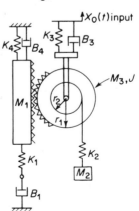

$X_0(t)$ input

K_4

K_3

B_4

B_3

M_3, J

M_1

r_2

r_1

K_1

B_1

K_2

M_2

Figure P. 2.35

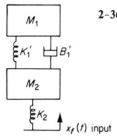

Figure P. 2.36(a)

2-36. As engineers for the N. O. Bountz & Smoth Ride Trailer Company, we are asked to specify the spring, shock absorber, and tire characteristics for a new lightweight trailer. In order to do this we must analyze the dynamics of the trailer.

I.   For a first approximation, we assume that the trailer body does not rotate but only moves vertically. This results in the following model of the trailer. See Fig. P. 2.36(a).

(a) Does the approximation of only vertical motion seem reasonable? Why?

(b) Draw the free body diagram.

(c) Write the dynamic equations for the trailer, assuming that the input is a change in the position of the ground side of the K_2 spring.

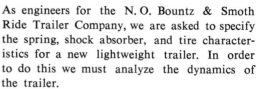

Figure P. 2.36(b)

II. A more exact model of the trailer is seen by looking in at the rear, Fig. P. 2.36(b).

In order to solve this problem, we make the following assumptions: (1) The angles through which the body and axle will rotate are small. (2) The centers of gravity move only in the vertical direction. (3) All the axle-wheel mass is concentrated in the wheels.

(d) What is the significance of assumption (1)?

(e) Draw the free body diagram.

(f) Write differential equation(s) describing the dynamics of the system. Note: The trailer is subject to two inputs, one at each wheel.

2-37. Given the spring mass system in Fig. P. 2.37, draw the complete free body diagrams and express all forces in terms of y_1, $\dot{y}_1$, $\ddot{y}_1$, y_2, $\dot{y}_2$, and $\ddot{y}_2$.

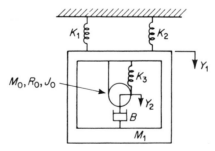

Figure P. 2.37

2-38. Write equations of motion, for the system in Fig. P. 2.38 assuming damping coefficient B_1 between bearing and shaft; shaft is massless.

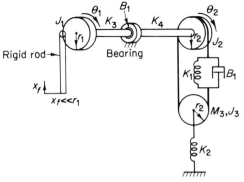

Figure P. 2.38

2-39. There is a coefficient of friction μ between the cylinder M_0 and the block M_1 of the system shown in Fig. P. 2.39.

(a) Draw the free body diagrams for the system, assuming that the cylinder will roll without slipping.

(b) Write the equations of motion.

(c) Comment on conditions necessary for equations to be valid.

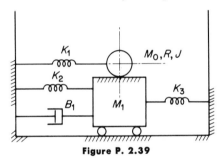

Figure P. 2.39

2-40. A tone arm for a cheap record player may be modeled as shown in Fig. P. 2.40. Write equations of motion. Note: *cg* is not at pivot point.

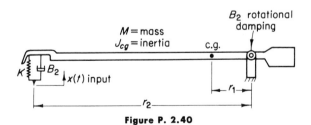

Figure P. 2.40

2-41. (a) How many degrees of freedom for the system in Fig. P. 2.41?

(b) Write equations of motion.

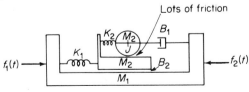

Figure P. 2.41

37

2-42. Derive equations for the system shown in Fig. P. 2.42.

2-43. (a) Draw the free body diagrams for the system in Fig. P. 2.43.
(b) Write the equation of motion in the following form:

$$M_{eq}\ddot{y} + B_{eq}\dot{y} + K_{eq}y = 0$$

Bearings are frictionless.

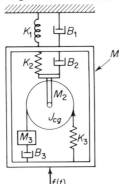

Figure P. 2.42

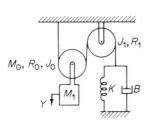

Figure P. 2.43

2-44. A homogeneous bar of mass M, length L, and moment of inertia J (about the center of mass) is constrained as shown in Fig. 2.44. Write the equations of motion for the bar, using the linear displacements of the center of mass and the angular displacement of the bar as the coordinates. Assume the cart never leaves the ground.

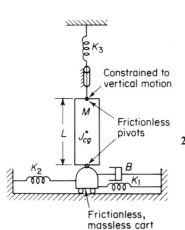

Figure P. 2.44

2-45. (a) Draw the free body diagram for the system in Fig. P. 2.45.
(b) Solve for x and x_1.

The system shown is a type of tapefeeding mechanism whereby M and the coupled system mechanically filter out variations in the tape-feeding speed.

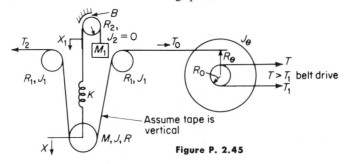

Figure P. 2.45

3 Formulation of Differential Equations in Electrical Systems

3.1 Introduction

We have seen in Chap. 2 how the basic concepts and laws of physics, along with the definitions of mechanical system elements, can be used to formulate systems of linear differential equations which characterize mechanical systems. We have seen that three special linear mechanical elements —mass, spring, and dashpot, and two sources—force and motion (with rotational counterparts)—provide a basis for characterizing a wide variety of mechanical systems. Linear relationships involving two variables, force and displacement (torque and angle), define these mechanical parameters. We recognize that these linear elements only approximate true systems, but that meaningful engineering results can be obtained through their use.

There is a completely analogous situation for electrical systems. We shall find that three basic electrical elements—the resistor, the capacitor, and the inductor—can be used to characterize completely many electrical systems. We shall see that the input-output variables of voltage and current or charge are the time-varying quantities which may be observed and measured and which appear in relations defining electrical elements. We shall learn that two basic laws, viz., those due to Kirchhoff, govern the formulation of the differential equations which characterize the electrical systems to be studied.

It will be shown that computational work can be reduced by normalizing the system equations. A set of checking procedures will also be presented to be used to minimize errors in the model formulation.

As in the case of the mechanical systems, we shall lean heavily on the basic concepts normally developed in a second year physics course. Some of these concepts may be discussed in the physics course after they are needed in dynamic systems. This should cause no major difficulty because it is possible to formulate and solve differential equations in electrical systems without complete knowledge of the physical bases on which the variables are related. However, should this situation occur, the student is strongly urged to make a special effort to fill in such gaps when they are considered in depth in his physics course.

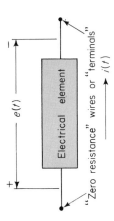

Fig. 3.1. The two-terminal electrical element.

We shall discuss certain electrical elements in the order in which they are often presented in a college physics course. From the dynamic systems point of view, these elements will be considered as "two-terminal electrical elements" in which a current $i(t)$ goes "through" and a potential or voltage drop $e(t)$ exists "across" the element (see Fig. 3.1).

Complete definitions of current and voltage are being (will be) developed in your physics course. It is sufficient to say here that a current i^* denotes the drift motion of carriers of electrical charge q in an electrical conductor. In solid metallic conductors, the charge carriers are electrons (carrying negative charge) and the current i is measured in terms of the rate of flow of these charges. A unit negative charge q of 1 coulomb passing a point in a conductor per second constitutes a current i of 1 ampere. Current is defined positively in the opposite direction to the flow of negative charge. Currents measured in the laboratory can range from micromicroamperes (10^{-12} amps or $\mu\mu$a) as found in radiation detectors; microamperes (10^{-6} amps or μa) found in photoelectric devices; milliamperes (10^{-3} amps or ma) found in transistors and vacuum tubes; 1–10 amps in home appliances; and thousands of amperes in large transmission lines. The flow of charge-carrying electrons in metallic conductors is somewhat analogous to the flow of water in pipes.

Voltage or potential, e, in electrical systems is analogous to

---

*i and $i(t)$ are used interchangeably to mean the same thing. In general, lower case letters are used to represent time-varying quantities and upper case letters for steady DC quantities. Exceptions are found in vector and complex number notations.

pressure in hydraulic systems and just as pressure is required to produce a flow of water in a pipe, voltage is required to produce a flow of current in a wire. Pressure may be defined in terms of the height of a column of water, or in terms of the work required to lift a unit volume of water to a given height. In the same way voltage may be defined in terms of the work required to move a unit charge in a potential field (that field due to another unit charge).

As you will discover, the proper definitions of voltage and current are far more complex than implied by the analogy of water in pipes. For our purposes, it will be sufficient if we visualize current as a flowing stream of charge-carrying particles which can neither be created nor destroyed within a circuit element (therefore, whatever goes in must come out). Voltage is a measure of the potential energy of a stream as it enters or leaves a circuit element, and voltage drop is the change in potential energy across the terminals of a two-terminal circuit element.

3.2   The Capacitor or Condenser

The electrical capacitor (or condenser) is shown in Fig. 3.2. Either form shown in Fig. 3.2(a) or (b) may be used in circuit notations. In the case of Fig. 3.2(b), the curved side identifies the electrode nearest the outside of the capacitor or if the capacitor is electrolytic, it identifies the negative electrode. Equations will be given for the relationship between the current $i(t)$ flowing through a capacitor and the voltage drop $e(t)$ across the capacitor. It is im-

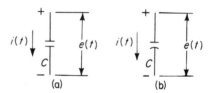

Fig. 3.2.   The capacitor or condenser showing voltage and current convention. (a) Common symbol. (b) Curved side of symbol identifies the outermost electrode or the negative electrode if it is an electrolytic capacitor.

portant to remember that the algebraic signs occurring in the equations which will be presented are consistent with the notation shown in Fig. 3.2. Thus a positive voltage drop is considered to produce a positive current flow in the direction of higher to lower voltage.

Physically, a capacitor may be visualized as two large metallic plates or foil separated by a very thin dielectric material. Sometimes the area is made variable as in a tuning condenser in a radio. Energy is stored in a capacitor by reason of the electrostatic field which exists between the plates when a voltage is impressed across the plates. The capacitance (or capacity), C, is a measure of the amount of charge which can be stored for a given potential difference across the plates.

By bringing the plates very close together, the capacitance increases and more charge can be stored for a given voltage. Very small capacitors are now being made through vacuum deposition techniques where films of metal and dielectric only a few molecules thick are possible. It is important, of course, that a current does not flow through the dielectric and if the voltage applied to a capacitor is too high, the dielectric may break down and cause the capacitor to fail. Thus, capacitors are rated not only by their charge-storing ability but also in terms of the maximum voltage which may be applied across their terminals.

Equation 3.1 shows the defining relationship for capacitance C:

$$q(t) = Ce(t) \tag{3.1}$$

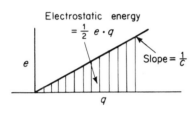

Fig. 3.3. Voltage vs. charge for a linear capacitor.

where q is the charge on the capacitor and e is the voltage across it. Figure 3.3 illustrates how work is done when voltage is increased across the plates of a condenser. The area represents the energy stored. Two basic equations relating to voltage and current in capacitors may be written.

$$i = \frac{dq}{dt} = C\frac{de}{dt} \quad [\text{ampere}] \tag{3.2}$$

$$e = \frac{1}{C}\int_{t_0}^{t} i\,dt + \left[\begin{array}{c}\text{voltage on}\\ \text{capacitor at } t_0\end{array}\right] \tag{3.3}$$

The capacitance C is defined by either Eq. 3.1 or 3.2. Since most differential equations will be written for voltage and current, Eq. 3.2 will be found most useful. The reciprocal of the capacitance as it appears in Eq. 3.3 is given the special name of *elastance*. These defining relationships with units are shown below:

$$C = \text{capacitance in } \textit{farads} \text{ or } \left[\frac{\text{ampere}}{\text{volt/second}}\right] \text{ or } \left[\frac{\text{coulomb}}{\text{volt}}\right]$$

$$\frac{1}{C} = \text{elastance in } \textit{darafs} \text{ or } \left[\frac{\text{volt}}{\text{ampere-second}}\right] \text{ or } \left[\frac{\text{volt}}{\text{coulomb}}\right]$$

The energy stored in a capacitor may also be written as in Eq. 3.4.

$$\text{Energy stored} = V = \frac{1}{2}eq = \frac{1}{2}Ce^2 = \frac{1}{2C}q^2 \quad [\text{joules}] \tag{3.4}$$

These plus signs hold for the assumed positive directions shown in Fig. 3.2. The positive derivative of voltage implies, of course, that it is becoming larger.

A capacitor having a capacitance of one farad would be very large.

The largest capacitors normally used in radio and electronic equipment are measured in microfarads (10^{-6} farads). The smallest capacitors have capacitances measured in micromicrofarads (sometimes called picofarads or 10^{-12} farads and written $\mu\mu f$). The average tuning capacitor in an AM radio has a maximum capacitance of around 400 micromicrofarads. Figure 3.4 shows some typical capacitors.

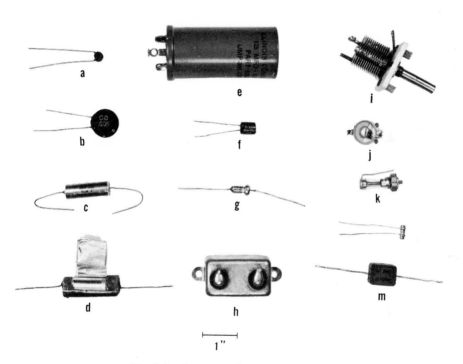

Fig. 3.4. Some typical capacitors.
a. Miniature disk ceramic capacitor—0.001 microfarad, 10 volt.
b. General purpose disk ceramic capacitor—0.005 μF, 600 v.
c. Paper tubular capacitor—0.1 μF, 200 v.
d. Cutaway view of a paper tubular capacitor showing foil plates and paper dielectric.
e. High-capacitance, medium-voltage electrolytic capacitor—120 μF, 350 v.
f. Miniature low-voltage electrolytic capacitor—30 μF, 10 v.
g. Miniature low-voltage tantalum capacitor—10 μF, 250 v.
h. Oil filled "bath tub" capacitor—5 μF, 600 v.
i. Air dielectric variable capacitor—8–50 $\mu\mu F$, 500 v.
j. Ceramic variable—4–25 $\mu\mu F$, 400 v.
k. Piston type variable capacitor—0.5–3 $\mu\mu F$, 1000 v.
l. Tubular ceramic capacitor—200 $\mu\mu F$, 600 v.
m. Mica capacitor—336 $\mu\mu F$, 400 v.

3.3   The Inductor or Choke

The inductor stores electrical energy by virtue of the magnetic field which is established when a current flows in it.

Figure 3.5 shows the symbol for the inductor and Eqs. 3.5 and

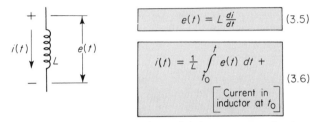

$$e(t) = L \frac{di}{dt} \tag{3.5}$$

$$i(t) = \frac{1}{L} \int_{t_0}^{t} e(t) \ dt + \begin{bmatrix} \text{Current in} \\ \text{inductor at } t_0 \end{bmatrix} \tag{3.6}$$

Fig. 3.5.   Symbol and defining equations for the inductor.

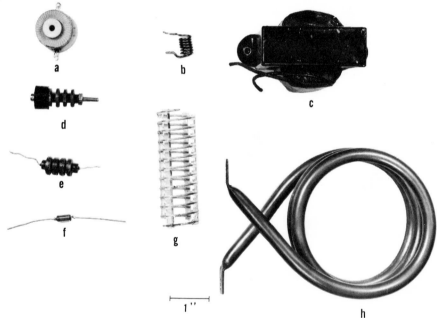

Fig. 3.6.   Some typical inductors.
a. Radio-frequency choke—single pi, 40 mh.
b. High-frequency choke—10 μh.
c. High-inductance choke with laminated core—8 h.
d. Adjustable core coil—3–8 mh.
e. Four-pi, radio-frequency choke—2.5 mh.
f. Polystyrene insulated radio-frequency coil—50 μh.
g. Radio-frequency coil for high currents—20 μh.
h. High-frequency heating coil.

☆   The positive signs in this equation relate to the chosen conventions in Fig. 3.5. A positive rate of change in current means that the current is increasing.

3.6 are the definitive equations in terms of voltage and current. As in the case of the capacitor, the positive signs for Eqs. 3.5 and 3.6 depend upon the convention chosen in Fig. 3.5, wherein a positive current *i* is assumed to flow in the direction of a voltage drop *e*. The inductance *L* of the inductor is defined by Eq. 3.5 and units are shown below. The energy stored in an inductor is given by Eq. 3.7:

$$L = \text{inductance in } [henries] \text{ or } \left[\frac{\text{volt}}{\text{ampere/second}}\right] \text{ or } \left[\frac{\text{weber-turns}}{\text{ampere}}\right]$$

$$\text{Energy stored} = U = \int ei\, dt = L\int \frac{di}{dt} i\, dt = \frac{1}{2}Li^2 \quad [\text{joules}] \quad (3.7)$$

Like capacitors, inductors come in many sizes and shapes. The smallest inductances occur in so-called radio-frequency coils and the largest in large chokes. Figure 3.6 shows some photographs of typical inductors with typical values of inductance.

3.4   The Resistor

Figure 3.7 shows the well-known symbol used to represent electrical resistance. Equations 3.8 and 3.9 are expressions of Ohm's law which defines the resistance in a linear resistor. The resistor does not store electrical energy in any form but rather dissipates it. This is done in the form of heat. While it is possible for other electrical elements to dissipate electrical energy in the form of electomagnetic radiation, this is usually neglected in the simple linear defining relationships. The resistance, *R*, and its inverse, conductance, are defined as below:

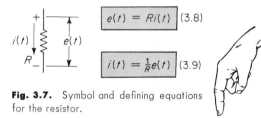

$$e(t) = Ri(t) \quad (3.8)$$

$$i(t) = \frac{1}{R}e(t) \quad (3.9)$$

Fig. 3.7. Symbol and defining equations for the resistor.

$$R = \text{resistance in [ohms] or } \left[\frac{\text{volt}}{\text{ampere}}\right]$$

$$\frac{1}{R} = \text{conductance [mhos] or } \left[\frac{\text{ampere}}{\text{volt}}\right]$$

The energy dissipated in a resistor is given by Eq. 3.10:

Once more the plus signs in the equation hold for the assumed directions and relative voltage magnitudes shown in Fig. 3.7.

Energy dissipated per unit time = power $= e \cdot i = Ri^2 = \dfrac{1}{R}e^2$ (3.10)

Resistors come in many sizes and shapes and are not only characterized by their resistance value but also by their power-handling capacitance and accuracy. Some typical resistors are shown in Fig. 3.8.

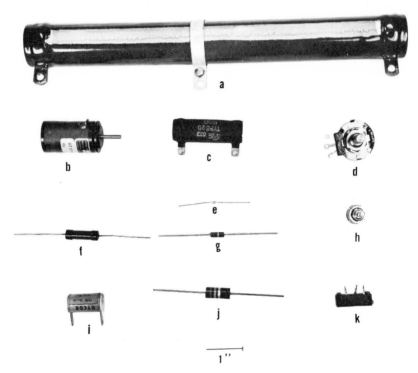

Fig. 3.8. Some typical resistors which can range in values from a few ohms to a few megohms.

a. High-power dissipation, adjustable wire-wound resistor—200 watt.

b. Ten-turn precision control—2 w.

c. Ten-watt, fixed, wire-wound resistance.

d. Carbon composition control—0.5 w.

e. Miniature carbon resistor—0.1 w.

f. 1 % tolerance, carbon-film resistor—1 w.

g. Common ½-watt carbon resistor.

h. Miniature carbon control—0.5 w.

i. Precision wire-wound resistance—0.5 w.

j. Two-watt carbon resistor.

k. Miniature adjustable trimming resistor.

3.5 Mutual Inductance

The inductor stores electrical energy by reason of the magnetic field which is produced when the current i flows within it. Since the magnetic field extends through space, it is possible for a second inductor in an electric circuit to come under the influence of this magnetic field. When this happens, the voltage drop in one will be found to be related not only to the current flowing through the inductor itself, but also to the current flowing through the second inductor whose magnetic field influences the first. In such cases, the second inductor is also influenced by the first in exactly the same way (in linear devices).* This influence between inductors due to the interaction of their fields is termed *mutual inductance*.

The case of mutual inductance is somewhat complicated because the field due to another coil may either aid or diminish the "self" field due to the current in an inductor. This situation is governed by the geometric relationships between the windings; however, it is common practice to denote the circuit diagram with special symbols which permit one to formulate the correct equations without needing to explore the geometry of construction. Let us consider two coils which are mutually coupled as shown in Fig. 3.9.

Currents i_1 and i_2 and voltage e_1 and e_2 are shown in a consistent notation. Self-inductance L_1 and L_2 are noted and a mutual inductance M which applies in either direction is defined. The relationship for the voltage drop e_1 is then given by Eq. 3.11 and e_2 by Eq. 3.12:

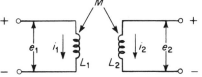

Fig. 3.9. Symbol and sign convention for two coils having mutual inductance, M.

$$e_1 = L_1 \frac{di_1}{dt} \pm M \frac{di_2}{dt} \qquad (3.11)$$

$$e_2 = L_2 \frac{di_2}{dt} \pm M \frac{di_1}{dt} \qquad (3.12)$$

At this point the signs in front of the mutual inductance terms are ambiguous because they depend upon the direction of currents i_1

---

*This is a special consequence of linearity and is called Maxwell's theorem of reciprocity.

and i_2 and on the orientation of the coils. The direction of the currents can be chosen arbitrarily but the orientation of the coils is generally fixed and we need to adopt some notation to specify this orientation on the circuit diagram. This is usually done by assigning dots to the top or bottom of each coil as shown in Fig. 3.10(a) and (b).

Knowing the location of the dots, we can apply the following rules:

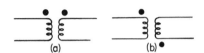

(a) If both currents enter (or both currents leave) through a dot then the voltage drop due to the mutual inductance will have the *same sign* as the voltage drop due to the self-inductance.

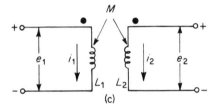

(c)

(b) If one current enters by a dot and one current leaves by a dot then the voltage drop due to the mutual inductance will have the *opposite sign* to the voltage drop due to the self-inductance.

Thus, for the example shown in Fig. 3.10(c) we find

$$e_1 = L_1 \frac{di_1}{dt} + M \frac{di_2}{dt}$$

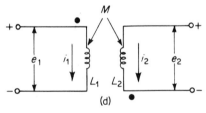

(d)

Figure 3.10

and

$$e_2 = L_2 \frac{di_2}{dt} + M \frac{di_1}{dt}$$

because both i_1 and i_2 enter by a dot.

On the other hand in Fig. 3.10(d), i_1 enters by a dot and i_2 leaves by a dot. Therefore, we find

$$e_1 = L_1 \frac{di_1}{dt} - M \frac{di_2}{dt}$$

and

$$e_2 = L_2 \frac{di_2}{dt} - M \frac{di_1}{dt}$$

  Everybody has trouble getting the signs right in equations having mutual inductances. Success comes with practice and careful bookkeeping. Good luck!

If three coils are mutually coupled as in Fig. 3.11 then three sets of symbols are required with three different mutual inductances. It is assumed that each coil is influenced by the magnetic field of the other two coils. In general, this relationship will be determined by the geometrical orientation of the three coils. The circles show the relative orientation of coils 1 and 2, the squares denote the orientation of coils 2 and 3, and the triangles show the orientation of coils 1 and 3.

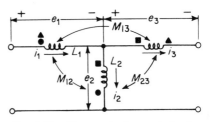

Fig. 3.11. Three mutually-coupled cells.

Applying the rules just defined we obtain the following expressions for voltages e_1, e_2, and e_3.

$$e_1(t) = L_1 \frac{di_1}{dt} - M_{12} \frac{di_2}{dt} - M_{13} \frac{di_3}{dt} \tag{3.13}$$

$$e_2(t) = L_2 \frac{di_2}{dt} - M_{12} \frac{di_1}{dt} + M_{23} \frac{di_3}{dt} \tag{3.14}$$

$$e_3(t) = L_3 \frac{di_3}{dt} - M_{13} \frac{di_1}{dt} + M_{23} \frac{di_2}{dt} \tag{3.15}$$

3.6   Sources of Voltage and Current

3.6–1   THE VOLTAGE SOURCE

The concept of a voltage or a current source is sometimes confusing because, in fact, all real sources of voltages are also sources of current and vice versa. The identity of a source depends upon which of these two variables may be considered substantially independent. A voltage source is a source of electrical power in which the voltage may be considered as an independent variable input to the circuit. This means physically that whatever current is required to maintain a specified voltage drop across the load can be supplied by the voltage source. Thus, in a voltage source the current is the dependent variable and the voltage is assumed independent of the current.

In Fig. 3.12, we see a voltage source supplying a series of resistors which may be switched into different combinations. Since each resistor

Everyone has trouble with voltage and current sources. A current source always
has a voltage and a voltage source always has a current. Both should always be
shown on any circuit diagram. To be a source, one or the other must be independent,
then the remaining one is dependent. You have to figure it out.

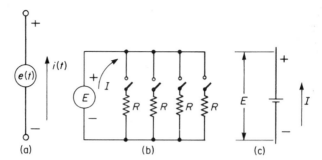

Fig. 3.12. (a) Symbol for a voltage source. Note current $i(t)$ is dependent and flows from $(-)$ to $(+)$. (b) Voltage source, E, must maintain constant voltage no matter how many resistors are switched in. (c) Symbol for a DC battery.

is equal, it is seen that current from the voltage source must be directly proportional to the number of resistors switched in. It is the characteristic of the voltage source that it maintains a given voltage E no matter how many resistors are switched in or out. The transformer which supplies voltage to your home may be considered such a voltage source. No matter how many appliances or lights are turned on in your home, the voltage supply remains substantially the same. Of course we are immediately aware from this example that the voltage source which supplies home power is not, in fact, a perfect voltage source because we know that as one increases the number of appliances in a home, the voltage drops and the lights, for example, may dim a bit when the freezer goes on. We see then that the voltage source is an ideal concept, only approached in practice.

Other examples of voltage sources include the common wet and dry batteries, voltage power supplies for electronic equipment which are often regulated to maintain a constant voltage, and various types of AC and DC rotating generators.

3.6–2 The Current Source

The current source is symbolically the inverse of the voltage source. While the elements from which it is made may be similar, it is designed to produce whatever voltage is necessary for a circuit to maintain the total current at a fixed value. Figure 3.13 shows the symbol for a current source in which current is the independent variable and the resultant voltage is the dependent variable.

In Fig. 3.13(b) a circuit is shown which may be switched to different positions, each one requiring a different voltage if the current is to be maintained constant. The current source I is capable of changing its voltage across whatever number of resistors is chosen so that

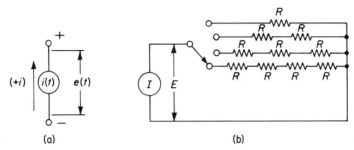

Fig. 3.13. Symbol for a current source. Note voltage, $e(t)$, is dependent on current, $i(t)$, which flows from $(-)$ to $(+)$. (b) Current source, I, most remain constant no matter which branch of series resistors is chosen.

the current through these resistors is constant. Since the resistors are of equal values, it may be seen that the voltage required is directly proportional to the number of resistors in series. Examples of current sources are somewhat harder to find and are not quite so familiar. The transistor is perhaps the most common device which may be viewed as substantially a current source. Power supplies specially designed for constant current are available commercially.

While it is true that a concept of a pure current or voltage source is ideal, it finds great use in circuit analysis for it is often possible to consider a nonideal source as composed of a combination of an ideal voltage or current source and other circuit elements. We shall see later how this may be done when formulating equivalent circuits; but for the present, we shall develop systems of equations for electrical circuits from the point of view of ideal voltage and current sources.

3.7   Remarks on Linearity

In Chap. 2 when we discussed mechanical system elements, you will recall that a great deal was said about when such elements might be considered linear and when they could not. A similar set of remarks is appropriate for electrical system elements although, in general, electrical elements are far more linear; that is, they can be manufactured so that they operate in a linear region for the purpose of the circuit in which they are used. The question of when an electrical element is linear and when it is not is really contained in the engineering decision of whether a single equation of the form of Eqs. (3.2), (3.3), (3.5), (3.6), (3.8), and (3.9) can be used to characterize completely the element for the range of variables in question.

Consider a wire-wound resistor which may be a coil of high resistance wire wound on a ceramic core. Physically it appears like the coil of the inductor and one may question whether it is a resistor or an inductor or both. The fact is, of course, that it is not only both a resistor and an inductor, but it may even exhibit a certain amount of capacitance. It is called a resistor because the resistance is very large compared to its inductance and for most uses, the voltage drop may be described by Ohm's law. However, when such a resistor is used in a very high frequency radio or radar system, even the small inductance may be sufficient to control the current-voltage relationship. Contrarily, coils designed for large inductance also have electrical resistance which may be very small compared to the inductance of the elements, but when a perfectly steady current flows through an inductor, the amount of current is determined by its resistance and not its inductance.

Remarks like these may be extended for all electrical system elements. It is important for the student to recognize that he is dealing with a system of idealized linear relationships which may or may not adequately describe the system which is being studied. He must exercise judgment in applying such relationships and deriving useful engineering information from his results. In addition, the question of *linearity* and the validity of any theoretical model of a physical device can often be answered only by experiment. The success of an engineering system will often depend on the ability of the engineers to *predict* what will happen before large sums of money are committed to make the system. This predictive ability depends to a great extent on the validity of the mathematical models used to make the prediction. The performance of components of a system can be evaluated by experiment to insure that their mathematical representation is valid. Unfortunately, manufacturers of system components often are not able to supply such performance data and it remains for the system designer to perform these verifying experiments himself.

The mathematical model for each of the three basic elements and the two sources described is based on an idealization of real elements. Often it is necessary to measure experimentally the voltage across a resistor and the current through it in order to determine the resistance R used in the mathematical model of the element. In some kinds of resistors, the resistance may change with current and so it will be necessary to use a straight-line approximation for this current-voltage relation in order to determine a value of R to use in the mathematical model. The same kinds of experiments may be necessary to model the capacitive and inductive elements and sources of current and voltage. In formulating a conceptual model of an electrical system, it is often necessary to perform such experiments in order to determine the unknown parameters in the model, while in the mechanical system, it

is sometimes necessary to determine parameters such as damping, spring gradient, or mass for a particular element in the system by experiment.

In addition to the elements described previously in detail, there is a much larger number of elements which are specifically designed to be highly nonlinear in character. The growth of semiconductor technology has permitted the design of many passive and active elements. The common diodes used for rectification are examples. Other

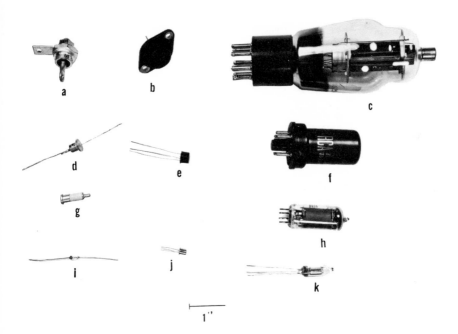

Fig. 3.14. Some nonlinear circuit elements.

a. High-current semiconductor diode used as a power rectifier—capacity, 20 amp.

b. Power transistor used for power amplifiers and regulating circuits —50 w.

c. Power pentode vacuum tube used in power amplifiers—150 w.

d. Medium current semiconductor diode used in power supplies—750 ma capacity.

e. Medium power transistor used in general purpose circuits—500 mw.

f. Metal vacuum tube—10 w.

g. Microwave diode used as a mixer.

h. Miniature vacuum-tube pentode voltage amplifier.

i. Miniature general purpose semiconductor diode—maximum current 60 ma.

j. Low-power transistor—100 mw.

k. Subminiature vacuum-tube triode voltage amplifier.

diodes which have unusual current-voltage characteristics such as tunnel diodes and zener diodes have emerged as important and useful circuit elements. A different class of nonlinear elements are the active elements which include vacuum tubes, transistors, and other modulating devices. Such elements make great amplification of electrical signals possible. Generally speaking, they modulate a source of power so that an output signal may more or less faithfully represent an input signal but at much higher voltage or current level. Elements such as those previously described are among the very large number of devices available to the electronic engineer. Most of these nonlinear elements will be ignored in the remainder of this course but the student may be assured that the techniques to be developed around the three linear elements and two sources previously presented may be extended to analyze circuits involving all electrical elements. Figure 3.14 shows some of the nonlinear elements mentioned.

3.8 Kirchhoff's Loop and Node Laws

The concept of an electric current as an indestructible flow of charge-carrying particles and of voltage as a measure of the relative potential energy at a point in an electric circuit leads to the two basic laws of Kirchhoff.

When three or more conducting wires join at a point in an electric circuit, a node is created.* It is assumed that a node has no essential properties of its own in that its resistance, capacitance, and inductance are all zero. It may be seen that if it is not possible for a node to store an electric charge then all charge which enters the node must also leave. This leads to Kirchhoff's *node theorem* which states that *the algebraic sum of all currents entering and leaving the node must be zero,* see Fig. 3.15. Notice the similarity between the node law and the sum of forces at a point in a mechanical system. The role of these two physical laws is identical in the formulation of differential equations of electrical and mechanical networks. This is stated in simple form in Eq. 3.16, Kirchhoff's current or node law:

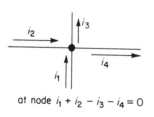

at node $i_1 + i_2 - i_3 - i_4 = 0$

Fig. 3.15. Kirchhoff's current or node law,

$$\sum_{\text{node}} i_n(t) = 0 \qquad (3.16)$$

Electric circuits are formed by interconnecting electric elements

---

*The case of two wires joining is considered to be a single conductor and not a node.

in various combinations. Such combinations of elements are sometimes called networks. We shall deal with a number of simple kinds of networks in later sections. When current flows in a circuit, voltage differences must exist between various points in the network; it is clear that various points will be at different potential energies. As a consequence of the potential drop equations we have assumed for linear elements, it will be seen that paths following series of potential drops and rises along connected elements exist in networks. Generally, it is possible to start at one point in a network and find a number of paths going through various elements encountering various voltage drops and rises which ultimately lead back to the original point. If one starts on such a path, or loop as it is sometimes called, from a point with a certain potential energy (or voltage) and returns to the same point, it is clear that the energy at that point cannot have changed. Thus, any changes in potential energy encountered in traversing such a loop must be compensated for by opposite changes to return to the original level. This statement leads to Kirchhoff's second law —his so-called *loop theorem*. It states that *the total sum of voltage drops and rises around any loop in an electric circuit must equal zero.* This is stated simply in Eq. 3.17 and an example of the resulting "loop equations" is illustrated in Fig. 3.16. Kirchhoff's voltage or loop law:

$$\sum_{\text{loop}} e_n(t) = 0 \quad \text{(around a loop)} \qquad (3.17)$$

The circuit shown in Fig. 3.16 has three loops or paths involving circuit elements. Accordingly, three equations involving the voltage drop around each of these loops may be written as shown in the figure. Note, however, that any one of those three equations may be derived from any of the other two, thus showing that one of the equations is not unique or independent. This is a noteworthy characteristic of all electric circuits and may be generalized in special rules in the science of network topology.

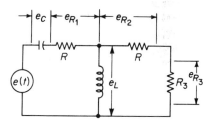

(1) $e_C + e_{R_1} + e_L - e(t) = 0$

(2) $e_L + e_{R_2} + e_{R_3} = 0$

(3) $e_C + e_{R_1} + e_{R_2} + e_{R_3} - e(t) = 0$

Fig. 3.16. Loop equations for an electric circuit. Note: Eq. (3) may be derived directly from Eq. (1) and Eq. (2). Therefore, it is not unique.

3.9   Loop and Node Equations

We have described the basic element equations and the physical laws involved in combining these element equations into a system differential equation. The next step in modeling an electrical system is that of drawing a diagram of the system and defining the system variables. As in the mechanical system, the signs of these variables can also be important. For example, the directions of currents should be assumed and the polarity of voltages established. These directions of current flow and voltage polarities should then be followed carefully in writing the system equations. The choice of signs for the currents and voltages to be determined, that is, the dependent variables in the system, is arbitrary; so that if the actual directions of current flow and actual voltage polarities turn out to be opposite to that chosen, they will appear with opposite signs in the solutions.

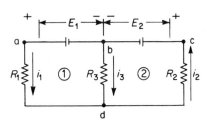

Fig. 3.17.   A two-loop circuit.

Consider a so-called "two-loop" circuit as shown in Fig. 3.17 (there are 2 nodes, b and d).

We shall proceed first with the technique of analysis known as *branch current analysis*. Individual, so-called branch currents, i_1, i_2, and i_3 have been assumed to flow in the branches of the circuit. They are noted in Fig. 3.17. Any directions may be assumed positive but having

once labeled the circuit, one must stick with the assumption made. One node and two loop equations may be written which involve the three unknown currents. These are given in Eqs. 3.18, 3.19, and 3.20.

node $i_1 \quad\quad - i_2 \quad + i_3 = 0$ (3.18)

loop (1) $-R_1 i_1 + R_3 i_3 + E_1 = 0$ (3.19)

loop (2) $-R_3 i_3 - R_2 i_2 - E_2 = 0$ (3.20)

In Eqs. 3.18, 3.19, and 3.20 each voltage *drop* has been given a minus sign. Note that when one "crosses" an element when traversing a loop against the current, so to speak, a voltage *rise* occurs. Also note that the proper sign for rise or drop for the voltage sources E_1 and E_2 must be included. It is common practice to revise the equations

☆   We really mean this statement about assuming initial current flows to be positive in any direction we choose. Don't bother trying to spot the correct direction—if your assumed direction is wrong, the current will come out minus indicating that it flows in the other direction.

so that the source or independent voltages or currents appear on the right-hand side of the equations. It is also common practice to change the signs in the equations so that voltage drops end up with positive signs. With a little practice it is possible to write the equations in this form immediately. Such equations are shown in Eqs. 3.21, 3.22, and 3.23. It is also usual to group terms with corresponding variables in the same column:

Eq. 3.19 becomes $\quad + R_1 i_1 \qquad\qquad - R_3 i_3 = E_1 \qquad\qquad$ (3.21)

Eq. 3.20 becomes $\qquad\qquad + R_2 i_2 + R_3 i_3 = -E_2 \qquad\qquad$ (3.22)

Eq. 3.18 repeats $\qquad i_1 - \quad i_2 + \quad i_3 = 0 \qquad\qquad$ (3.23)

The solution of a set of equations like Eqs. 3.21, 3.22, and 3.23 is straightforward and can be done either by reducing two sets of equations to two equations and two unknowns or by the application of Cramer's rule using determinants. Since Cramer's rule leads to an explicit expression for each of the unknowns, it is preferred. In this case the unknown currents may then be expressed as follows:

$$i_1 = \frac{\begin{vmatrix} E_1 & 0 & -R_3 \\ -E_2 & R_2 & R_3 \\ 0 & -1 & 1 \end{vmatrix}}{\begin{vmatrix} R_1 & 0 & -R_3 \\ 0 & R_2 & R_3 \\ 1 & -1 & +1 \end{vmatrix}}$$

$$= \frac{+R_3 E_1 + R_2 E_1 - R_3 E_2}{+R_2 R_3 + R_1 R_3 + R_1 R_2} = \frac{(R_2 + R_3)E_1 - R_3 E_2}{R_2 R_3 + R_1 R_3 + R_1 R_2} \qquad (3.24)$$

$$i_2 = \frac{\begin{vmatrix} R_1 & E_1 & -R_3 \\ 0 & -E_2 & R_3 \\ 1 & 0 & 1 \end{vmatrix}}{+R_2 R_3 + R_1 R_3 + R_1 R_2}$$

$$= \frac{(-R_1 E_2 + R_3 E_1 - R_3 E_2)}{R_2 R_3 + R_1 R_3 + R_1 R_2} = \frac{R_3 E_1 - (R_1 + R_3)E_2}{R_2 R_3 + R_1 R_3 + R_1 R_2} \qquad (3.25)$$

$$i_3 = \frac{\begin{vmatrix} R_1 & 0 & E_1 \\ 0 & R_2 & -E_2 \\ 1 & -1 & 0 \end{vmatrix}}{+R_2 R_3 + R_1 R_3 + R_1 R_2}$$

$$= \frac{-R_2 E_1 - R_1 E_2}{+R_2 R_3 + R_1 R_3 + R_1 R_2} = \frac{-R_2 E_1 - R_1 E_2}{R_2 R_3 + R_1 R_3 + R_1 R_2} \qquad (3.26)$$

If you've never heard of Cramer's rule, look it up in a math book on determinants. If that's too much trouble, ask any mathematician.

The foregoing analysis assumed that there were *three* unknown branch currents. A more economical method of approach which would, in this case, yield two sets of equations immediately is that of the so-called *loop current approach.* Since the elements are linear and the laws of superposition hold, it may be assumed that there are flowing in $(n-1)$ loops of a circuit $(n-1)$ loop currents. In elements which are common to more than one loop, we shall find more than one loop current flowing. Equations written on this basis may be illustrated by referring to Fig. 3.18 which is similar to Fig. 3.17. The loop currents are generally designated by a curved arrow somewhere near the center of the loop in question. While it makes no difference, loop currents are generally assumed to circulate clockwise.

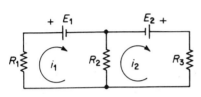

Fig. 3.18. Assumed loop currents in circuit of Fig. 3.17.

Loop equations are written as before, noting that in this case both currents i_1 and i_2 flow through R_2. The sign of the terms generated must be consistent with the direction in which the loop is being traversed and the direction in which the current is assumed to flow. If care is taken at this point, equations having correct signs will result. Equations 3.27 and 3.28 are the loop equations thus produced. As before, it is desirable to group all terms for individual variables in common columns and to put the driving or input functions on the right-hand side of the equations.

$$(R_2 + R_1)i_1 \qquad - R_2 i_2 = -E_1 \qquad (3.27)$$

$$-R_2 i_1 + (R_2 + R_3)i_2 = +E_2 \qquad (3.28)$$

Although perhaps overly complicated for this case, Cramer's rule permits an explicit solution for i_1 and i_2. Note that i_1 and i_2 are not quite the same currents assumed in Fig. 3.17, for in each case their directions are different. Note also that Eq. 3.18 which relates current i_3 to i_1 and i_2 is essentially self-contained within the loop current analysis.

$$i_1 = \cfrac{\begin{vmatrix} -E_1 & -R_2 \\ +E_2 & +(R_2 + R_3) \end{vmatrix}}{\begin{vmatrix} (R_2 + R_1) & -R_2 \\ -R_2 & (R_2 + R_3) \end{vmatrix}} = \frac{-(R_2 + R_3)E_1 + R_2 E_2}{(R_2 + R_1)(R_2 + R_3) - R_2^2}$$

$$= \frac{R_2 E_2 - (R_2 + R_3)E_1}{R_1 R_2 + R_2 R_3 + R_1 R_3} \qquad (3.29)$$

Once again, it doesn't matter if you guess wrong, just stick to your original assumption and see what happens.

$$i_2 = \frac{\begin{vmatrix} R_2 + R_1 & -E_1 \\ -R_2 & +E_2 \end{vmatrix}}{R_1 R_2 + R_2 R_3 + R_1 R_3} = \frac{(R_2 + R_1)E_2 - R_2 E_1}{R_1 R_2 + R_2 R_3 + R_1 R_3} \qquad (3.30)$$

Equations 3.29 and 3.30 produce the same answers as Eqs. 3.24 and 3.26 except for the sign differences which are accounted for by the fact that we have assumed currents in Fig. 3.18 which are opposite to those assumed in Fig. 3.17. The technique applied for the loop current analysis is quite general and will be employed in a number of circuits to be studied in this book.

A third approach which can be used to analyze a circuit is known as the *node-pair voltage* method. This method entails defining voltages between pairs of nodes in addition to defining branch currents.

For example, in the circuit shown in Fig. 3.17 we have two nodes, at b and d, and three branch currents. With the node-pair voltage approach we define e_{bd} as the voltage between the nodes as indicated in Fig. 3.19.

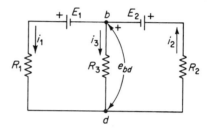

Note that we have to specify that one node of the pair across which the voltage is defined is at a higher potential than the other. In this case we have chosen node b and this is indicated by placing

Fig. 3.19. Assumed node-pair voltage representation.

a plus $(+)$ sign adjacent to b. In writing the equations for the circuit the assumed potential gradient must always be observed.

We start the solution by applying the node law for each node in terms of the branch currents, i.e.,

$$i_2 - i_3 - i_1 = 0 \quad \text{node } b$$

$$i_1 + i_3 - i_2 = 0 \quad \text{node } d$$

One of these equations is obviously redundant so we proceed using the equation for node b only.

We then make use of the element equations to obtain an expression for each branch current in terms of E_1, E_2 and the node-pair voltage e_{bd}, i.e.,

$$i_3 R_3 = e_{bd}$$

$$i_1 R_1 = e_{bd} + E_1$$

A little time spent on showing plus and minus signs on the circuit diagram really pays dividends here.

$$i_2 R_2 = -E_2 - e_{bd}$$

Solving these equations for the currents and substituting in the node equation yields

$$-\frac{E_2}{R_2} - \frac{e_{bd}}{R_2} - \frac{e_{bd}}{R_3} - \frac{e_{bd}}{R_1} - \frac{E_1}{R_1} = 0$$

This results in the following expression for e_{bd},

$$e_{bd} = -\frac{E_2 R_1 R_3 + E_1 R_2 R_3}{R_1 R_2 + R_1 R_3 + R_2 R_3}$$

Substituting in the element equations yields the individual branch currents in terms of the resistances and the voltages E_1 and E_2. For example, in the case of i_1 we find

$$i_1 = \frac{e_{bd} + E_1}{R_1}$$

$$= \frac{E_1}{R_1} - \frac{1}{R_1}\left[\frac{E_2 R_1 R_3 + E_1 R_2 R_3}{R_1 R_2 + R_1 R_3 + R_2 R_3}\right]$$

or

$$i_1 = \frac{E_1(R_2 + R_3) - E_2 R_3}{R_1 R_2 + R_1 R_3 + R_2 R_3}$$

This is, of course, the same result as obtained in Eq. 3.24.

The example does not illustrate the node-pair voltage method to the best advantage because it was a relatively simple circuit. However, it did enable us to solve the problem without using determinants. Had there been more branches in the circuit we could have demonstrated more effectively the time and labor saved by using the node-pair voltage method.

Briefly then, we can use any one of three methods to obtain electrical circuit equations. Any method can be used on any circuit though one method will usually be better than the other two, depending on the nature of the circuit. Sometimes it is desirable to use two methods in order to check the results.

A rigorous treatment of the network topology considerations required to generalize the use of these techniques is beyond the scope of this text and the interested student should consult a textbook on electrical network analysis.

Even with considerable experience in the use of the various methods, the engineer often finds it necessary to proceed on the basis of trial and error, i.e., he selects an approach and sees where it leads him. If it becomes clear part way through the analysis that a different method might lead to an easier solution then he would be well advised to change his method.

The following general recommendation will usually prove helpful in deciding which method to use at the first attempt.

If the number of node-pair voltages is less than the number of loop currents required to analyze the circuit then the node-pair voltage method should be adopted. (The branch current method seldom leads to the easiest solution.)

Usually a good deal of common sense and puzzle-solving ability are required to derive the most useful, "neat" set of differential equations. While the methods proposed in this book may not lead immediately to such a neat set, they will produce correct sets of equations and constitute a useful technique for all engineering students.

We shall proceed with our discussion of loop and node equation formulation by means of a series of examples. These examples are intended to embrace most questions which will arise in formulating equations for electric circuits comprised of linear elements.

3.10   Differential Operator Notation

Before proceeding with examples of circuits, a new, useful notation will be introduced. It is proposed to replace the symbol d/dt for the operation of differentiation by the single letter D and the process of integration $\int dt$ by the inverse of D, i.e., $1/D$. *For the purpose of this text this is merely a change in notation and has no other significance.* You will learn later that rigorous mathematical significance can be ascribed to similar-appearing operational notations when they are used to identify mathematical operators such as the Heaviside operator p and the Laplace operator s. Confusion can arise because the Heaviside and Laplace operators appear in transformations of differential equations in exactly the same way as the operator D does.

Let it be remembered that for our purposes D merely replaces the Newtonian dots or the differential operator d/dt. Higher derivatives are indicated by exponents so that the second derivative, for example, is represented by D^2. The advantage of this notation is that a variable itself can be "factored" out of all terms in which it appears, and the terms containing D may be treated according to the normal rules of algebra. Thus an equation of the form of Eq. 3.31 may appear as in Eq. 3.32.

This assumes that you have managed to define the *minimum* number of node-pair voltages and the *minimum* number of loop currents. It is very easy to define too many of both.

    Laplace transforms are really great. You're certain to hear about them again.

$$A_3\frac{dy^3}{dt^3} + A_2\frac{dy^2}{dt^2} + A_1\frac{dy}{dt} + A_0 y = B_2\frac{dx^2}{dt^2} + B_1\frac{dx}{dt} + B_0 x \quad (3.31)$$

$$(A_3 D^3 + A_2 D^2 + A_1 D + A_0)\, y\,(t) = (B_2 D^2 + B_1 D + B_0)\, x\,(t) \quad (3.32)$$

This has great implications in rearranging differential equations to solve explicitly for certain variables. It should be borne in mind, however, that when this is done, one must always be able to revert to the original differential equation form as a check on the correctness of the notation. Equations 3.33 and 3.34 follow accordingly from Eq. 3.32.

$$y(t) = \frac{B_2 D^2 + B_1 D + B_0}{A_3 D^3 + A_2 D^2 + A_1 D + A_0} x(t) \quad (3.33)$$

$$\frac{y}{x}(t) = \frac{B_2 D^2 + B_1 D + B_0}{A_3 D^3 + A_2 D^2 + A_1 D + A_0} \quad (3.34)$$

There are even occasions when it is useful to represent the polynomial expression in the numerator and denominator of Eq. 3.34 as a product of their algebraic factors as in Eq. 3.35. In this expression z_n represents the roots of the numerator and p_n represents the roots of the denominator.

$$\frac{y}{x}(t) = \frac{(D - z_1)(D - z_2)}{(D - p_1)(D - p_2)(D - p_3)} \quad (3.35)$$

Equation 3.35 seems a "far cry" from Eq. 3.31, but it has been arrived at through notation change and algebraic manipulation only.

3.11   Examples of Differential Equations in Electric Circuits

3.11-1: Single Loop *RC* Unit (Fig. 3.A).

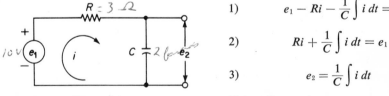

$$R = 3\,\Omega$$

$$10\,V\ e_1 \qquad C = 2 \qquad e_2$$

Figure 3.A

1) $\quad e_1 - Ri - \dfrac{1}{C}\displaystyle\int i\,dt = 0$

2) $\quad Ri + \dfrac{1}{C}\displaystyle\int i\,dt = e_1$

3) $\quad e_2 = \dfrac{1}{C}\displaystyle\int i\,dt$

Using D notation,

$$\left(R + \frac{1}{CD}\right)i = e_1$$

$$\frac{E_2}{E_1} = \frac{1}{1 + RCD}$$

4 time constants
4) of curve voltage /
time

This may seem like pure magic—it does to most people. However, it works and after a while you will become used to it.

1   63.2 %
2   86.5 %
3   95 %
4   98 %

$$Time - RC$$

$$\frac{1}{RC}$$

$$\left(\frac{1}{RC}\right) + D$$

5)
$$i = \frac{e_1}{R + 1/CD} = \frac{CDe_1}{RCD + 1}$$

6)
$$e_2 = \frac{1}{CD}i = \frac{e_1}{RCD + 1}$$

which may be returned to differential equation form:

7)
$$(RCD + 1)e_2 = e_1$$

8)
$$RC\frac{de_2}{dt} + e_2 = e_1$$

3.11-2: Two Loop Circuit with Voltage Source (Fig. 3.B).

1) $R_1 i_1 + \frac{1}{C}\int i_1\, dt$

$\qquad -\frac{1}{C}\int i_2\, dt = e$

2) $-\frac{1}{C}\int i_1\, dt + L\frac{di_2}{dt}$

$\qquad +\frac{1}{C}\int i_2\, dt + R_2 i_2 = 0$

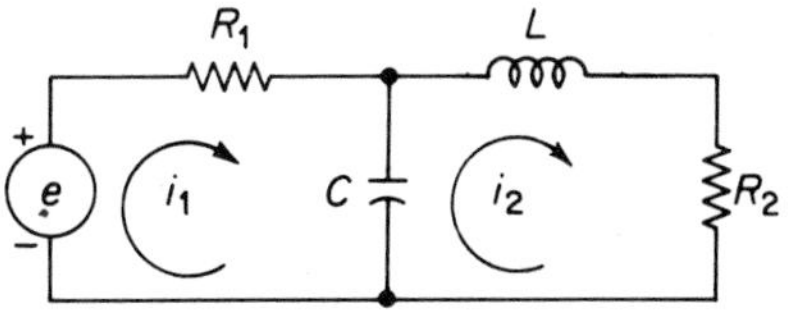

Figure 3.B

which yields

3)
$$\left(R_1 + \frac{1}{CD}\right)i_1 - \frac{1}{CD}i_2 = e$$

4)
$$-\frac{1}{CD}i_1 + \left(LD + \frac{1}{CD} + R_2\right)i_2 = 0$$

i_1 and i_2 may be represented explicitly from Eqs. 3 and 4 using Cramer's rule.

$$i_1 = \frac{\begin{vmatrix} e & -1/CD \\ 0 & (LD + 1/CD + R_2) \end{vmatrix}}{\begin{vmatrix} (R_1 + 1/CD) & -1/CD \\ -1/CD & (LD + 1/CD + R_2) \end{vmatrix}}$$

$$= \frac{(LD + 1/CD + R_2)e}{(R_1 + 1/CD)(LD + 1/CD + R_2) - 1/C^2D^2}$$

$$= \frac{(LD + 1/CD + R_2)e}{R_1 LD + [(R_1 + R_2)/CD] + L/C + R_1 R_2}$$

$$= \frac{(LCD^2 + R_2 CD + 1)e}{R_1 CLD^2 + (L + R_1 R_2 C)D + R_1 + R_2}$$

$$i_2 = \frac{\begin{vmatrix} R_1 + 1/CD & e \\ -1/CD & 0 \end{vmatrix}}{\begin{vmatrix} (R_1 + 1/CD) & -1/CD \\ -1/CD & (LD + 1/CD + R_2) \end{vmatrix}} = +\frac{e/CD}{\Delta}$$

$$= \frac{e}{R_1 CLD^2 + (L + R_1 R_2 C)D + R_1 + R_2}$$

3.11-3: *RLC* Parallel Circuit with Voltage Source

At first glance Fig. 3.C looks like a 3-loop circuit, thus we proceed to solve for loop currents i_1, i_2, and i_3.

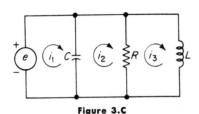

1) $\dfrac{1}{C}\displaystyle\int i_1\,dt - \dfrac{1}{C}\int i_2\,dt \qquad\qquad = e$

2) $-\dfrac{1}{C}\displaystyle\int i_1\,dt + \dfrac{1}{C}\int i_2\,dt + Ri_2 - Ri_3 = 0$

3) $\qquad\quad -Ri_2 + Ri_3 + L\dfrac{di_3}{dt} \quad = 0$

Figure 3.C

We might now proceed with Cramer's rule to solve for i_1, i_2, and i_3 but let us first try a branch current analysis. The figure may be redrawn to show that there are only two nodes (Fig. 3.D).

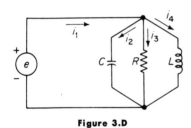

We now see that the voltage e exists across each element as an independent variable, thus:

$$e = \frac{1}{C}\int i_2\,dt = Ri_3 = L\frac{di_4}{dt}$$

Figure 3.D

or

$$i_2 = C\frac{de}{dt}; \qquad i_3 = \frac{1}{R}\,e; \qquad i_4 = \frac{1}{L}\int e\,dt$$

which gives the currents directly—no reduction is needed!

We see that $i_1 = i_2 + i_3 + i_4 = (CD + 1/R + 1/LD)\,e$. The same result will come from the application of Cramer's rule to Eqs. 1, 2, and 3 above which the student may verify if he desires. This example illustrates the importance of branch current analysis in certain cases.

3.11-4: *RLC* Parallel Circuit with Current Source (Fig. 3.E).

As in Ex. 3.11-3 we may proceed with a loop analysis. Note that i_1 is identical to i and not dependent. To write a loop equation involving the current source we must include the dependent voltage rise e_i across the source.

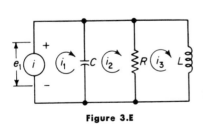

1) $\qquad + e_i + \dfrac{1}{C}\displaystyle\int i_2\,dt = \dfrac{1}{C}\int i\,dt$

2) $\qquad + \dfrac{1}{C}\displaystyle\int i_2\,dt + Ri_2 - Ri_3 = \dfrac{1}{C}\int i\,dt$

Figure 3.E

3)　　　$-Ri_2 + L\dfrac{di_3}{dt} + Ri_3 = 0$

But are there really three unknowns and three equations? Let
us try a branch current analysis
again. Show the dependent voltage
e across all elements. Note that
$e = e_i$ (Fig. 3.F).

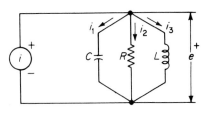

Figure 3.F

4)　　　　　　　$i_1 + i_2 + i_3 = i = C\dfrac{de}{dt} + \dfrac{1}{R}e + \dfrac{1}{L}\int e\, dt$

5)　　　　　　　$\left(CD + \dfrac{1}{R} + \dfrac{1}{LD}\right)e = i$

Equation 5 is the classic second order differential equation for the parallel *RLC* circuit. Note that one equation (not three) suffices to describe
the system. Sometimes Eq. 5 is rewritten in the following form:

6)　　　　　　　$\left(LCD^2 + \dfrac{L}{R}D + 1\right)e = LD\,i$

or

7)　　　　　　　$LC\dfrac{d^2e}{dt^2} + \dfrac{L}{R}\dfrac{de}{dt} + e = L\dfrac{di}{dt}$

3.11-5:　*RLC* Series Circuit with Voltage and Current Sources (Figs.
　　　　3.G and 3.H).

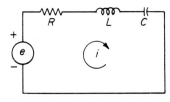

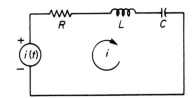

Figure 3.G　　　　　　　　　　　　　**Figure 3.H**

1)　　　　　　　$Ri + L\dfrac{di}{dt} + \dfrac{1}{C}\int i\, dt = e$

2)　　　　　　　$\left(LD + R + \dfrac{1}{CD}\right)i = e$

3)　　　　　　　$(LCD^2 + RCD + 1)i = CD\,e$

or

4)
$$LC\frac{d^2i}{dt^2} + RC\frac{di}{dt} + i = C\frac{de}{dt}$$

$$e_R = iR$$

$$e_L = L\frac{di}{dt}$$

$$e_C = \frac{1}{C}\int i\,dt$$

Since i is given, there is no governing over-all equation.

3.11-6:   3 Node-6 Loop Circuit; Voltage Source (Fig. 3.I)

Since there are 3 nodes and 6 loops, redraw the circuit as a node circuit (Fig. 3.J) and define node-pair voltages e_1 and e_2.

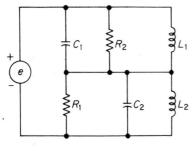

Figure 3.I

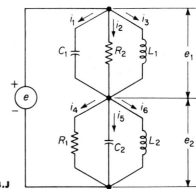

Figure 3.J

1) $e_1 + e_2 = e$

2) $i_1 + i_2 + i_3 = i_4 + i_5 + i_6$ 2 equations-1) and 3)

or   2 unknowns-e_1 and e_2

3) $C_1\frac{de_1}{dt} + \frac{1}{R_2}e_1 + \frac{1}{L_1}\int e_1\,dt = \frac{1}{R_1}e_2 + C_2\frac{de_2}{dt} + \frac{1}{L_2}\int e_2\,dt$

or

4) $\left[C_1 D + \frac{1}{R_2} + \frac{1}{L_1 D}\right]e_1 = \left[\frac{1}{R_1} + C_2 D + \frac{1}{L_2 D}\right]e_2$

3.11-7:   Circuit with Both Voltage and Current Source (Fig. 3.K)

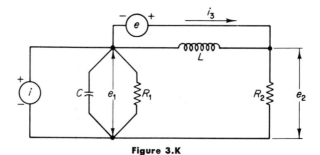

Figure 3.K

With 3 nodes and 4 loops a node-pair voltage analysis seems indicated. Since we shall sum currents, the unknown dependent current through the source e must appear as a dependent variable. Node-pair voltages e_1 and e_2 may be chosen as the other two dependent variables.

1) $$C\frac{de_1}{dt} + \frac{1}{R_1}e_1 + i_3 = -\frac{1}{L}\int e\, dt + i$$

2) $$e_1 - e_2 = -e$$

3) $$+\frac{1}{R_2}e_2 - i_3 = -\frac{1}{L}\int e\, dt$$

For example, to solve for e_2:
Eq. 1 and Eq. 3 can be combined to yield, Eq. 4

4) $$C\frac{de_1}{dt} + \frac{1}{R_1}e_1 + \frac{1}{R_2}e_2 = +i$$

Equations 4) and 2) can be combined to yield,

$$\left(CD + \frac{1}{R_1} + \frac{1}{R_2}\right)e_2 = i + e\left[CD + \frac{1}{R_1}\right]$$

3.11-8:   Circuit with 3 Mutually Coupled Inductors (Fig. 3.L)

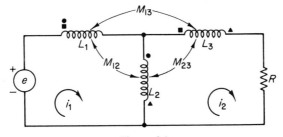

Figure 3.L

It is more difficult to maintain a physical "feel" for mutual inductance problems, and a more systematic approach to writing the equations is required. The student is advised to write the net voltage *drop* associated with each inductor before writing the loop equations.

$$e_{L_1} = L_1\frac{di_1}{dt} + M_{12}\frac{di_1}{dt} - M_{12}\frac{di_2}{dt} + M_{13}\frac{di_2}{dt}$$

$$e_{L_2} = L_2\frac{di_1}{dt} - L_2\frac{di_2}{dt} + M_{12}\frac{di_1}{dt} + M_{23}\frac{di_2}{dt}$$

$$e_{L_3} = L_3\frac{di_2}{dt} + M_{23}\frac{di_1}{dt} - M_{23}\frac{di_2}{dt} + M_{13}\frac{di_1}{dt}$$

Loop equations are, therefore,

1) $(L_1 + L_2 + 2M_{12})Di_1 - (+L_2 + M_{12} - M_{23} - M_{13})Di_2 = e$

2) $(-L_2 - M_{12} + M_{23} + M_{13})Di_1 + (L_2 + L_3 - 2M_{23})Di_2 + Ri_2 = 0$

3.12 Mechanical Network Diagrams

For an electrical system we have seen that the components of the system (resistors, capacitors, inductors, etc.) can be regarded as two-terminal elements where a current goes "through" and a voltage drop exists "across" the element.

We have also seen that electrical networks are formed by interconnecting these two-terminal elements in various combinations and that a number of techniques are available to derive the differential equations for such networks.

These same techniques can sometimes be applied to mechanical systems if the concept of the "through" and "across" variable is used to redraw the mechanical system in the form of a network of two-terminal devices. The problem then becomes one of writing a set of network equations from this topographical arrangement.

To understand how mechanical elements can be considered to be two-terminal devices we need to refer back to Chap. 2. Here it was shown that each element (mass, spring, or damper) could be completely characterized by a differential equation.

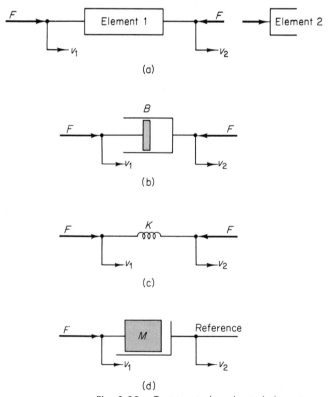

Fig. 3.20. Two-terminal mechanical element representation.

In the case of a spring, the difference in displacement of the ends is proportional to the applied force. For the damper, the difference in velocity of the ends is proportional to the applied force; and for the mass, it was shown by d'Alembert's principle that the force is proportional to the acceleration of the mass relative to the ground. Thus each of these elements could be characterized as a two-terminal device having an input and an output with a force acting upon it.

More generally, each element can be represented by a box with a line entering and leaving it as shown in Fig. 3.20. The line represents the force on the element and the positive direction of force is denoted by the input arrow. The input of the element is the point where the force enters and the output the point where it leaves. *The "leaving" force is in the same direction as the "entering" force when one considers the action of the element on whatever is connected to its output.*

Thus the force on an element can be thought of as passing through the element and force is, therefore, a "through" variable.

In addition since each element has a difference in position, velocity, or acceleration across the input and output terminals, this variable (position, velocity, or acceleration) can be considered as an "across" variable.

The differential equation for each of the basic mechanical elements can be written in terms of their "through" and "across" variables as follows.

(1) *The Spring.* For a spring the input force is related to the difference in position of the two ends of the spring. The spring is represented schematically by a coil of gradient K. For the assumed force direction as shown in Fig. 3.20,

$$F = K(x_1 - x_2) + K\delta_0 = K \int (v_1 - v_2)\, dt \qquad (3.36)$$

(2) *The Damper.* In the case of the damper, from the previous discussion referring to Figs. 2.6 and 3.20, there is a relationship between the "through" variable (force) and the "across" variable (velocity). As before the damper is represented by a cylinder and piston. The force on the damper can be expressed as follows:

$$F = B\,(v_1 - v_2) \qquad (3.37)$$

(3) *The Mass.* The mass can be considered a two-terminal mechanical element provided that one of the terminals is made a reference terminal. This reference terminal can have a nonzero position or it can be moving with a constant velocity; however, it may not be

accelerating with reference to the absolute reference frame. For most engineering calculations the surface of the earth may be taken to have zero acceleration. Under these circumstances the acceleration of the other terminal of the mass element is directly related to the force "through" the mass element by d'Alembert's principle. The mass is represented by a box with a letter inside denoting the amount of mass. The reference terminal is shown as an L not connected to the mass because unlike the terminals of the other elements it is not physically connected to it. As long as the reference is not accelerating then force can be expressed in terms of the acceleration of the nonreference terminal which is the acceleration of the mass itself and we can write

$$F = M \frac{dv_1}{dt} \quad \text{where} \quad \frac{dv_2}{dt} = 0 \tag{3.38}$$

These definitions are equivalent to the definitions that were presented previously. The only differences are that each element has deen represented by an equation and a two-terminal drawing including the mass, and they have been defined in terms of the velocity variables instead of position variables. These basic definitions can now be used to derive a set of differential equations for a mechanical system. The concept of the "through" and "across" variable will be used. Instead of isolating the masses in the system, an equivalent two-terminal circuit will be drawn for the mechanical system. The differential equations will be written from this circuit in much the same way as the differential equations were written for an electrical network. However several important points should be remembered.

(a) In addition, it will be recognized that the velocities of any element terminals which are connected together must be equal. This relation can be called a *compatibility* requirement.

(b) Also, it will be recognized that the force into any junction in this circuit is equal to the force out of that junction. This result evolves from applying d'Alembert's principle to a point in a mechanical circuit. Since a point has no mass, the sum of the forces at that point must be zero.

(c) As before, a velocity which is a known function of time is considered a velocity source. A force which is a known function of time is a force source. These sources will be represented schematically by circles with the magnitude of the source shown inside and the direction denoted by an arrow.

The method can be illustrated by the following example in Fig. 3.21. The example will be first analyzed using the free body diagram method as presented in Chap. 2.

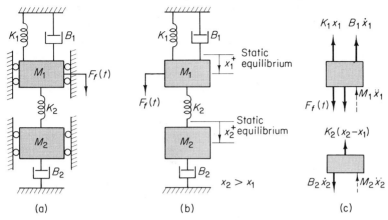

Fig. 3.21. Example using "free body" method.

From this free body diagram the differential equations can be written almost by inspection by using Eq. 2.4a to obtain

$$M_1\ddot{x}_1 + B_1\dot{x}_1 + (K_1 + K_2)x_1 = K_2 x_2 + F_f(t) \qquad (3.39)$$

$$M_2\ddot{x}_2 + B_2\dot{x}_2 + K_2 x_2 = K_2 x_1 \qquad (3.40)$$

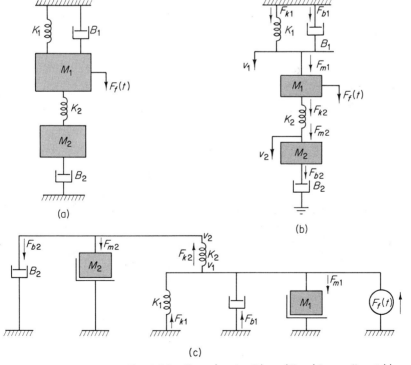

Fig. 3.22. Example using "through" and "across" variables.

The element equations and their equivalent two-terminal networks can be used to analyze this same system. As before, the mechanical system is drawn and the elements are assigned parameter values (Fig. 3.22). In addition the velocity of each terminal of each element is given an assumed direction, noticing that the compatibility equations require that only two velocities need to be defined. Also the force through each element is given an assumed direction. These force and velocity variables are assigned a letter. Now using the concept of a mass, damper, or spring element the original diagram can be redrawn in terms of a two-terminal mechanical circuit. Notice that the reference terminal for each of the masses M_1 and M_2 is shown to be ground. From this representation using the fact that the net force into a connection must be zero, the differential equations for the system can be written and are shown below, assuming that "ground" has zero velocity and acceleration.

$$K_1 \int (0 - v_1)\, dt \ = F_{k1}$$

$$B_1 (0 - v_1) \qquad = F_{b1}$$

$$M_1 \frac{dv_1}{dt} \qquad = F_{m1}$$

Element equations   (3.41)

$$K_2 \int (v_1 - v_2)\, dt = F_{k2}$$

$$B_2 v_2 \qquad = F_{b2}$$

$$M_2 \frac{dv_2}{dt} \qquad = F_{m2}$$

$$F_{k1} + F_{b1} = F_{m1} + F_{k2} - F_f(t)$$

Continuity equations   (3.42)

$$F_{k2} = F_{m2} + F_{b2}$$

These equations can then be combined to eliminate all the forces F_{k1}, F_{b1}, F_{m1}, F_{k2}, F_{m2}, and F_{b2}. The equations can be written then in terms of v_1, v_2, $F_f(t)$ and the parameters of the system M_1, M_2; B_1, B_2; and K_1, K_2. The resulting equations are

$$-K_1 \int v_1\, dt - B_1 v_1 = M_1 \frac{dv_1}{dt} + K_2 \int (v_1 - v_2)\, dt - F_f(t)$$

(3.43)

$$K_2 \int (v_1 - v_2)\, dt = M_2 \frac{dv_2}{dt} + B_2 v_2$$

or

$$M_1 \frac{dv_1}{dt} + B_1 v_1 + (K_1 + K_2) \int v_1 \, dt = K_2 \int v_2 \, dt + F_f(t)$$

$$M_2 \frac{dv_2}{dt} + B_2 v_2 + K_2 \int v_2 \, dt = K_2 \int v_1 \, dt$$

(3.44)

These equations are directly equivalent to the differential equations derived using d'Alembert's principle and the isolating the free bodies in the system. This can be seen by substituting $\dot{x}_1$ for v_1 and $\dot{x}_2$ for v_2 in the equations. The resulting differential equations are then written in terms of the terminal positions in the system rather than the velocities. Then the result is identical to that obtained from the free body diagrams.

Although we shall use the mechanical network concept from Sec. 3.14 to demonstrate similarities between electrical and mechanical systems, we do not recommend it as a general method for analyzing mechanical systems. This is because it can lead to great complexity when used to solve systems other than straightforward spring-mass-damper combinations. The free body diagram approach, on the other hand, can be used with equal facility on all mechanical systems and is therefore a much more satisfactory method.

3.13 Mathematical Model, Checking Methods

The processes outlined for mechanical systems and electrical systems will yield a mathematical model for these classes of systems. Often however, this mathematical model may become quite complicated algebraically and it is possible for the engineer to make errors. It is convenient, then, to have some way to check one's results. These check can take many forms.

The most common types of errors in the formulation of mathematical models are:

(a) algebra errors
(b) sign errors
(c) errors in physical reasoning
(d) errors in mathematical models of physical system elements
(e) dimensional inconsistency

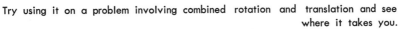

Try using it on a problem involving combined rotation and translation and see where it takes you.

This is really useful material. Everyone makes mistakes, especially when equations contain many terms and coefficients. Checking takes time but it is worth it in the end. We urge you to use these methods.

3.13–1 ALGEBRA ERRORS

Occasionally in combining system element equations to form a mathematical model for the entire system, terms may be lost or combined incorrectly. Such errors can be detected by carefully going over every step of the analysis. However, this is tedious and one often repeats an error. The presence of such errors can often be detected by using the requirement of dimensional consistency of the equation. The equal sign in an equation denotes that the quantities on either side are equal in magnitude and dimension.

For example, Eq. 6 of Ex. 3.11-4 is

$$\left(LCD^2 + \frac{L}{R}D + 1\right)e = LDi$$

Checking dimensions of each term gives

$$\left(\frac{\text{volt}}{\text{ampere/sec}} \times \frac{\text{ampere} - \text{sec}}{\text{volt}} \times \frac{1}{\text{sec}^2} + \frac{\text{volt/ampere/sec}}{\text{volt/ampere}} \times \frac{1}{\text{sec}} + 1\right)\text{volt}$$
$$= \frac{\text{volt}}{\text{ampere/sec}} \times \frac{\text{ampere}}{\text{sec}}$$

Hence, the equation checks dimensionally. Whenever the dimensions do not check, there are three possibilities: 1) an error in algebra has been made, 2) an error in assigning the dimensions has been made, or 3) a physical law has been used incorrectly.

3.13–2 SIGN ERRORS

Errors in sign result usually from inconsistent applications of physical laws and sign conventions or in subsequent algebraic manipulation. It is possible to check signs of certain terms in differential equations from a determination of the stability of the system described but these techniques cannot be presented at this point. One must, therefore, rely on systematic application of originally chosen sign conventions and on checking algebraic manipulations.

Sign errors, algebraic errors, and errors in physical reasoning can often be detected by simplifying the system differential equations in a rather formalized way. Three ways in which this may be done are:

1. LET SOME OF THE SYSTEM VARIABLES AND THEIR DERIVATIVES GO TO ZERO OR INFINITY. For example in the case of a mechanical system, this represents a condition where the system is at rest, nonaccelerating, at zero velocity, or perhaps at some limit of motion. The resulting differential equation has fewer terms. Then the signs and magnitudes of the simpler expression can be compared to the assumed sign conventions and the basic physical equations for the elements to check for inconsistencies.

For example:

$$m\ddot{x} + B\dot{x} + Kx = {'F}$$

If the system is at rest, $\ddot{x} = \dot{x} = 0$, hence, $Kx = F$. This tells us that the system will come to rest at a new equilibrium position, distance F/K from the old one, which is correct.

If $x = \ddot{x} = 0$ the system is moving with a constant velocity and is just passing the point of zero spring deflection. Then,

$$B\dot{x} = F$$

Thus a positive force causes a proportional positive velocity. Again this is correct according to our chosen sign conventions and physical equation for a damper.

If $x = \dot{x} = 0$ the system is just starting to accelerate and has no velocity or displacement at this instant. Then,

$$m\ddot{x} = F$$

According to the chosen sign and d'Alembert's principle this is correct. A positive force will cause a positive acceleration.

In this way we look at the system differential equation at particular instants of time at which some of the variables and/or their derivatives are zero. This enables us to reduce the equation to a simpler one in order to apply the sign convention chosen and the particular physical equations which represent each element.

2. LET SOME OF THE SYSTEM PARAMETERS GO TO ZERO OR INFINITY. This has the effect of replacing the system with a simpler one in which the signs and magnitudes of the terms can easily be checked by the assumed sign convention and element equations. In mechanical systems letting B or $K = 0$ is equivalent to assuming no connection while B or $K = \infty$ is equivalent to a solid connection. Similarly, $M = 0$ represents zero mass while $M = \infty$ is equivalent to a solid ground connection.

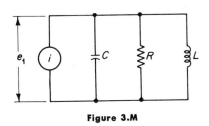

Figure 3.M

In electrical circuits when $R = \infty$ an open circuit exists and when $R = 0$, the circuit becomes a solid connection, etc. Example 3.11-4 can be reduced for checking using this approach (Fig. 3.M).

$$\left[LCD^2 + \frac{L}{R}D + 1\right]e = LDi$$

If $L = R = \infty$, the inductor and resistors are assumed to be open circuits; the circuit then reduces to Fig. 3.N

The equation for this circuit can be written by inspection.

$$e = \frac{i}{CD}$$

If the original differential equation is divided by L to prevent indeterminant forms, then we have

$$\left[CD^2 + \frac{D}{R} + \frac{1}{L}\right]e = Di$$

which becomes

$$CD^2e = Di \qquad \begin{matrix} L \longrightarrow \infty \\ R \longrightarrow \infty \end{matrix}$$

or

$$e = \frac{i}{CD}$$

Hence the chosen sign and form of the LCD^2e term is correct. In a similar way we could check the $(D/R)e$ term by letting $L = \infty$, $C = 0$; then the original circuit would become Fig. 3.O, hence, $e = Ri$.

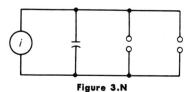

Figure 3.N

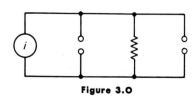

Figure 3.O

If the original differential equation is again divided by L and the limits taken on L and C we obtain

$$\frac{De}{R} = Di$$

Hence, $e = Ri$, which checks the sign and form of the resistance term.

The form of the e term could be checked by letting $R = \infty$ and $C = 0$. This approach must be employed with some care because the correspondence between limiting values of system parameters and physical conditions which cause them must be known. For instance, it must be recognized that $C = 0$ corresponds to an open circuit as $R = L = \infty$ does. In addition the differential equations must usually be manipulated to prevent terms taking the form $0/0$, ∞/∞, or ∞ which would make the reduction difficult.

3. WHEN MULTIPLE INPUTS OCCUR IT IS USEFUL TO ASSUME THAT ALL BUT ONE OF THEM IS ZERO, THEN EXAMINE THE SIMPLER EXPRESSION IN LIGHT OF THE CHOSEN SIGN CONVENTIONS AND PHYSICAL EQUATIONS GOVERNING THE SYSTEM. Example 3.11-7 can be examined in this way, as shown in Fig. 3.P. The resulting equations are

4)
$$\left[CD + \frac{1}{R_1} \right] e_1 + \frac{1}{R_2} e_2 = i$$

2)
$$-e_1 + e_2 = e$$

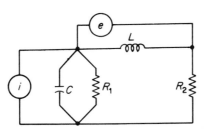

Figure 3.P

If $e = 0$, then since a voltage source was assumed for e, L is shorted out. The resulting circuit is in Fig. 3.Q for which we can write

$$i = CDe_2 + \frac{e_2}{R_1} + \frac{e_2}{R_2} \quad \text{and} \quad e_1 = e_2$$

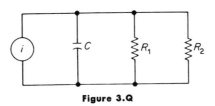

Figure 3.Q

Returning to the system equations, if $e = 0$ they become

$$e_1 = e_2$$

$$\left(CD + \frac{1}{R_1} + \frac{1}{R_2}\right)e_2 = i$$

which are the same as the derived equations for the reduced circuit when $e = 0$.

We could also let $i = 0$ which would amount to assuming an open circuit through the current source, as shown in Fig. 3.R. This circuit could be analyzed to develop a differential equation for it.

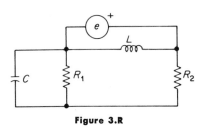

Figure 3.R

$$e = e_2 - e_1$$

$$\left[CD + \frac{1}{R_1}\right]e_1 + \frac{1}{R_2}e_2 = 0$$

which are the same as the derived equations when $i = 0$.

3.13–3   ERRORS IN ELEMENT MODELS

Often the elements in mechanical, electrical, hydraulic, thermal, etc., systems are not easily described by simple mathematical equations. We are forced to make simplifying assumptions and it is a good idea to verify these assumptions by experimentally checking the element models. In this process we subject the element to a set of known inputs and observe its outputs. On the basis of the mathematical model of the element we predict what the outputs will be for these known inputs and compare the results. If the predicted response is close enough to the actual response, we assume that the model is correct. For example, we might check the resistance R_1 in Fig. 3.17 by performing a simple e versus i test as in Fig. 3.S.

The line passing through data points should have a slope of R_1 if the model is correct. In addition if the voltage across the resistor is changing with time, there should be no variations from this straight line if the average voltage is plotted versus the average current. If this is not the case, as may occur in wire-wound resistances, then the resistor has some inductance and/or capacitance. Therefore, our model for R_1 would not be correct.

These checking methods present a number of ways to check a

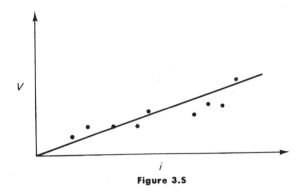

Figure 3.5

mathematical model. Since important decisions involving money and manpower may be made on the basis of such models, their validity should be well established whenever possible.

3.14 Summary of Mathematical Modeling Methods

In Chaps. 2 and 3 mechanical and electrical systems were represented by mathematical equations. The process is described as mathematical modeling. Several approaches have been outlined but they all have involved some basic modeling principles.

(a) Draw a system diagram showing the basic elements.
(b) Define variables, assign letters to the variables, note them on the diagram, and establish a sign or direction for each variable.
(c) Write the element equations in terms of the variables.
(d) Using physical laws, combine the element equations based on the system diagram.
(e) Variables may be redefined for convenience or computation.
(f) Check equations for sign compatibility, correct dimensions, and correct physical reasoning.

3.15 Analogy—Mechanical and Electrical Systems

The "through" and "across" variable concept as developed in Sec. 3.12 for mechanical systems is much more appropriate in the application of Kirchhoff's laws to electrical systems. We may consider voltage as an "across" variable since we can define a voltage across each terminal of an electric element. Current may be considered a "through" variable since each element has a flow of current through it. The element equations define the the relationship between these two variables. One then observes the analogy between force and current which are both

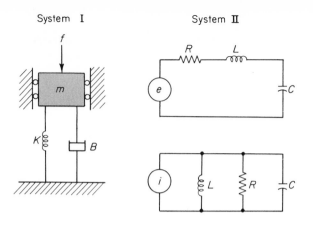

System I   System II

Figure 3.T

"through" variables and velocity and voltage which are both "across" variables.

Many mechanical and electrical systems have the same mathematical model. This can be illustrated by formulating the mathematical model for the two systems in Fig. 3.T; one mechanical, one electrical.

Both systems will be analyzed using the "through" and "across" variable approach.

(a) Variable definition (Fig. 3.U):

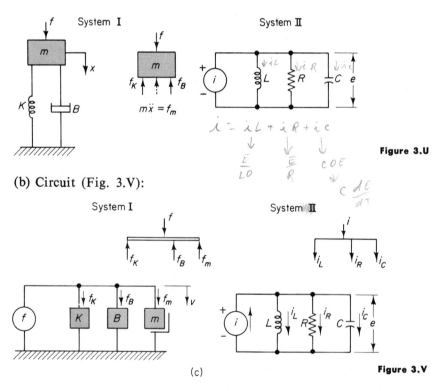

System I   System II

$$m\ddot{x} = f_m$$

$$i = i_L + i_R + i_c$$

$$\frac{E}{LD} \qquad \frac{E}{R} \qquad COE$$

$$C\frac{dE}{dT}$$

Figure 3.U

(b) Circuit (Fig. 3.V):

System I   System II

(c)

Figure 3.V

(c) Element differential equations:

System I   System II

$$K \int (v - 0)\, dt = f_K \qquad i_L = \frac{1}{L} \int e\, dt$$

$$B(v - 0) = f_B \qquad i_R = \frac{1}{R} e$$

$$M\frac{dv}{dt} = f_m \qquad i_C = C\frac{de}{dt}$$

(d) Circuit law application:

System I   System II

Sum of forces into a junction is zero (d'Alembert's principle).   Sum of currents into a junction is zero (Kirchhoff's node equation).

$$f = f_K + f_B + f_m \qquad\qquad i = i_L + i_R + i_C$$

(e) Substitution of the element equation into circuit law relations:

$$f = K \int v\, dt + Bv + M\frac{dv}{dt} \tag{3.45}$$

$$i = \frac{1}{L} \int e\, dt + \frac{1}{R} e + C\frac{de}{dt}$$

Notice that the resulting two differential equations are identical in form. If the following correspondence is made, they are identical and the two systems are analogous to one another.

$$f \longleftrightarrow i \qquad B \longleftrightarrow \frac{1}{R}$$

$$v \longleftrightarrow e$$

$$K \longleftrightarrow \frac{1}{L} \qquad M \longleftrightarrow C$$

A set of values exists for R, L, and C which will give a voltage-time response that is identical to the velocity-time response of a mechanical system with a given B, R, and M. Thus the velocity-time response of the mechanical system mass to a change in force could be determined by subjecting the analogous electrical system to a change in current and observing the resultant voltage-time response. This is the basis of one method of analogue computation. In this type of analogue computer we build an electrical circuit (which has the same differential equations as the system we wish to investigate) and then use the correspondence of voltages and currents to our system variables to investigate the system response.

Note that the series RLC circuit shown in Fig. 3.23 is described by an equation of *form* identical to Eq. 3.45 as follows:

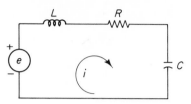

Fig. 3.23. Series LRC circuit.

$$e = \frac{1}{C} \int i \, dt + Ri + L\frac{di}{dt}$$

However, the role of velocity and current is reversed and the system parameters R, L, and C appear inverted with C and L interchanged. The analogous variables are then

$$f \longleftrightarrow e \qquad B \longleftrightarrow R$$

$$v \longleftrightarrow i$$

$$K \longleftrightarrow \frac{1}{C} \qquad M \longleftrightarrow L$$

The circuit in Ex. 3.11-4 is called the *dual* of the circuit in Ex. 3.11-5. While most electrical circuits have duals, it is often impossible to define the dual of a mechanical system (circuit).

The analogy, however, is only as good as the correspondence of the differential equations. For example remember that for a mechanical damper, the force was not exactly proportional to the difference in velocity of the damper terminals. Often this relationship is only an idealization of the real situation. In the same manner, the inductor in the analogous circuit will not always have a constant inductance L. These changes in inductance and damping are usually not the same. Consequently, an analogy can break down when the correspondence between elements does not hold. It is important to remember that there may be situations in which an analogy will break down when using this method to analyze or model a system.

The example above illustrated the "through" and "across" variable approach applied to mechanical and electrical systems. The method can also be applied to fluid and thermal systems. It is very tempting to use this method exclusively and develop an equivalent electrical circuit for every type of system because the methods of electrical circuit analysis are highly developed and the transition from circuit to differential equation can be formulated very quickly on the basis of the topology of the circuit. However, the analogies between resistance, inductance, capacitance, and the system variables are difficult to define when complex mechanical systems are considered. This is the main pitfall of the "through" and "across" variable approach as a general method.

Problem

3-1. Find the equivalent inductance and capacitance of the systems below.

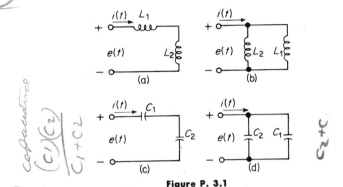

(a)

(b)

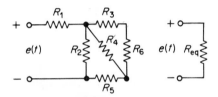

(c)

(d)

Figure P. 3.1

3-2. (a) Find the equivalent resistance R_{eq} of the following circuit. Hint: Simplify circuit so various combinations can be seen more easily.

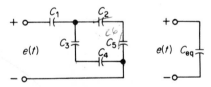

Figure P. 3.2a

(b) Find the equivalent capacitance C_{eq} of the following circuit.

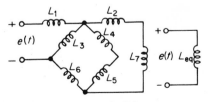

Figure P. 3.2b

(c) Find the equivalent inductance L_{eq} of the following circuit. Assume no mutual inductance occurs (between separate inductors).

Figure P. 3.2c

3-3. For capacitance, resistance, and inductance, write the equation relating

$i(t)$ to $e(t)$ for the following assumed voltage polarities and current directions. The box represents the element. ($\mp$) e_1 and e_2 are voltages supplied to terminals shown.

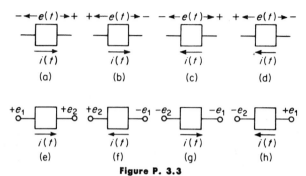

(a)   (b)   (c)   (d)

(e)   (f)   (g)   (h)

Figure P. 3.3

3-4. Which of the following are permissible, assuming ideal elements? Why? Reduce the combination to one source where possible. Assume the terminals are connected to some load.

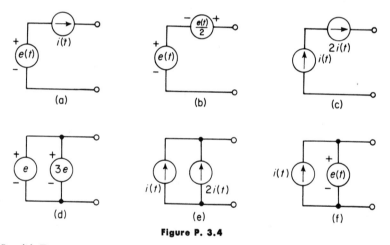

(a)   (b)   (c)

(d)   (e)   (f)

Figure P. 3.4

3-5. (a) Draw a graph of $e(t)$ versus R_2. How does R_1 affect $e(t)$?
(b) How does R_1 affect $e(t)$ in this circuit?

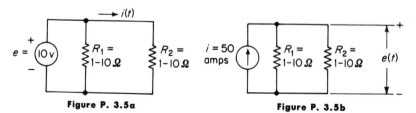

Figure P. 3.5a   **Figure P. 3.5b**

3-6. (a) Draw a graph of $i(t)$ versus R_2. How does R_1 affect $i(t)$?
(b) How does R_1 affect $i(t)$?

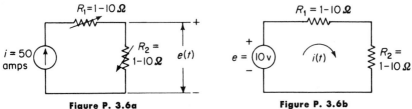

Figure P. 3.6a   **Figure P. 3.6b**

3-7. Determine the current through the battery and through the 2-ohm resistor in the following circuit.

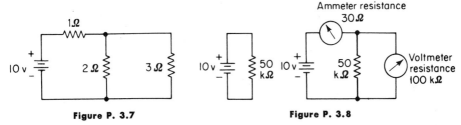

Figure P. 3.7   **Figure P. 3.8**

3-8. Determine the effects of adding the given ammeter and the given voltmeter on the current through the battery in the shown in Fig. P. 3.8 circuit.

3-9. Write an expression (differential equation) for the system in Fig. P. 3.9.

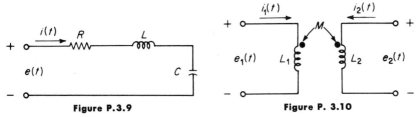

Figure P.3.9   **Figure P. 3.10**

3-10. Obtain the mathematical model (system differential equations) for the system in Fig. P. 3.10.

3-11. (a) Find the equivalent inductance of the system shown below.
(b) What is the equivalent inductance of the system if L_1's dot is moved to the other side of its coil? Can you obtain an inequality between L_1, L_2, and M?
(c) What is the equivalent inductance of the system shown in Fig. P. 3.11c.

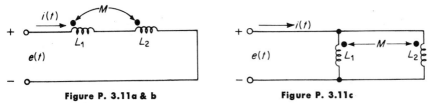

Figure P. 3.11a & b   **Figure P. 3.11c**

3-12. (a) Solve for e_0 by loop methods in the system in Fig. P. 3.12.

(b) Solve for e_0 by node-pair voltages.

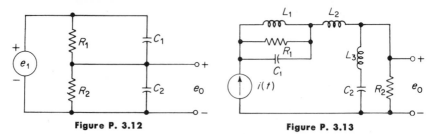

Figure P. 3.12   Figure P. 3.13

3-13. Solve for e_0 in the system shown in Fig. P. 3.13.

3-14. Write the differential equation for the circuit in the figure and find $e_{out}(t)/e(t)$, using operator $(D = d/dt)$ notation.

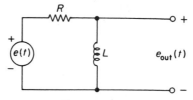

Figure P. 3.14

3-15. Write the differential equations for the circuit in Fig. P. 3.15.

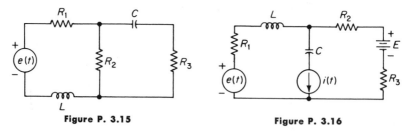

Figure P. 3.15   Figure P. 3.16

3-16. Write the differential equations for the circuit in Fig. P. 3.16.

3-17. Solve for e_0 for each of the following diagrams.

3-18. Derive the equations for the diagrams in Fig. P. 3.18.

3-19. At time $t = 0^-$, all currents and voltages in the circuit shown in Fig. P. 3.19 are zero (except battery voltage E). At time $t = 0$, switch S is suddenly closed. Write the differential equations for the circuit which apply from time $t = 0^+$. Equations are to be in terms of e_1, e_2, system parameters, and D.

3-20. A network of resistances, together with a galvanometer, keys, and a battery as shown in Fig. P. 3.20, is known as a Wheatstone bridge. In portable form it can be used for quickly measuring resistance. When the key circuits are closed, current from the battery flows through adjustable resistances R_1, R_2, R_3, and unknown resistance R_x. The direction of current flow through R_4 will depend upon the potential difference across

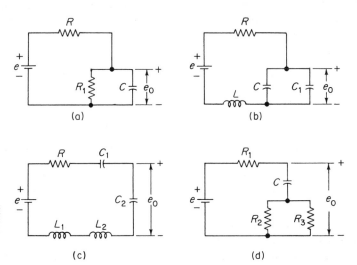

Figure P. 3.17

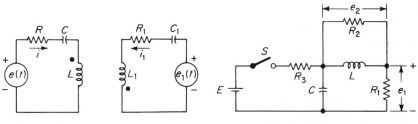

Figure P. 3.18   **Figure P. 3.19**

R_4. Clearly for some set of R_1, R_2, and R_3, no current can flow through the galvanometer circuit. Derive an expression for R_x at this time.

3-21. In addition to solving for e_0, for the circuit shown in Fig. P. 3.21 state:
(a) The number of loops.
(b) The number of nodes.
(c) The number of branches.

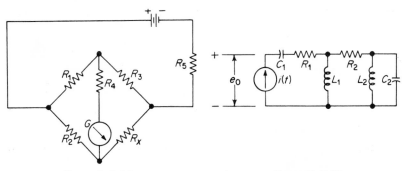

Figure P. 3.20   **Figure P. 3.21**

3-22. Derive the differential equation for e_0 in terms of e_1 for the given network, using the *node-pair voltage method* or any other method.

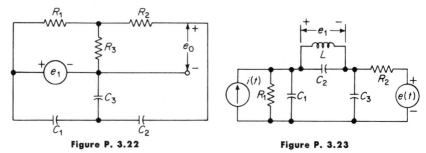

Figure P. 3.22   Figure P. 3.23

3-23. For the circuit shown in Fig. P. 3.23 express e_1 as a function of system parameters and $i(t)$ and $e(t)$, using $D(p)$ notation.

3-24. (a) Find one equation relating e_0 to e_1 in this system.
(b) If in (a) we are told to assume $R_1C_1 = R_2C_2$, what does the relation in (a) simplify to? What is the signifigance of your result?

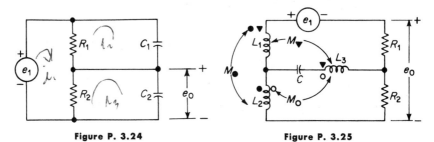

Figure P. 3.24   Figure P. 3.25

3-25. Find a set of equations that could be used to describe the dynamics of the network in Fig. P. 3.25.

3-26. Solve for e_0 by loop method in the diagram.

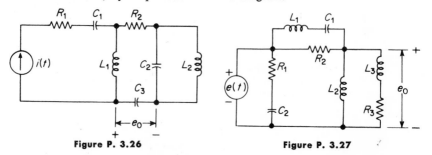

Figure P. 3.26   Figure P. 3.27

3-27. Solve for e_0 in Fig. P. 3.27 by node method. How many loop equations would you need if you solved this by the loop method?

3-28. Find differential equations of the circuit shown in Fig. P. 3.28.

3-29. Some part of a distortion analyzer looks like Fig. P. 3.29. Write sufficient equations to solve for e_0.

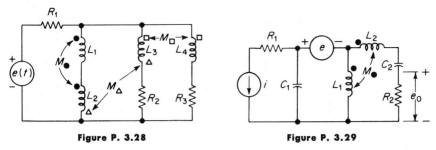

Figure P. 3.28   Figure P. 3.29

3-30. Use any method you choose to find e_0 as a function of $i(t)$ in the system shown.

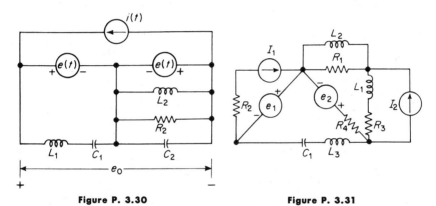

Figure P. 3.30   Figure P. 3.31

3-31. Set up equations for *either* loop or node analysis of the system in Fig. P. 3.31.

3-32. Solve the network shown by either loop or node analysis (only write equations, do not solve them).

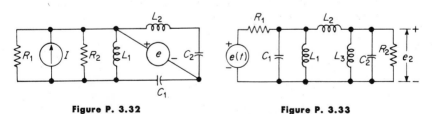

Figure P. 3.32   Figure P. 3.33

3-33. The network shown in Fig. P. 3.33 represents the interstage network found in some vacuum tube amplifiers. Write the differential equations for the circuit, using the nodal method of analysis. How many loop equations would be required?

3-34. For the following model of a single stage transistor amplifier, derive sufficient equations to solve for e_0 such that you could eliminate all unknowns. Do not combine or reduce your equations.

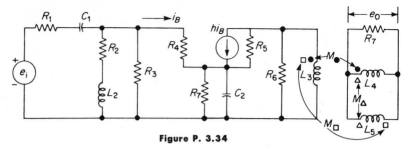

Figure P. 3.34

3-35. This cathode follower DC amplifier (a), may be modeled as in (b). Find $e_0 = f(e_{in}, g, c, \mu, R_p, R_k, R_g, R_6, R_7)$ i.e., eliminate e_g. Assume no current flows through output terminals. Note: The source μe_g puts out a voltage that is μ times the voltage e_g seen across R_g and R_k.

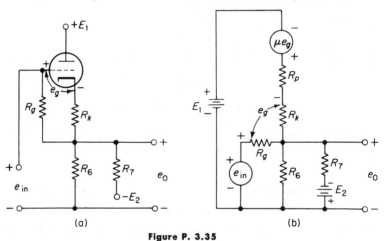

Figure P. 3.35

3-36. Draw a network diagram and write equations. The only external force is gravity. Initial conditions at $t = 0$: system is held by M_1, with springs compressed for $t < 0$. Let go of M_1 at $t = 0$.

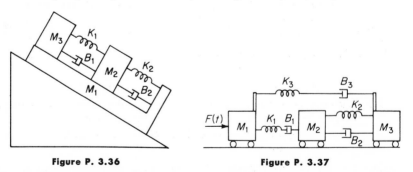

Figure P. 3.36   **Figure P. 3.37**

3-37. Draw a network diagram and write equations with motion resulting from $F(t)$ as shown in Fig. P. 3.37.

3-38. Draw a network diagram and write equations. Pulleys have *zero* mass and only translational motion of M_1, M_2, and frame are allowed. Assume small displacements.

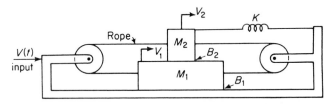

Figure P. 3.38

3-39. For the mechanical system shown, find
(a) The current-force or mass-capacitance electrical analogue.
(b) The voltage-force or mass-inductance electrical analogue.
(c) The equations for the mechanical system, and for each analogue; write down the equivalence of coefficients among them.

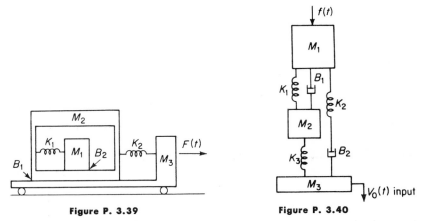

Figure P. 3.39   **Figure P. 3.40**

3-40. For the system shown in Fig. P. 3.40, draw the two analogues.

3-41. Given the following mass-*inductance* analogy for some mechanical system, draw the mass-*capacitance* electrical analogue for the same mechanical system.

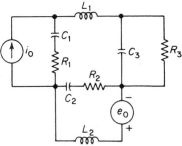

Figure P. 3.41

4 Functional Block Diagrams

4.1 Introduction

In Chaps. 2 and 3 we discussed the formulation of differential equations in mechanical and electrical systems. The methods of approach to mechanical and electrical systems will be found applicable in a wide variety of other situations including hydraulic, pneumatic, and chemical systems. The differential equation is a mathematical model of a system to be analyzed. An alternate model which contains not only all of the information given in a differential equation but also further information about the structure of a system is the *functional block diagram*. Block diagrams which indicate relationships between variables in a system have been widely used and developed.

Functional flow diagrams can be structured from either the block point of view or the so-called signal flow point of view. In the block diagram, the variables are represented by flow lines and the characteristics of system elements are contained within blocks. The signal flow diagrams place the variables within circles and show the system element characteristics in association with flow lines. There are advantages and disadvantages associated with both points of view. We shall limit our presentation to that of the functional block diagram primarily because this viewpoint leads to direct association with an analogue computer program diagram. In addition to providing a basis for analogue computation, the block diagram essentially embodies a "program" for digital or pencil and paper numerical solutions to dynamic problems. This latter aspect of the block diagram will be illustrated in Chap. 5.

4.2 Functional Block Diagram

A particular form or class of differential equations will be found to characterize most of the systems to be studied, not only in this course but throughout all fields of engineering. We have seen that the mass-spring-dash pot system has an equation of the form

$$M\frac{d^2x}{dt^2} + B\frac{dx}{dt} + Kx = F(t) \tag{4.1}$$

Other systems may have effects due to higher time derivatives so that Eq. 4.2 may be written in the general form,

$$a_n\frac{d^n x}{dt^n} + a_{(n-1)}\frac{d^{(n-1)} x}{dt^{(n-1)}} + \cdots + a_1\frac{dx}{dt} + a_0 x = F(t) \tag{4.2}$$

Equation 4.2 is a *constant-coefficient-linear-differential equation*. We shall be concerned primarily with block diagrams which are based on such equations, and we shall find that only three basic block notations or operations are required for the construction of these diagrams. These are: addition, multiplication by a constant, and integration.* Looking ahead to the use of an analogue computer, we shall find that these three linear operations may be embodied in electrical computing units which perform the operations indicated. We shall find that all the linear equations discussed previously can be represented and solved in a computer comprised of only these three linear elements.

4.3 Addition in Block Notation

Addition is the first operation to be considered. It is represented by a small circle usually drawn about one-quarter of an inch in diameter as in Fig. 4.1. Generally, equations involving addition are arranged so

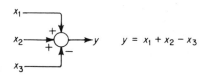

$$y = x_1 + x_2 - x_3$$

Fig. 4.1. Addition (and subtraction)— block diagram notation.

---

*Many other operations may be shown in block notation; e.g., differentiation, squaring, multiplication of two or more variables, square root, logarithm taking, etc. In this text these other operations will usually be represented by a block-enclosing a graph which indicates the function input-output relationships.

Sometimes the plus sign is only implied. Don't be surprised if we omit it in some of our block diagrams. ☆

that one variable is considered as the sum (or difference) of a number of other variables. Note that subtraction is accomplished through the addition of a negative quantity.

4.4 Multiplication by a Constant in Block Notation

All other operations (except addition and subtraction) are indicated within a box or block notation. These blocks are commonly drawn about three-eighths or one-half inch on a side, although this is purely a matter of convenience. Many kinds of operations could be included within this notation. We shall limit our attention to only two; the first is the simple process of multiplication by a constant or simple gain. Figure 4.2 shows this notation.

The block notation goes somewhat further than the simple equation notation. Included in the block notation is a concept of causality or causal relation. Thus in Fig. 4.2, y may be thought of as something more than just the instantaneous product of c times x. The diagram indicates x moving from left to right into the box and y resulting therefrom. Thus, y may be thought of as the result of the cause, x. It may be considered the output where x is the input. y may be considered a dependent quantity while x is independent. These remarks do not apply quite so appropriately to the simple process of multiplication by a constant, for it is clear that we could say that x is equal to $1/c$ times y. However, we shall see that there are cases where this point of view is quite valid, and in particular, the process of integration may be viewed in this manner. Operations which involve time variations lend themselves particularly to this interpretation because cause and effect can be defined only in the context of a flowing time stream. We shall see this in the second process that of integration.

$x \longrightarrow \boxed{c} \longrightarrow y \qquad y = cx$

Fig. 4.2. Multiplication by a constant or simple gain.

4.5 Integration with Respect to Time in Block Notation

Integration with respect to time is a fundamental dynamic operation and can be represented as shown in Fig. 4.3

$y(t_1)$ is called an *initial condition*. Figure 4.4 shows how it is defined.

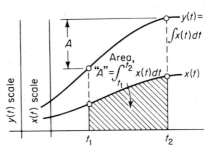

$$y(t) = \int_{t_1}^{t} x(t)\,dt + y(t_1)$$

Fig. 4.3. Integration with respect to time.

If

$$y(t) = \int x(t)\,dt \tag{4.3}$$

then

$$y(t_2) - y(t_1) = \int_{t_1}^{t_2} x(t)\,dt \tag{4.4}$$

or

$$y(t_2) = \int_{t_1}^{t_2} x(t)\,dt + y(t_1) \tag{4.5}$$

We adopt the integral sign as our notation for integration, the simplest label which will serve through most of this course. We have also used $1/D$ to denote integration. We will use either of these two symbols in our diagrams. The block notation shows the initial condition added in after the integration. Thus, the integration process in block notation computes the change in $y(t)$ between two time limits with the initial value added in later.

Fig. 4.4. $x(t)$ and its integral $y(t)$ plotted on the same diagram.

4.6 Differentiation in Block Notation

We might easily define a fourth block to represent the process of differentiation, and it might seem logical to do so since we are going to represent equations in which differentiation is the main process. We shall find, however, that it is possible to formulate our diagrams either in terms of integrations or in terms of differentiations or combinations of both. Any differential equation, for example, can be

This is harder to understand than one would expect. Think back to the basic integration concepts you learned in calculus. See if you can put them into this point of view.

arbitrarily integrated on both sides to a form which is purely integral or a combination of integrals and derivatives. Such equations are called integro-differential equations. But we shall find that it is always advantageous to formulate our diagrams in terms of only integral operations and that this may be easily done. All machine computers (analogue and digital) are far more stable and accurate when performing integration rather than differentiation. For this reason we shall merely indicate the possibility of the derivative notation but shall not plan to use it in our formulations

4.7 Block Diagram Construction

We shall now demonstrate how the three linear operations of addition, integration, and multiplication by a constant are used to synthesize or construct a block diagram. The first step is to rearrange the defining differential equation so that the *highest derivative* is considered as the sum of all other terms. Thus Eq. 4.2 would become Eq. 4.6. The

$$a_n \frac{d^n x}{dt^n} = F(t) - a_{(n-1)} \frac{d^{(n-1)} x}{dt} - \cdots - a_1 \frac{dx}{dt} - a_0 x \qquad (4.6)$$

addition symbol is used to represent Eq. 4.6 as shown in Fig. 4.5.*

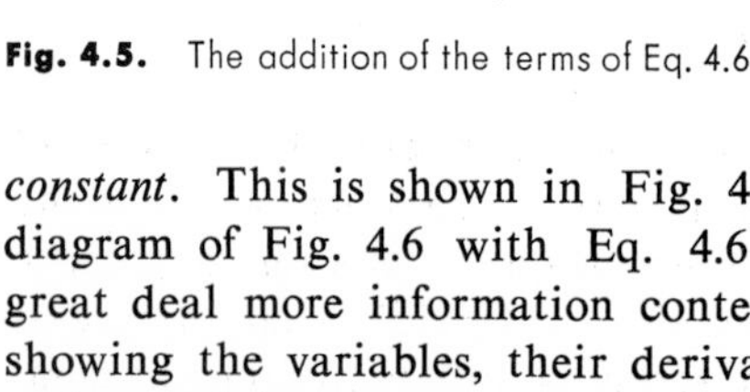

Fig. 4.5. The addition of the terms of Eq. 4.6.

Figure 4.5 is essentially equivalent to Eq. 4.6 with the exception that a causal notation has been introduced. The highest derivative seems to be the effect of all other terms in the equation. It is this rather arbitrary procedure which allows us to complete our block diagram using only the remaining notations of *integration* and *multiplication by a constant*. This is shown in Fig. 4.6. It is interesting to compare the diagram of Fig. 4.6 with Eq. 4.6 which it represents. One sees a great deal more information content in the diagram. In addition to showing the variables, their derivatives, and coefficients, the feedback and causal loops appear as well as initial conditions. The inherent parts of the equation, the outputs, and the inputs are brought out in topological form. The significance of these observations must await continued reinforcement throughout this course to become clear. At

---

*If all terms are to be summed, plus signs are omitted.

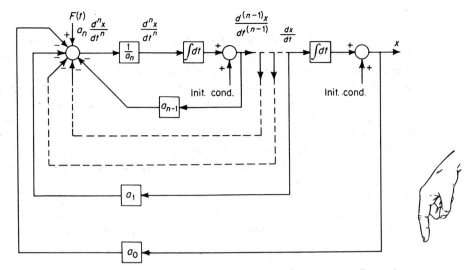

Fig. 4.6. Complete block diagram of constant coefficient linear differential equation, viz. Eq. 4.6.

this point, these remarks are intended to alert the student to concepts which will become more real later.

4.8 Block Diagrams of Linear Mechanical Elements

The equations for the linear mechanical elements given in Chap. 2 are shown in Fig. 4.7 with their corresponding block diagrams. The block diagrams shown in Fig. 4.7 are perhaps the first one might

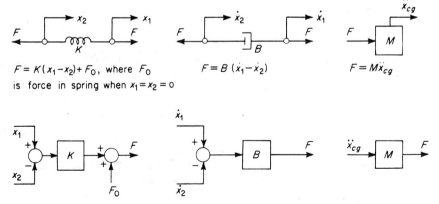

Fig. 4.7. Mechanical system elements and possible block diagrams.

 This block diagram applies equally to the original mechanical differential analyzer invented by Vannevar Bush and to a modern analogue computer. If you can figure it out, you will have gone far toward understanding how to use an analogue computer.

draw. However, some thought about the causal relationships indicated might suggest that they are inappropriate. For the spring, for example, one may not think of the deflection as producing the force, but rather the reverse. That is, a spring does not deflect until a force is applied (exception: a bimetallic strip which exerts force when temperature is changed). Likewise, a shock absorber does not move until a force is applied. In the same manner but perhaps more so, it is hard to visualize a force resulting from an acceleration in a mass. It is, therefore, proposed that the block diagrams indicated in Fig. 4.8 are more closely related to a natural causal interpretation of the facts. We arbitrarily solve for x_1 as the dependent quantity, given x_2 and the force. Note the use of the integration operation where the dashpot and mass are involved in order to produce not only in the

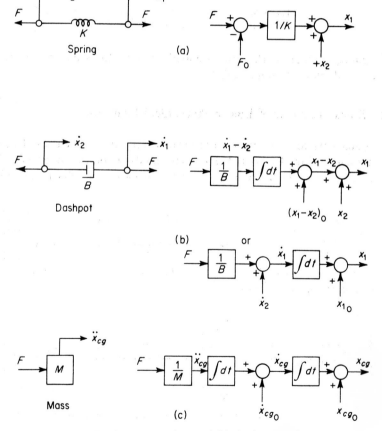

Fig. 4.8. Natural causal block diagrams for mechanical system elements.

velocity and acceleration but also the actual position. Actually, the foregoing depends entirely on a point of view and neither form of diagram is "correct" as distinct from another.

It is obvious that the foregoing diagrams would be similar but with different constants for the rotational equivalents of the linear elements which they represent.

We shall conclude our discussion of the functional block diagram with a collection of diagrams for some typical mechanical systems (see Fig. 4.9). A few electrical systems are included in section 4.9.

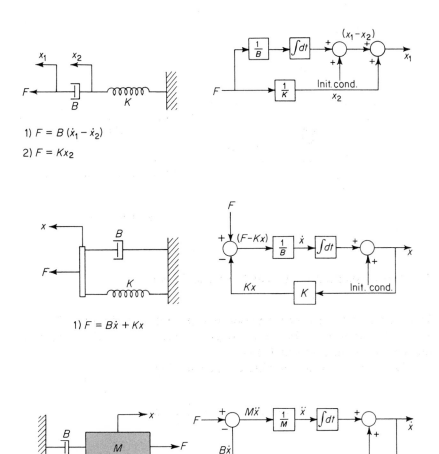

1) $F = B(\dot{x}_1 - \dot{x}_2)$

2) $F = Kx_2$

1) $F = B\dot{x} + Kx$

1) $\Sigma F = F - B\dot{x} - M\ddot{x} = 0$

Fig. 4.9. Some typical mechanical system block diagrams.

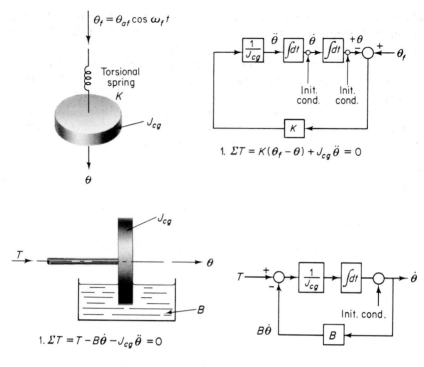

1. $\Sigma T = K(\theta_f - \theta) + J_{cg}\ddot{\theta} = 0$

1. $\Sigma T = T - B\dot{\theta} - J_{cg}\ddot{\theta} = 0$

Figure 4.9 *(cont.)*

4.9   Block Diagram for Linear Electrical Circuits

The differential equations representing examples at the end of Chap. 3 can also be written in block diagram form. First of all consider the simple circuits shown below.

Example 3.11-4 has a differential equation:

$$i = C\frac{de}{dt} + \frac{1}{R}e + \frac{1}{L}\int e\,dt$$

The functional block diagram obtained from this equation is similar in form to that of the mass-spring-dashpot system, see Fig. 4.12.

The differential equation for Ex. 3.11-5 is:

$$Ri + L\frac{di}{dt} + \frac{1}{C}\int i\,dt = e$$

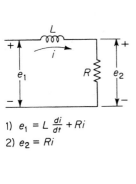

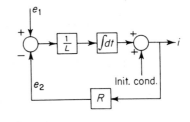

1) $e_1 = L\dfrac{di}{dt} + Ri$

2) $e_2 = Ri$

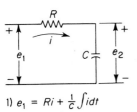

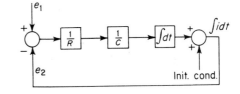

1) $e_1 = Ri + \dfrac{1}{c}\int i\,dt$

2) $e_2 = \dfrac{1}{c}\int i\,dt$

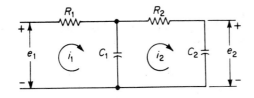

$$e_1 = i_1 R_1 + \frac{1}{C_1}\int (i_1 - i_2)\,dt$$

$$0 = i_2 R_2 + \frac{1}{C_1}\int (i_2 - i_1)\,dt + \frac{1}{C_2}\int i_2\,dt$$

$$e_2 = \frac{1}{C_2}\int i_2\,dt$$

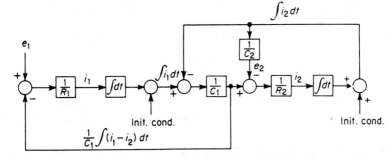

Fig. 4.10.   Some typical electrical block diagrams.

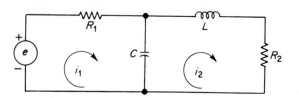

The differential equations for Example 3.112 are:

$$R_1 i_1 = e + \frac{1}{C} \int (i_2 - i_1)\, dt$$

$$L \frac{di_2}{dt} = -R_2 i_2 - \frac{1}{C} \int (i_2 - i_1)\, dt$$

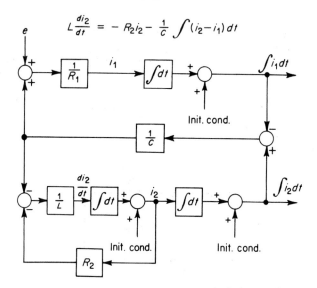

Fig. 4.11. Block diagram for Example 3.11–2.

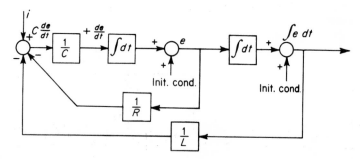

Fig. 4.12. Block diagram for Example 3.11–4.

which results in the block diagram of Fig. 4.13. For Ex. 3.11-6 we have the differential equations

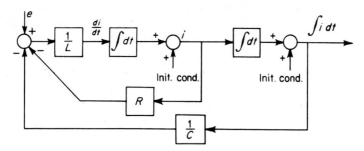

Fig. 4.13. Block diagram for Example 3.11–5.

$$e_1 + e_2 = e$$

$$C_1 \frac{de_1}{dt} = -\frac{1}{R_2} e_1 - \frac{1}{L_1} \int e_1 \, dt + \frac{1}{R_1} e_2 + C_2 \frac{de_2}{dt} + \frac{1}{L_2} \int e_2 \, dt$$

which are shown in block diagram form in Fig. 4.14.

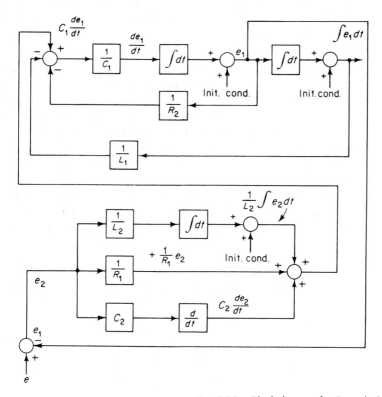

Fig. 4.14. Block diagram for Example 3.11–6.

In all of these examples we have written the differential equations using the methods of Chaps. 2 and 3 and then used the block diagram notation to form a picture of the differential equation. The order of these steps is most important. It is tempting to formulate the block diagram directly from the schematic drawing of the system, but this approach is loaded with pitfalls. Often initial conditions, the effects of one element on another, and other parts of the mathematical model are ignored by going directly to the block diagram from the system schematic drawing.

4.10 Block Diagram Reduction

The block diagram can be more than a way of drawing a picture of a set of differential equations. The diagram can be used to reduce a set of equations to a single equation, express a given variable in terms of other variables, and, in general, aid in the manipulation of a differential equation. If the differential equation is a constant-coefficient-linear-differential equation, a set of rules can be devised to reduce the block diagram to its simplest form. In order to accomplish this reduction, the D notation is used. Any block diagram can be reduced to a single block involving an algebraic equation in D, connecting each input or initial condition with the output. However, most of these rules apply only to constant-coefficient-linear-differential equations. Like any set of rules, they can be misapplied to produce erroneous results. Consequently, in this text a less powerful but general approach will be devised which does not depend on a set of rules. The method consists of taking the block diagram representing a set of equations and using it to write a single (reduced) equation which is then used to draw a reduced block diagram.

Consider the block diagram for the system analyzed in Fig. 4.9. This is redrawn in Fig. 4.15 using the D notation. The system input is T and we also have to specify an initial condition $\dot{\theta}_0$. The required

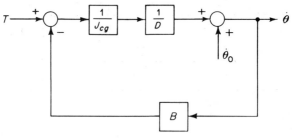

Figure 4.15

output is $\dot{\theta}$, hence we have to derive an equation for $\dot{\theta}$ in terms of the input T and the initial condition $\dot{\theta}_0$.

Starting at the first summing junction, this tells us that we must subtract the term $B\dot{\theta}$ from input T to obtain the function $(T - B\dot{\theta})$. This function is then multiplied by $1/J_{cq}$ and $1/D$ to obtain $(T - B\dot{\theta})$ $(1/J_{cg})(1/D)$ which represents one of the inputs to the second summing junction, the other input being $\dot{\theta}_0$.

We now write that the sum of the inputs to the second summing junction is equal to the output $\dot{\theta}$. i.e.,

$$[T - B\dot{\theta}]\left(\frac{1}{J_{cg}}\right)\left(\frac{1}{D}\right) + \dot{\theta}_0 = \dot{\theta}$$

This is the required differential equation. However, it is not yet in the final reduced form since we have $\dot{\theta}$ terms on both sides of the equation.

Collecting the $\dot{\theta}$ terms and performing some algebraic manipulation we finally obtain an expression for $\dot{\theta}$ as follows,

$$\dot{\theta} = \frac{T + J_{cg}D\dot{\theta}_0}{J_{cg}D + B}$$

In order to draw the reduced block diagram it is convenient to break down the right-hand side of the equation into functions of T and $\dot{\theta}_0$, respectively, i.e.,

$$\dot{\theta} = T\frac{1}{J_{cg}D + B} + \dot{\theta}_0\frac{J_{cg}D}{J_{cg}D + B}$$

The functional block diagram representing this equation is shown in Fig. 4.16.

Notice that in this simplest form of the functional block diagram both the input T and the initial condition $\dot{\theta}_0$ are connected by a single block to the output. Hence this simplest form can be used to specify $\dot{\theta}(t)$ given $T(t)$ and $\dot{\theta}_0$.

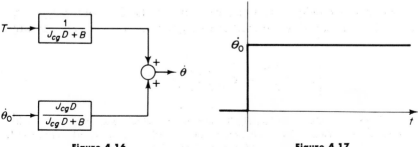

Figure 4.16   Figure 4.17

It is important to remember that $\dot{\theta}_0$ is an initial value of $\dot{\theta}(t)$ which is suddenly applied at $t = 0$ and is then held constant throughout the solution (the reader should refer to Sec. 4.5 for a review of the role of $\dot{\theta}_0$). In this case, it can be shown that the form of $\dot{\theta}_0$ is as in Fig. 4.17. This is known as a step function and its effect on the system will be discussed in Chap. 5.

The example just presented is relatively straightforward and we were able to write the reduced equation by inspection. Sometimes it will be necessary to write several equations which then have to be combined to obtain the reduced equation relating all the inputs and initial conditions to the output.

Consider Fig. 4.18 which shows the block diagram for Ex. 3.11-5. Since the number of outputs is reduced during the reduction process we must decide ahead of time which ones we are interested in. Let us assume, in this case, that we wish to know the current i.

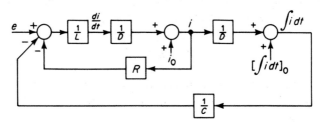

Fig. 4.18. Block diagram for example 3.11–5.

We commence by writing the inputs and initial conditions, etc. That is

input: $\qquad\qquad\qquad\qquad\qquad\qquad e$

initial conditions: $\qquad\qquad\qquad\qquad i_0, \left[\int i\,dt\right]_0$

output: $\qquad\qquad\qquad\qquad\qquad\qquad i$

As in the previous example, we start at the first summing junction and work our way through the diagram until we reach output i.

$$\left[e - \frac{\int i\,dt}{C} - Ri\right]\left(\frac{1}{L}\right)\left(\frac{1}{D}\right) + i_0 = i$$

 Think carefully about the full significance of the initial condition. It is not just a number or a symbol. It has a physical meaning which must be clearly understood. Sketches such as shown in Fig. 4.17 are a great aid to understanding.

Output i, however occurs in the middle of the diagram and we have not yet incorporated the last operation involving the integration of i. We do this by writing a second equation as follows:

$$i\left(\frac{1}{D}\right) + \left[\int i\,dt\right]_0 = \int i\,dt$$

Substituting this for $\int i\,dt$ in the first equation yields a single differential equation for the system.

$$\left[e - \frac{i/D + \left[\int i\,dt\right]_0}{C} - Ri\right]\frac{1}{LD} + i_0 = i$$

Collecting the i terms and simplifying yields

$$i = \frac{eCD - \left[\int i\,dt\right]_0 D + i_0 LCD^2}{CLD^2 + CRD + 1}$$

This is the reduced equation and from it we are able to draw the reduced block diagram shown in Fig. 4.19.

As noted previously, the initial conditions $[\int i\,dt]_0$ and i_0 are constants for $t > 0$ and zero at $t < 0$.

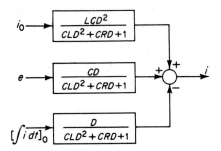

Fig. 4. 19. Reduced block diagram.

In this way any block diagram representing a set of equations can be reduced to its simplest form where each of the inputs and initial conditions is connected by a single block to the output.

4.11 Summary

The functional block diagram serves a number of uses. First and foremost it gives us a picture of the differential equation(s) which helps us to visualize the relationships between the system inputs,

initial conditions, and outputs. In addition, it serves as a plan to indicate how the equations can be reduced to a simpler form.

For linear differential equations with constant coefficients, the
diagram can always be reduced to one where each input and initial
condition is connected by a single block to the output. Reductions
are usually possible with other more complicated types of differential
equations.

Finally, the block diagram is useful as a circuit diagram for an
analogue computer solution or a flow diagram for a digital computer
solution.

Problems

4-1. (a) Obtain the differential equation to describe the angular velocity of
this rotational system.
(b) Draw the block diagram.

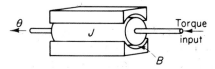

Figure P. 4.1

4-2. The figure shows an amplifier and loud speaker combination. The cone
of the speaker (which makes the noise) may be approximated as in
the sketch where its mass, spring, and damping are shown as separate
elements; the applied force is directly proportional to the current
supplied by the amplifier.

The differential equation for the amplifier current which results
when an input voltage e_0 is applied is as follows:

$$L\frac{di}{dt} + Ri + \frac{1}{C}\int i\,dt + K_2\dot{x} = K_3 e_0$$

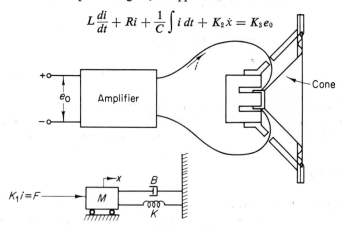

Figure P. 4.2

Derive the other equation (i.e., for the mechanical system) and then carefully draw the functional block diagram for the complete system.

4-3. Draw functional block diagrams to represent the following:
(a) Figure P. 4.3
(b) $J_1\ddot{\theta}_1 + K_1\theta_1 - K_2\theta_2 = T$,
$J_2\ddot{\theta}_2 + (K_1 + K_2)\theta_2 - K_1\theta_1 = 0$.

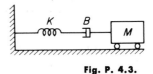

Fig. P. 4.3.

4-4. Reduce the following functional block diagrams to systems in which each input or initial condition is connected via a single block to one summing unit from which the output is obtained directly. Derive the auxilary equations for each step in the reduction.

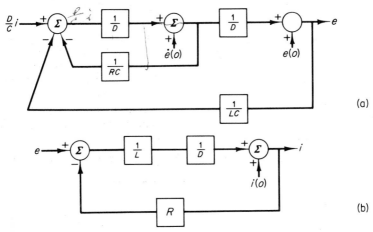

(a)

(b)

Figure P. 4.4

4-5. Reduce the following block diagram and obtain the differential equation.

4-6. Draw block diagrams for the following systems shown with their differential equations.

Linearized equations

$$A_1\frac{dh_1}{dt} + K_1 h_1 = Q_{in}$$

$$A_2\frac{dh_2}{dt} + K_2 h_2 - K_1 h_1 = 0$$

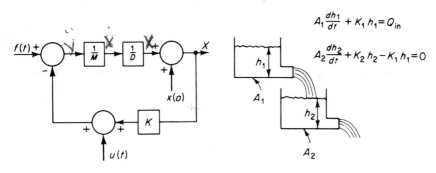

Figure P. 4.5   **Figure P. 4.6(a)**

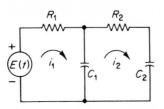

$$R_1 \frac{di_1}{dt} + \frac{1}{C_1}(i_1 - i_2) = \frac{dE(t)}{dt}$$

$$R_2 \frac{di_2}{dt} + \left(\frac{1}{C_1} + \frac{1}{C_2}\right)i_2 - \frac{1}{C_1}i_1 = 0$$

Figure P. 4.6(b)

4-7. A piston of mass M fits in a closed cylinder of cross-sectional area A. When the piston is in its central position $(x = 0)$, it is in equilibrium and the pressure on each side is P_0. The gas in the cylinder is assumed to follow Boyle's law, i.e., the pressure times the volume equals a constant. The piston is moved a distance x and then released. Write the equations of motion and draw the resulting block diagram. Assume viscous friction between piston and cylinder wall. The width of the mass: $W \ll L$.

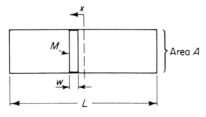

Figure P. 4.7

4-8. Write the equation for the following block diagram, including the initial conditions.

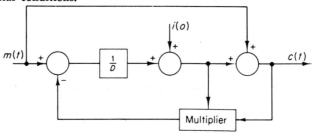

Figure P. 4.8

4-9. Write the differential equation for the following block diagram.

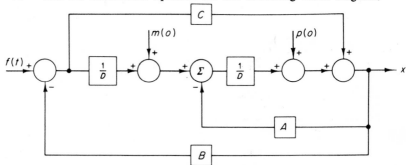

Figure P. 4.9

4-10. Write the equation for the block diagram (include all initial condition effects).

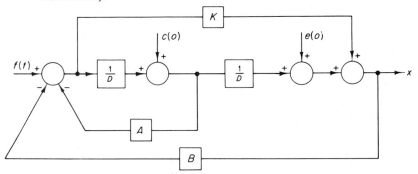

Figure P. 4.10

4-11. (a) Draw a block diagram for $D(D^2 + KD + M)X + AX = (D + C)f(t)$
(b) Reduce the block diagram.

4-12. Given the following block diagram, derive the differential equation.

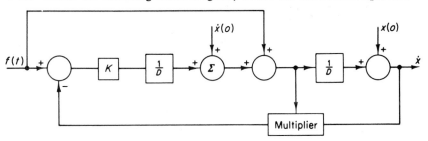

Figure P. 4.12

4-13. Given the following block diagram, write the differential equation.

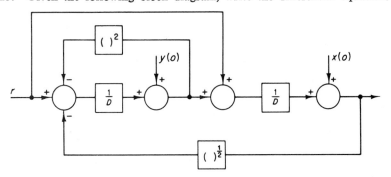

Figure P. 4.13

4-14. The block diagram for a DC motor with position and armature current feedback is shown below. Derive the differential equation for this system. *Do not reduce!* In case you are interested:
$T_1 =$ torque applied to motor by load

r = voltage reference input proportional to desired position

θ = output position

R_a, L = armature resistance and inductance

K_b = motor back emf constant

K_t = motor torque constant

J = motor inertia

K_p = feedback gain

R_s = source resistance

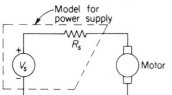

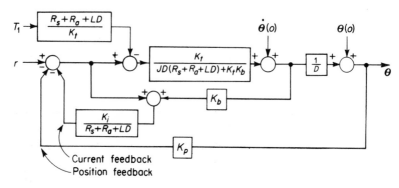

Current feedback

Position feedback

Figure P. 4.14

5 The Solution of First Order Differential Equations

5.1 Introduction

In this chapter we propose to develop a number of new concepts and techniques. We shall do this in the context of a specific example which is sufficiently complex so that a number of different points will be raised. Generalizations will be made in specific instances. A unique system will be studied from a number of points of view. We shall see that the system is characterized by so-called nonlinear differential equations. These equations will be solved by a simple numerical technique. We shall then transform these equations into linear form and develop a general technique for solving the class of linear differential equations of which these equations are members.

5.2 Illustrative Example

A problem studied in some detail in this chapter is the motion of a paratrooper who has just left his aircraft on his descent to the earth. We shall study a means to calculate his velocity, both horizontally and vertically, at various periods of time before he opens his parachute. This problem will require a number of simplifications before we can obtain solutions. It is in this way, typical of all engineering problems, wherein the problem actually solved is really a simplified model of the original system.

Among the factors which we shall approximate are the effects of air resistance, the effect of changing air density, and the effect of change in frontal area presented by the paratrooper as he rotates while falling. Figure 5.1 illustrates the problem.

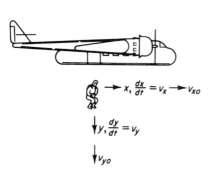

Let us use x to designate the horizontal direction and y the vertical direction. The origin of coordinates will be taken as that point in space where the man is located just after he leaves the aircraft. At this time the initial velocity in the horizontal direction is the same as that of the aircraft and the vertical velocity will be essentially zero (gravity having had a negligible amount of time to act). We shall consider his motion in each direction individually and assume that there is no effect of one upon the other. We

Fig. 5.1. Paratrooper having just bailed out; v_{x0} (initial horizontal velocity) is that of aircraft; v_{y0} (initial vertical velocity) is essentially zero.

know that his total motion is the vector sum of these two orthogonal components. Thus, his vertical descent may be characterized by a single equation in the vertical direction and his horizontal motion will be characterized by a single equation in the horizontal direction. Furthermore, we shall concern ourselves here with his velocity only. We know that if we have a complete description of his velocity in both directions over a period of time it is simple to determine his position, since we know that the distance traveled over a period of time is given by the integral of the velocity with respect to time over that interval of time.

The aircraft is flying at 5,000 feet on a normal day with very little wind blowing. The aircraft velocity is 180 mph. Joe, our paratrooper, has practiced many jumps and has learned to count a period of ten seconds accurately. We shall study his velocity during the first ten seconds of free fall before be pulls his ripcord. We want to calculate his velocity at any instant of time following his jump. We shall be satisfied initially with a table or plot of these velocities, but we might prefer an expression that not only defines Joe's velocity in this particular instance, but also anyone else's velocity given a different speed, height, and other parameters. In the first case we seek an empirical solution which is applicable only to Joe in this particular jump. In the second case we seek an analytical solution which has greater generality. We shall discover, however, that it is not always easy to find either one at will.

5.3 Equation Formulation

Figure 5.2 shows the horizontal (x) and vertical (y) components of forces which act upon Joe. We shall assume these forces act through his center of gravity. Shown are the force of gravity, the two components of the force due to air resistance, and the two components of inertia force. Since we are only interested in his velocity, the forces are written in terms of the velocity components. Note also that since we are dealing with velocity and its changes, we do not require an absolute reference frame.

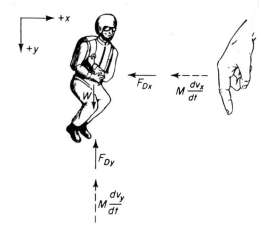

The next step is to express the dependent forces as functions of the dependent variable. As pointed out before when dealing with mechanical elements, this step requires the application of basic physics to the problem. The science of fluid mechanics permits

Fig. 5.2. Forces acting on Joe (free body diagram).

us to define relationships for the amount of force which is applied to a body moving through a fluid such as water or air. It is, however, beyond the scope of this text to develop in detail the principles of fluid mechanics which would clearly explain these relationships. We shall, therefore, merely write the result. It may be well-known to most readers that the resistance to movement of a body in air is proportional generally to its frontal area, the square of its velocity, and the density of the air. In addition the force is materially affected by the shape of the body. This shape effect is taken care of in a drag-force formula by a coefficient that gives the ratio of the actual drag to that which would be computed from Newton's quadratic resistance law given below.

$$\text{Newton's drag formula} = \tfrac{1}{2}A\rho v^2 \qquad (5.1)$$

Thus the drag force on a body is often computed from Eq. 5.2.

$$F_D = \tfrac{1}{2}C_D A\rho v^2 \qquad (5.2)$$

where:

Accelerations and displacements can be easily determined if $v(t)$ is known. Have you ever tried graphical integration or differentiation?

C_D = coefficient of drag

A = effective frontal area

ρ = density of air (in mass units, e.g., pound-second^2/feet^4)

v = velocity relative to air

The drag coefficient C_D is usually determined through experimental means in a wind or water tunnel and the factor of $\frac{1}{2}$ is purely arbitrary.

We may now write the equations of motion as Eqs. 5.3 and 5.4.*

$\Sigma F_x = 0$

$$M\frac{dv_x}{dt} + \frac{1}{2}C_D A\rho v_x^2 = 0 \qquad (5.3)$$

---

*Equation 5.3 may be easily integrated by "separating variables" as follows:

$$\frac{dv_x}{dt} + av_x^2 = 0$$

$$\frac{dv_x}{v_x^2} = -a\,dt$$

$$\int v_x^{-2}\,dv_x = -a\int dt$$

$$v_x = \frac{1}{at+c}$$

When $t=0$; $v_{x0} = 1/c$

$$v_x = \frac{1}{at+1/v_{x0}}$$

Equation 5.4 does not lend itself to direct integration but the solution may be obtained from a table of integrals.

$$\frac{dv_y}{dt} + av_y^2 = F \qquad F = \frac{W}{M}$$

$$\frac{dv_y}{dt} = F - av_y^2$$

$$\int \frac{dv_y}{F/a - v_y^2} = a\int dt$$

Let $c^2 = F/a$: the solution is valid if $F/a \geqq 0$.

$$\frac{1}{2c}\ln\frac{c+v_y}{c-v_y} = at + B$$

$$\ln\frac{c+v_y}{c-v_y} = 2act + 2cB$$

$$\frac{c+v_y}{c-v_y} = e^{2act+2cB}$$

$$v_y = c\left[\frac{e^{2act+2cB}-1}{e^{2act+2cB}+1}\right]$$

$\ln_e x = y$

$x = e^y$

Find B from initial conditions $v_y = 0$ at $t = 0$

We are actually cheating here to make the solution simpler. The v_x^2 term in Eq. 5.3 should be $v_x v$ and the v_y^2 term (Eq. 5.4) should be $v_y v$. Equation 5.3 is absolutely correct at the start of the fall and Eq. 5.4 is absolutely correct at the end of the fall; neither is correct in between. If we used the correct equations we would have to solve them simultaneously to obtain v.

$$\Sigma F_y = 0$$

$$M\frac{dv_y}{dt} + \frac{1}{2}C_D A\rho v_y^2 = W \tag{5.4}$$

These are differential equations that happen to be nonlinear differential equations, called so because the variable appears in the equation as squared instead of to the first power only (linear). There are many ways in which equations become nonlinear, but this will be discussed later.

Our task is to solve these equations; or in this case really, to find out what v_x and v_y are at each point in time. While it is possible to find an analytic form of solution for these particular nonlinear equations, they will be left to a course on differential equations. However, it is possible to easily obtain v_x and v_y as a function of time for the single set of data which apply to this problem using a stepwise descent calculation which is similar to that used on a digital computer. This we shall now proceed to do.

5.4　Determination of Data and Coefficients (Importance of Engineering Judgment)

The following values may be taken to represent a reasonable set of conditions that might occur. We have assumed that the air density is constant during the entire drop of the man (this is quite reasonable during the first ten seconds); we shall assume a constant frontal area for Joe, despite the fact that we know this must change materially as he rotates about in free fall; and we shall assume a coefficient of drag based on a cylinder about the size and shape of a man. These assumptions are typical of those required for solution of an engineering problem. The fact that the data are therefore neither accurate nor precise should be kept in mind when deciding on the accuracy needed in mathematical analysis and, of course, in the interpretation and use of the results.

Table 5.1　Assumed Data for Chapter 5 Example

W = Joe's weight = 193 lb	$C_D = 1.2$
M = Joe's mass = $193/32.2 = 6.0$ lb-sec²/ft (or slugs)	$v_{x0} = 180$ mph = 264 ft/sec
$A = 3$ ft² (assumed average)	$v_{y0} = 0$
ρ = Air mass density = 2.4×10^{-3} lb-sec²/ft⁴ [standard conditions]	

Substituting numbers into Eqs. 5.3 and 5.4, we have

$$6\frac{dv_x}{dt} + 4.32 \times 10^{-3}v_x^2 = 0$$

or

$$\frac{dv_x}{dt} + 7.2 \times 10^{-4}v_x^2 = 0 \tag{5.5}$$

$$6\frac{dv_y}{dt} + 4.32 \times 10^{-3}v_y^2 = 193$$

or

$$\frac{dv_y}{dt} + 7.2 \times 10^{-4}v_y^2 = 32.2 \tag{5.6}$$

Equations 5.5 and 5.6 are interesting to compare. It is seen that the left-hand sides of these equations are identical, but in one case the right-hand side is zero and in the other the right-hand side is not. Thinking back to the components of motion of the physical system which they describe, we realize that for horizontal motion parallel to the earth's surface, there are no forces other than air resistance acting on the body. When moving in the vertical direction, however, we see that the force of gravity provides a constant pull. It is common practice to arrange all the terms in a differential equation which are functions of a dependent variable on the left side and those terms which relate to the effect of the environment or the input to the system on the right-hand side. We might then ask the question, "In the case of Eqs. 5.5 and 5.6, how can anything happen if the effect of the environment is zero on the system as indicated by the right-hand side of the equation equaling zero?" The answer to this, of course, is contained in the fact that the man leaves the aircraft with an initial horizontal velocity and his motion is one of slowing down to zero in the horizontal direction. We note that this initial velocity does not appear in the differential equation. In the case of the vertical descent, his initial velocity is zero, but we know he must accelerate due to the steady force of gravity.

Thus, we see that systems can respond both to a constant external effect (its input) and it may respond (behave) due to a set of initial conditions which exists at the time a solution begins (viz., $t = 0$).

5.5 Functional Block Diagrams

Let us now draw functional diagrams for each of these equations. We shall see that some additional information is inherent in these diagrams; namely, the presence of initial conditions and the feedback nature of

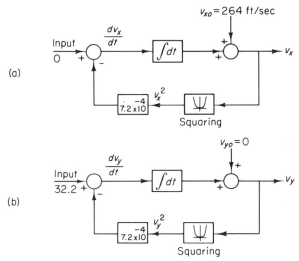

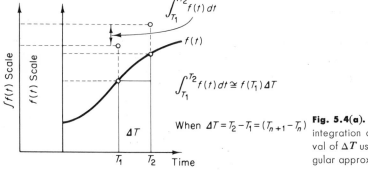

Fig. 5.3. Functional block diagrams for (a) Eq. 5.5 and (b) Eq. 5.6.

the drag force. These block diagrams are shown in Fig. 5.3(a) and (b).

REAB

5.6 Solution of Nonlinear Equations—Discrete Solution Technique

It is easy, however, to solve this problem approximately with pencil and paper. All we need is to recall the basic process of integration and to devise a systematic means for performing integration numerically on a piece of paper (the other functional block operations are simple arithmetic). We remember that the integral of a function with respect to time between T_1 and T_2 is identically the area under the curve of this function between T_1 and T_2. Now, if T_1 and T_2 are not very far apart and the function varies slowly, the area under the curve may be taken to be the area under the rectangle formed by drawing

$$\int_{T_1}^{T_2} f(t)\, dt$$

$f(t)$

$$\int_{T_1}^{T_2} f(t)\, dt \cong f(T_1)\, \Delta T$$

When $\Delta T = T_2 - T_1 = (T_{n+1} - T_n)$

Fig. 5.4(a). Discrete integration over interval of ΔT using rectangular approximation.

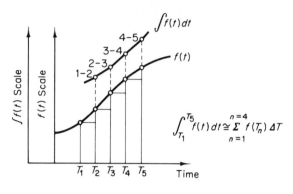

Fig. 5.4(b). Discrete integration over large interval obtained by summing a number of rectangular areas.

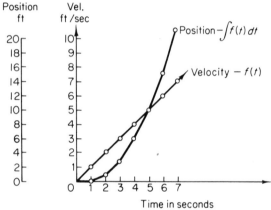

Fig. 5.4(c). Plot of sample integration carried out in Table 5.2.

a horizontal line through the value of the function at T_1. See Fig. 5.4. It is important to choose ΔT sufficiently small so that $f(t)$ reasonably approximates a horizontal line over the interval of computation.

Figure 5.4 shows how the integral over a longer period of time may be approximated as the sum of a series of small rectangular areas.

The computation can now be carried out conveniently in tabular form. Figure 5.4(c) shows how one might integrate a linearly increasing velocity to produce a parabolic position versus time function.

☆   It might seem more accurate to use a trapezoidal approximation with a chord running between points T_1 and T_2 on the curve. We cannot do this here because it is the value of the function at T_2 which we are trying to find. Under the circumstances, the rectangular approximation is good enough. Of course, having gone through the problem once, we might repeat it using a trapezoidal approximation based on the previously determined results.

Table 5.2 Illustration of Tabular Integration—Linearly Increasing
Velocity ($\Delta T = 1$ sec)

Time	Given Velocity ft/sec	$f(T_n)\Delta T =$ Position Change	Position	
T_n		from T_n to T_{n+1}	At n	At $n+1$
0	0	0×1	0	0
1	1	1×1	0	1
2	2	2×1	1	3
3	3	3×1	3	6
4	4	4×1	6	10
5	5	5×1	10	15
6	6	6×1	15	21

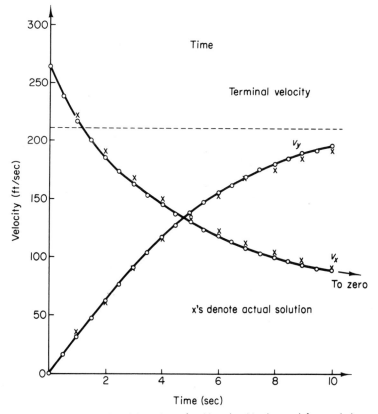

Fig. 5.4(d). Plots of $v_x(t)$ and $v_y(t)$ obtained from tabular computations in Tables 5.3 and 5.4 as compared with actual solutions.

Figure 5.4(c) shows a plot of the velocity and the resulting position as determined in the computation of Table 5.2. It may be seen that numerical work in Table 5.2 is very simple and thus we are now in a position to readily compute the time integral of a function of time, especially if it is given to us in terms of discrete values separated by equal and small increments.

The foregoing discussion has been presented so that we can, by means of paper and pencil, perform the process of continuous integration with respect to time. We are now able to do on paper what an analogue computer integrating component does electrically. The object of all of this is to put ourselves into such a position that we can now perform all of the computations indicated by the block diagrams of Fig. 5.3(a) and (b). Addition and multiplication by a constant, squaring, or any other nonlinear instantaneous relationship may be handled readily in a tabular computation.

The block diagram shown in Fig. 5.3(a) illustrates the causal flow and feedback nature of the problem we wish to solve. At any instant of time $t = T_n$, we can determine the acceleration from the velocity and the input. That is:

$$\text{Input}|_{t=T_n} - 7.2 \times 10^{-4} v_x^2|_{t=T_n} = \frac{dv_x}{dt}\Big|_{t=T_n} \tag{5.7}$$

v_x at time $t = T_{n+1}$ can then be obtained by assuming that the acceleration dv_x/dt is constant over the interval $T_n < t < T_{n+1}$ and equal to its value at $t = T_n$.

Then,

$$\int_{T_n}^{T_{n+1}} \frac{dv_x}{dt}\, dt \approx \frac{dv_x}{dt}\Big|_{t=T_n} \Delta T \tag{5.8}$$

so that,

$$v_x|_{T_{n+1}} = v_x|_{T_n} + \frac{dv_x}{dt}\Big|_{t=T_n} \Delta T \tag{5.9}$$

At $T_n = 0$, $v_{x0} = 264$ ft/sec; from Eq. 5.7,

$$\frac{dv_x}{dt}\Big|_{t=0} = 0 - 7.2 \times 10^{-4}(264)^2 = -50.1$$

and then from Eq. 5.9,

     This is a very powerful tool which provides unlimited scope for dealing with all kinds of equations. Once you have mastered it you can stop worrying about nonlinear differential equations.

$$v_x|_{T_{n+1}} = 264 + (-50.1)\Delta T$$

The process continues to develop $v_x|_{T_n}$ in a step by step manner. $v_x|_{T_{n+1}}$ becomes the new $v_x|_{T_n}$ at each step.

We shall now present a complete tabular computation for the solution of a variation of velocity as a function of time for each of the situations represented in Fig. 5.3(a) and (b). The choice of ΔT is essentially an engineering assumption. It is difficult to set the proper value a priori. Perhaps the best procedure is to make a guess and calculate a few points. If the functions do not, in fact, vary radically over these periods, the choice is probably good (a choice of ΔT smaller than necessary should be avoided since there are computational errors inherent at each step and one can reduce the problem to the point where the computational errors may be larger than the changes in variables).

Tabular computations for v_x and v_y appear in Tables 5.3 and 5.4 with the results of the computations plotted in Fig. 5.4(d).

We now see that Joe reaches a vertical speed of about 200 ft/sec in about 10 sec. He slows down from his initial horizontal velocity of 264 ft/sec to 85 ft/sec in the same 10 sec. We can predict his terminal

Table 5.3   Solution for $v_x(t)$; Eq. 5.5 ($\Delta T = 0.5$ sec)

T	$v_x(T_n)$	*INPUT*	$v_x^2(T_n) \times 10^{-4}$	*Input* -7.2×10^{-4} $v_x^2(T_n)$	$\left.\dfrac{dv_x}{dt}\right|_{t=T_n} \Delta T$	$v_x(T_{n+1})$
0.0	264.0	0	7.00	−50.4	−25.2	238.8
0.5	238.8	0	5.72	−41.2	−20.6	218.2
1.0	218.2	0	4.79	−34.5	−17.2	201.0
1.5	201.0	0	4.05	−29.2	−14.6	186.4
2.0	186.4	0	3.49	−25.2	−12.6	173.8
2.5	173.8	0	3.02	−21.8	−10.9	162.9
3.0	162.9	0	2.65	−19.1	− 9.5	153.4
3.5	153.4	0	2.36	−17.0	− 8.5	144.9
4.0	144.9	0	2.10	−15.2	− 7.6	137·3
4.5	137.4	0	1.89	−13.6	− 6.8	130.5
5.0	130.5	0	1.71	−12.4	− 6.2	124.3
5.5	124.3	0	1.55	−11.2	− 5.6	118.7
6.0	118.7	0	1.41	−10.2	− 5.1	113.6
6.5	113.6	0	1.29	− 9.2	− 4.6	109.0
7.0	109.0	0	1.19	− 8.6	− 4.3	104.7
7.5	104.7	0	1.10	− 7.95	4.0	100.7
8.0	100.7	0	1.01	− 7.28	3.64	97.06
8.5	97.06	0	0.946	− 6.81	3.41	93.65
9.0	93.65	0	0.88	− 6.34	3.17	90.48
9.5	90.48	0	0.82	− 5.91	2.95	87.53
10.0	87.53	0	0.77	− 5.54	2.77	84.76

Table 5.4 Solution for $v_y(t)$; Eq. 5.6 ($\Delta T = 0.5$ sec)

T	$v_y(T_n)$	INPUT	$v_y^2(T_n)$ $\times\,10^{-4}$	$-7.2v_y^2(T_n)$ $\times\,10^{-4}$	*Input* -7.2×10^{-4} $v_y^2(T_n)$	$\left.\dfrac{dv_y}{dt}\right\|_{t=T_n}(\Delta T)$	$v_y(T_{n+1})$
0.0	0.0	32.2	0.0	0.0	32.2	16.1	16.1
0.5	16.1	32.2	0.026	0.19	32.01	16.0	32.1
1.0	32.1	32.2	0.103	0.75	31.45	15.7	47.8
1.5	47.8	32.2	0.229	1.65	30.55	15.25	63.05
2.0	63.05	32.2	0.4	2.88	29.32	14.6	77.65
2.5	77.65	32.2	0.61	4.39	27.81	13.9	91.55
3.0	91.55	32.2	0.83	5.96	26.24	13.12	104.67
3.5	104.67	32.2	1.10	7.9	24.3	12.2	116.87
4.0	116.87	32.2	1.36	9.8	22.4	11.2	128.1
4.5	128.1	32.2	1.65	11.9	20.3	10.2	138.5
5.0	138.5	32.2	1.92	13.9	18.4	9.2	147.7
5.5	147.7	32.2	2.18	15.7	16.5	8.3	156.0
6.0	156.0	32.2	2.44	17.6	14.6	7.3	163.3
6.5	163.3	32.2	2.68	19.3	12.9	6.5	169.8
7.0	169.8	32.2	2.88	20.8	11.4	5.7	175.5
7.5	175.5	32.2	3.09	22.2	10.0	5.0	180.5
8.0	180.5	32.2	3.26	23.4	8.8	4.4	184.9
8.5	184.9	32.2	3.41	24.6	7.6	3.8	188.7
9.0	188.7	32.2	3.60	25.9	6.3	3.2	191.9
9.5	191.9	32.2	3.70	26.6	5.6	2.8	195.7
10.0	195.7	32.2	3.83	27.6	4.6	2.3	198.0

or final constant velocity by noting that if he did reach a constant velocity, dv_y/dt would be zero. Thus, from Eq. 5.6 in which we set the $dv_y/dt = 0$, we see that v_{yf} (final value of v_y) may be determined by Eq. 5.10. Of course, we had no idea in the beginning how long it would take him to reach this speed.

$$0 + 7.2 \times 10^{-4}v_{yf}^2 = 32.2 \tag{5.10}$$

$$v_{yf} = \sqrt{\frac{32.2}{7.2} \times 10^4} = 212 \text{ ft/sec} = 145 \text{ mph}$$

We have "solved" this nonlinear differential equation using only simple addition, multiplication, subtraction, and division; using in addition a "program" as embodied in the block diagram and a "memory" as contained in the list of numbers in Tables 5.3 and 5.4. This is similar to the approach that is used in digital computation and suggests how a digital computer would be used to solve such a program. In a digital computer, the processes of multiplication and division are, in fact, done through addition and subtraction so that the power of the simplest kind of arithmetic is illustrated herein. We have used a simple approximate rule for integration. There are more sophisticated approximations possible which are generally employed in high speed computers. However, when one considers the assumptions which were made initially in formulating the problem it is questionable whether a more accurate integration method would be warranted even if a digital computer were used to solve the problem.

To summarize, by using discrete techniques the solution of a differential equation can be accomplished by solving algebraic equations of the type which you have solved many times before. For example, in Eq. 5.3 if we let

$$a_x = \frac{dv_x}{dt} \qquad (5.11)$$

Eq. 5.3 becomes

$$Ma_x + \tfrac{1}{2} C_D A \rho v_x^2 = 0 \qquad (5.12)$$

These are algebraic equations with two unknowns, $a_x(t)$ and $v_x(t)$. However, *a differential equation is an algebraic equation with unknown functions of an independent variable rather than unknown constants.* The methods of algebra allow you to solve algebraic equations of the form

$$f(x,y,z) = 0$$

$$g(x,y,z) = 0$$

$$h(x,y,z) = 0$$

as long as there are many equations as unknowns *and* the unknowns x, y, z are constants. In order to use the methods of algebra we chose to look at the velocity of the paratrooper at equally spaced instants of time, $t = n\Delta T$. This enabled us to write a set of n equations from Eq. 5.12 to solve for n pairs of $a_x(n\Delta T)$ and $v_x(n\Delta T)$.

$$Ma_x(n\Delta T) + \tfrac{1}{2} C_D A \rho v_x^2(n\Delta T) = 0 \qquad n = 0, 1, 2, \ldots \qquad (5.13)$$

However, this only allows us to determine v_x at one instant of time and then only if we know a_x at that instant, or vice versa. Consequently we need something to join the n pairs of equations. This is the role of the rectangular approximation to integration.

We could also obtain the joining equation by remembering the definition of the derivative and rewriting Eq. 5.11 to obtain

$$a_x(n\Delta T) = \lim_{\Delta T \to 0} \frac{v_x[(n+1)\Delta T] - v_x(n\Delta T)}{\Delta T} \qquad n = 0, 1, 2, \ldots$$

This modified form of Eq. 5.11 can then be used to link the n equations together. All that remains is a value for v_x to start off the process. This is $v_x(0)$, the initial condition. Then the $2n$ algebraic equations with $2n$ constant unknowns can be solved for $a_x(n\Delta T)$ and $v_x(n\Delta T)$.

In this way we have rewritten an algebraic equation with unknown functions of an independent variable (in this case, time) to obtain a set of algebraic equations in unknown constants. This second form is easily solved by the elementary rules of algebra to obtain values for the unknown functions at particular instants of time. This discrete approach to the solution of differential equations is basic to solving differential equations on a digital computer. The computer is capable of solving only algebraic equations but it does so at extreme speed. Hence we change the differential equations into a discrete time form to obtain values for the unknown function at particular instants of time. If the instants of time are close enough, the resulting values of the function can be plotted to obtain a smooth and accurate representation of the unknown function of time.

5.7 Linearization of Equations

Let us now seek a more general way to solve our problem. We shall derive, or rather we shall propose, a technique for solving these equations which leads to an analytic solution (functional representation) rather than a list of numbers or a plot of our answer. In dynamic systems we shall be primarily concerned with linear differential equations. As pointed out before, so far we have solved a nonlinear equation with simple, yet inherently extremely powerful, tools. Now, as we reach for an analytic solution, we must restrict our capabilities and concern ourselves only with linear equations and a few especially well-behaved nonlinear ones. This is because there are just very few nonlinear equations that may be solved analytically, i.e., for which there exist functional solution forms. Our example happens to be a reasonably well-behaved nonlinear equation for which there exists an analytic solution.* We shall pretend that a solution does not exist and proceed as we must in many nonlinear situations. That is, we shall replace our equation by one which is linear and we hope the solution will represent the behavior of our system within reasonable limits of accuracy.

In fact we should point out here, not only are we concerned with linear equations (those in which the dependent variables and derivatives appear in the first power only and not in products), but we shall require the coefficients of our equations to be constant. Note that our

*See footnote, page 116.

previous pencil and paper technique did not require this, but for a generalized analytical approach we must make this assumption. The general form of the equation we seek is given in Eq. 5.14. It is a *first order equation* since the highest derivative is only the *first* derivative.

$$\frac{dv_x}{dt} + av_x = 0 \qquad (5.14)$$

Let us first seek the solution of the equation which represents the horizontal motion of the paratrooper. The term av_x in Eq. 5.14 assumes that the drag force is proportional to velocity, rather than to velocity squared. The question of selecting an appropriate value for a in this linear term is one which requires engineering judgment. In this case, a possible method of proceeding would be to assume that a should be chosen so that the area under the drag force as a function of the velocity curve equals that for the square law case over the total range of velocity (see Fig. 5.5). This example shows clearly that the choice of a depends upon the actual velocity range covered.

The assumption shown in Fig. 5.5 leads to the following computation:

$$\frac{1}{2} a v_{x0}^2 = \frac{1}{3} \frac{C_D A \rho}{2M} v_{x0}^3$$

$$a = \frac{C_D A \rho}{3M} v_{x0} = \frac{1.2 \times 3 \times 2.4 \times 10^{-3} \times 264}{3 \times 6} = 0.127$$

$$\text{Units equation} = \left[\frac{\text{ft}^2 \cdot \text{lb sec}^2 \cdot \text{ft} \cdot \text{ft}}{\text{ft}^4 \cdot \text{sec} \cdot \text{lb} \cdot \text{sec}^2} \right] = \frac{1}{\text{sec}}$$

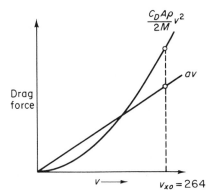

Fig. 5.5. Assumption of "equal areas" to determine *a*.

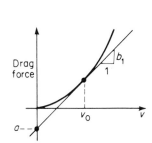

Fig. 5.6. Drag force versus velocity.

We might also use a more formalized method called small-signal linearization to linearize the nonlinear term $(C_D A\rho/2m)(v^2)$. If we were to restrict our analysis to small changes in v from its value v_0 at some operating point, we could represent this term by a tangent at v_0 to the drag force versus the velocity curve shown in Fig. 5.6.

This straight line approximation is then linear. Since it only involves v to the first power,

$$\frac{C_D A\rho}{2M}\,v^2 \approx b_0 + b_1 v$$

However, the accuracy of this approximation diminishes as v deviates from v_0. This process of linearization about an operating point can be mechanized by the Taylor series expansion of the nonlinear function to be linearized.

$$F_D(v) = F_D(v_0) + \frac{dF_D}{dv}\bigg|_{v=v_0}(v - v_0) + \frac{1}{2!}\frac{d^2 F_D}{dv^2}\bigg|_{v=v_0}(v - v_0)^2 + \ldots$$

As long as the derivatives of F_D are finite, the series converges to $F_D(v)$. If we restrict ourselves to small changes in v, that is,

$$v - v_0 \longrightarrow 0$$

then, higher order terms are small since

$$\frac{1}{2!}\frac{d^2 F_D}{dv^2}\bigg|_{v=v_0}(v - v_0)^2$$

is small because $(v - v_0)^2$ is small. We can then approximate,

$$F_D(v) \doteq F_D(v_0) + \frac{dF_D}{dv}\bigg|_{v_0}(v - v_0)$$

for small changes in v.

Thus, for the parachute problem:

$$\frac{C_D A\rho v^2}{2M} = \frac{C_D A\rho v_0^2}{2M} + \frac{C_D A\rho v_0}{M}(v - v_0)$$

$$= \frac{C_D A\rho v_0^2}{2M}\left(\frac{2v}{v_0} - 1\right)$$

which is a linear function of v. Notice, however, that if $v_0 = 0$,

---

☆   Note, a product of several variables or their derivatives can also be expanded in a Taylor series using partial derivatives.

$C_D A \rho v^2 / 2M = 0$ since the drag-force curve has zero slope for $v_0 = 0$. This approach is not too useful for the present problem because v varies over too wide a range to obtain useful answers by a small-signal linearization. We could, how-ever, use several small-signal linear models to approximate the system response as closely as we liked. This method is shown in Fig. 5.7 where four small-signal linear models are used to approximate the system re-sponse. The small-signal lineariza-tion method presents a general method of linearization which is applicable to all types of nonlinear-ities except those with infinite de-rivatives.

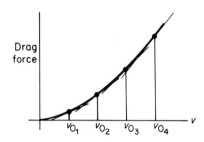

Fig. 5.7. Example of small-signal lineari-zation.

5.8 Graphical Solution by Tangent Approximation

Let us now proceed with a formal solution of Eq. 5.14. Its solution is some expression for v_x as a function of time which "satisfies" the equation. Thus both the function and its derivative, when substituted in, must be such that they are equal except for a constant of proportionality. Thus, we may rearrange Eq. 5.14 as follows:

$$\frac{dv_x}{dt} = -a v_x \qquad (5.15)$$

Equation 5.15 shows that if a is positive (as it is in our example), the velocity must at all times be proportional to the negative of its derivative. Furthermore of course, the slope itself is then proportional to the negative of the value of the velocity. Thus, if the velocity

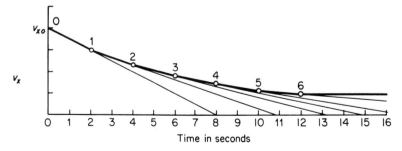

Fig. 5.8. $v_x(t)$ constructed from tangent approximations at 2 sec intervals.

drops to one-half its initial value, its rate of change must also drop to one-half its initial value. This relationship permits us to sketch the curve in terms of its slope readily as in Fig. 5.8.

The initial slope is seen to be $-av_{x0}$; from then on, we proceed to increase the slope proportionately as v_x decreases stepwise in time, much as we did in our tabular computations of a nonlinear equation. While the curve can be constructed approximately in this way, it is easier to work with an analytical solution. We shall, therefore, spend no more time on this form of graphical computation.

5.9 Direct Integration

We should also mention another quite practical approach to solving Eq. 5.14. This equation is a so-called "separable" equation. This means that the variables may be easily separated so that each side can be integrated separately in a straightforward manner using tables of integrals. Thus, if we write Eq. 5.14 as follows,

$$\frac{dv_x}{v_x} = -a\,dt$$

each side can then be integrated:

$$\ln v_x = -at + \ln A \quad \text{or} \quad \ln\frac{v_x}{A} = -at$$

$$Ae^{-at} = v_x \tag{5.16}$$

Equation 5.16 is thus the answer to our problem, for it gives the function of t which v_x must have in order to satisfy the equation. This method of approach seems straightforward, but it is deceptive for it works only in the simplest cases. Equation 5.14 is a member of the class of constant-coefficient-linear-differential equations which have the following form in general (also Eq. 4.2 in Chap. 4):

$$a_n\frac{dx^n}{dt^n} + a_{(n-1)}\frac{d^{(n-1)}x}{dt^{(n-1)}} + \ldots + a_0x = F(t) \tag{5.17}$$

5.10 The Exponential Solution Form

It is not practical to develop a table of integrals to cover all possible forms of Eq. 5.17. What is required is a single, general method for their solution. We propose to investigate a method of solution which will work for all constant-coefficient-linear-differential equations. We are led to a search for a general form of solution wherein the function and its derivatives must simply be constants times each other. This implies a function whose derivative has the same form as the function itself.

Many functions can be expanded into a power series; that is, as a sum of terms in which, in the case of dynamic systems, time appears in the form of increasing powers. Suppose the $f(t)$ we seek could be written as Eq. 5.18:

$$f(t) = a_0 + a_1 t + a_2 t^2 + a_3 t^3 + \ldots + a_n t^n \qquad (5.18)$$

where the a's are constants yet to be determined. The derivative of the series of Eq. 5.18 is

$$\frac{df(t)}{dt} = 0 + a_1 + 2a_2 t + 3a_3 t^2 + \ldots + na_n t^{n-1} \qquad (5.19)$$

These two series will be equal if the coefficients of terms containing t in identical powers are arbitrarily made equal. Thus, the series are equal if

$$a_1 = a_0 \qquad a_2 = \frac{a_1}{2} = \frac{a_0}{2} \qquad a_3 = \frac{a_2}{3} = \frac{a_0}{6} \qquad a_4 = \frac{a_3}{4} = \frac{a_0}{24} \qquad \text{etc.}$$

The following function, then, has the property we seek; namely, its derivative is the same function back again.

$$f(t) = \left(1 + t + \frac{t^2}{2!} + \frac{t^3}{3!} + \frac{t^4}{4!} + \ldots + \frac{t^n}{n!}\right) a_0 \qquad (5.20)$$

The function shown in Eq. 5.20 has a number of unusual properties. One perhaps unexpected property is revealed when two series for different values of t are multiplied together. Consider the following two series:

$$f(t_1) = \left(1 + t_1 + \frac{t_1^2}{2!} + \frac{t_1^3}{3!} + \ldots + \frac{t_1^n}{n!}\right) a_0$$

$$f(t_2) = \left(1 + t_2 + \frac{t_2^2}{2!} + \frac{t_2^3}{3!} + \ldots + \frac{t_2^n}{n!}\right) a_0$$

When these series are multiplied together, we obtain

$$f(t_1)f(t_2) = \left(1 + (t_1 + t_2) + \frac{(t_1 + t_2)^2}{2!} + \frac{(t_1 + t_2)^3}{3!} + \ldots + \frac{(t_1 + t_2)^n}{n!}\right) a_0^2$$

$$= f(t_1 + t_2) a_0^2$$

This indicates that $f(t)/a_0$ must be of the form (constant) to the power t, for we know that when such functions are multiplied together, their exponents add as required by our unique series. The constant associated with the series is the familiar e and may be found by evaluating the series where $t = 1$ as follows:

$$\frac{f(1)}{a_0} = 1 + 1 + \frac{1}{2!} + \frac{1}{3!} + \frac{1}{4!} + \ldots + \frac{1}{n!} = 2.718 = e$$

hence

$$f(t) = a_0 e^t = \left(1 + t + \frac{t^2}{2!} + \ldots + \frac{t^n}{n!}\right) a_0$$

The following are some of the rules for handling e^t:

$$\frac{d}{dt}(e^t) = e^t \qquad \int e^t \, dt = e^t + \text{constant}$$

$$\frac{d}{dt}(ae^{bt}) = abe^{bt} \qquad \int ae^{bt} \, dt = \frac{a}{b} e^{bt} + \text{constant}$$

$$e^{bt} e^{ct} = e^{(b+c)t}$$

These operations are illustrated in the plots of Fig. 5.9.

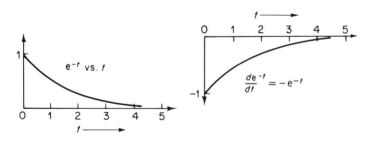

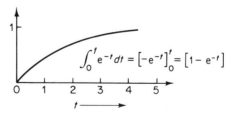

Fig. 5.9. Integral and derivative forms of e^{-t} showing identical shapes.

5.11   Solution of Linear Homogeneous Differential Equation (Eq. 5.14)

We have now "discovered" a form of solution which meets our original requirements; namely, that when differentiated, Eq. 5.20 returns to its original form. The technique of solution which we shall use over and over again for the solution of differential equations of the form of Eq. 5.17 consists simply of (1) assuming that our solution does, in fact, have the form of an exponential; (2) substituting this assumed solution back into the differential equation; and (3) evaluating the constants so that the assumed solution does, in fact, satisfy the equation. Let us then assume the following solution for Eq. 5.14,

$$v_x = Ae^{\lambda t} \tag{5.21}$$

When the assumed solution of Eq. 5.21 is substituted into Eq. 5.14, we obtain

$$\lambda Ae^{\lambda t} + aAe^{\lambda t} = 0$$

and since $Ae^{\lambda t}$ is not zero (if we are to have any solution at all), we may write

$$\lambda + a = 0 \quad \text{or} \quad \lambda = -a$$

Hence,

$$v_x = Ae^{-at} \tag{5.22}$$

Equation 5.22 is a solution of our original differential equation and agrees with the result obtained by direct integration (Sec. 5.8). The constant A has yet to be determined and, for the specific problem being studied, would be evaluated from initial conditions. At $t = 0$:

$$v_{x0} = 264\,\text{ft/sec} \quad\quad a = 0.127 \quad \text{(from page 127)}$$

$$\therefore 264 = Ae^0 = A$$

and

$$v_x = 264e^{-0.127t} \tag{5.23}$$

Equation 5.23 is the numerical solution for Eq. 5.14 for the parameters of our sample problem. A plot of Eq. 5.23 appears in Fig. 5.10. Also

---

You will meet situations requiring this kind of solution time and time again so don't leave this section until you are sure you understand the logic on which the solution is based.

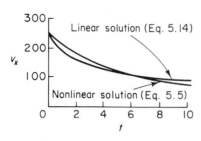

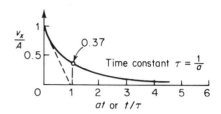

Fig. 5.10. Numerical solutions to Eqs. 5.5 and 5.14.

Fig. 5.11. Nondimensional solution to first order differential equation.

plotted in Fig. 5.10 is the more exact solution to the nonlinear equation as shown in Fig. 5.4(d). We see that the velocity at $t = 10$ sec is predicted with fair accuracy by the linear equation.

Equation 5.22 is very important and represents a solution to problems in many fields. We find that if it is nondimensionalized, a single solution may be drawn to apply to any problem which has a solution of its form. We noted that when a was evaluated, it had the units of 1/time. This is checked in Eq. 5.22 by the fact that the exponent of e must be nondimensional. It is common practice to refer to the reciprocal of a as the *time constant* of a system. We note also that the units of a coefficient a must be the same as the units of the variable and thus a nondimensional plot may be reproduced in which v_x/A is plotted against a nondimensional time parameter t/τ. This plot appears in Fig. 5.11.

The initial slope of the nondimensional curve of Fig. 5.11 may be seen to be identically -1 as follows:

$$\frac{d(v_x/A)}{d(t/\tau)}\bigg|_{t/\tau=0} = \frac{d(e^{-t/\tau})}{d(t/\tau)}\bigg|_{t/\tau=0} = -1e^0 = -1$$

The initial slope is then easy to sketch and if we note that after one time constant the curve has dropped to 37 per cent of its original value, the entire curve may be easily sketched. Numerical results can be obtained from Fig. 5.11 for any dimensional solution simply by evaluating the proper constant and time constant.

Figure 5.12 shows the nondimensional plot on semilog scale. The straight line result is probably not unexpected.

The plot of Fig. 5.12 is interesting from several points of view.

☆   The *time constant* is a very important parameter which is used in defining system response—look out for it.

☆   Students tend to dislike nondimensionalized solutions even though they are great labor-saving devices. You have to become used to them so why not start now?

First, it shows that by merely drawing a straight line on a piece of semilog paper, one may produce a permanent numerical solution to the first order equation which can be used in many engineering problems. Second, it affords an important way to determine the time constant and nature of the response of an actual system when experimental data have been recorded. If, in fact, the response of a real system when plotted on semilog paper does lie on a straight line, the slope of the line indicates the time constant (when plotted against time, the time constant is that value of time at which the variable has reduced to 37 per cent of its original value).

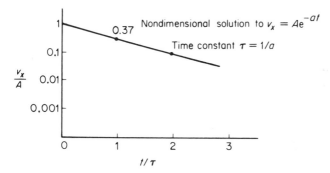

Fig. 5.12. Nondimensional solution to first order differential equation.

If a set of equivalent linear differential equations with constant coefficients can be written which describe the system, we again have a set of algebraic equations in unknown functions. For this example,

$$a_x = \frac{dv_x}{dt} \tag{5.24}$$

and

$$Ma_x + av_x = 0 \tag{5.25}$$

As before, a_x and v_x are not constants, but are changing with time so that the usual rules of algebra do not enable us to obtain a solution except by considering particular instants of time as we did in the solution of the nonlinear equations. Because Eqs. 5.24 and 5.25 are linear with constant coefficients, however, we can accomplish the solution by noticing that a class of functions exists which will satisfy the equation; namely,

$$v_x = Ae^{\lambda t}$$

Assuming the solution has this form, we obtain a set of algebraic equations for the constants A and λ. That is,

$$\lambda A e^{\lambda t} = a_x$$

and hence

$$M\lambda A e^{\lambda t} + a A e^{\lambda t} = 0$$

or

$$M\lambda A + a = 0$$

We have one equation and two variables but, as before, the solution depends on the initial conditions which must satisfy the equations to yield

$$v_x = v_x(0) \quad \text{at} \quad t = 0$$

hence

$$A e^{\lambda t} = A = v_{x0}$$

This is the second equation necessary to determine λ and A. Notice that we have been able to find a general equation for $v_x(t)$ by this process which allows us to investigate the effects on the response of changes in initial velocity $v_x(0)$, mass M, and resistance a.

Thus, we might generalize the process of solving a differential equation to a process in which we try to reduce a set of m equations for an unknown function and its $m-1$ derivatives into a set of algebraic equations with a finite number of constant unknowns. This summarizes the basic differences between the solution of algebraic equations for unknown constants and differential equations which must be solved for unknown functions.

5.12   Remarks on Linear Approximation

From an engineering point of view, the linear solution for final horizontal velocity after 10 sec agrees reasonably well with the non-linear solution. However, the difference between the two equations is really very great and the solutions are not close at all times. In many systems, however, the linear equation is often much closer to nature. In fact there are many devices where the damping, for example, is proportional directly to velocity or its equivalent. In such systems the linear equation predicts a performance with good accuracy. In other cases where the nonlinearity is "strong," the questions to be answered may concern themselves with only small changes in a variable. In such cases, the straight line representing a curve which varies only slightly between two points again leads to a linear differential equation and predicts performance accurately for small variations about an operating point.

5.13 Solution of Linear Equation for Vertical Descent, v_y

Let us now turn to the solution of the linear equation for the vertical component of descent. Here the equation will take the following form:

$$\frac{dv_y}{dt} + av_y = F(t) \qquad (5.26)$$

The left-hand side is the same as Eq. 5.14, but we see that the right-hand side now involves a function of time. In our case the right-hand side is a simple constant if we choose to define $t = 0$ at the instant after the paratrooper, Joe, leaves the airplane. The sequence of events are really a bit complicated because when he stands at the edge of the door, his gravity force is balanced by a force pushing up from the floor and thus there is no acceleration. The instant after he leaves the floor the net force on his body is that due to his weight. Thus, one might picture the right-hand side of the Eq. 5.26 as shown in Fig. 5.13.

This is the so-called step function which we first met in Sec. 4.9. The question of exactly what happens at $t = 0$ is important, but can be bypassed here if we assume that the events between $t = 0^-$ and $t = 0^+$ happen very fast compared to the changes in velocity

Fig. 5.13. Step change in external "force" $F(t)$ on Joe at $t = 0$.

under the free fall. It is sometimes convenient to adopt notation $t = 0^+$ to indicate the beginning of a solution for a differential equation in order for everyone to know that whatever transition events occurred around $t = 0$ at the beginning of the problem have been completed. We shall use $t = 0$ without the $+$ or $-$ except in those cases where their use will prevent ambiguity. Another way of expressing $F(t)$ in Eq. 5.26 is as follows:

$$F(t) = 0 \qquad t < 0$$

$$F(t) = \frac{W}{M} = g \qquad t > 0$$

Our next step is to evaluate *a* for the particular problem to be solved. We might proceed as before and assume an "equal area relationship" (see page 127) between 0 and 212 feet per second (remember, 212 was computed in Eq. 5.10 previously and is the known final or terminal velocity). However, in this case we have an additional constraint; namely, that the solution of the linear equation must produce the same terminal velocity as the solution of the nonlinear equation (previously, our terminal velocity was 0), and it may be seen that one assumption is incompatible with the other. Accordingly, let us derive a value for *a* for the linear equation so that the terminal velocity conditions are met. This means that *a* is given simply by

$$a = \frac{W/M}{v_{yf}} = \frac{32.2}{212} = 0.152 \frac{1}{\text{sec}}$$

Since we are now familiar with the time constant of a system, it may be immediately evaluated as $\tau = 1/a$ or 6.58 sec. How this time constant figures in the solution shall be seen as it develops.

Equation 5.26 then becomes Eq. 5.27:

$$\frac{dv_y}{dt} + 0.152v_y = 32.2 \tag{5.27}$$

The solution of Eq. 5.27 is not quite as simple as Eq. 5.14. The right-hand side causes trouble. It is obvious that we just can't substitute the proposed solution as before, for now the $Ae^{\lambda t}$ does not conveniently cancel out. This creates something of a dilemma, the solution of which is really not trivial. In fact, its solution depends upon new concepts which are inherent in the definition of linear systems. The following remarks are concerned with this issue but will probably not prove conclusive to the reader at this time. The reader will find, however, as his engineering experience broadens, that many instances of confirmation and elaboration arise.

The solution of Eq. 5.26 depends upon the fundamental property of a linear system; namely, *that its behavior resulting from two input effects is identical to the sum of the individual behaviors resulting from*

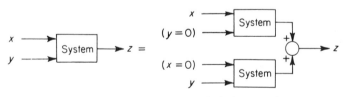

Fig. 5.14. Block diagram of superposition theorem.

 We are now embarking on a very important topic. Read it carefully and digest it.

each effect. This statement may be diagramed as in Fig. 5.14. This is one way of stating the law of superposition, or the superposition theorem, for linear systems. Another implication of the superposition theorem is that when the magnitude of an input to a linear system is increased, the output is also increased in proportion but is not altered in form. We know that no such system really exists, for all physical systems saturate or limit at some point. However, we also know that for a given range of operation, it is often possible to construct a system (for example, a hi-fi amplifier) which does, in fact, reproduce the input "faithfully" without distortion.

Now Eq. 5.27 describes the behavior of the system "a man in air" which has been linearized. The velocity resulting from the force of gravity is the behavior or output, and gravity force is the input. The block diagram of Fig. 5.3 shows this. Let us consider the behavior of the system as the sum of two parts:

(1) that due to gravity
(2) that which would result if no gravity were present

The second part is equivalent to setting the right-hand side of Eq. 5.27 equal to 0 and the resulting equation is identical in form to Eq. 5.14 which described the horizontal motion of the man. We found at that time that motion was possible (a solution would exist) even though no external forces were acting due to the initial velocity (initial condition). Thus, we propose to divide our solution into two parts; (1) that for the right-hand side equal to 0, an equation which we have already solved and know the answer to and (2) that for the right-hand side equal to 32.2. The significance of the superposition theorem now comes into play, for we shall further hypothesize that the total behavior (solution) is the linear sum of the two solutions which we propose to obtain.

The total solution to Eq. 5.27 is called the *general* solution. It is the sum of the *complementary* solution to the *homogeneous equation* (right side 0) and the *particular* solution (that which satisfies the equation when the right side is included).

In the study of dynamic systems, a desired solution is usually time varying and the complementary solution to the homogeneous equation can be realistically described as a *transient solution*. It results from the initial state of a system (e.g., initial displacement or velocity) and not from external effects. The block diagram of the homogeneous equation shows no input other than initial conditions [see Fig. 5.3(a)].

The particular solution is usually associated with some steady or repeating effect from the environment on the system (e.g., force of gravity, vibrations, and shocks). It is often called the *steady state* solution (even though many particular solutions are not "steady").

We shall adopt the subscript "tr" for transient and "ss" for steady state. The complete or general solution will carry no subscripts. (When we study sinusoidal solutions later on, we shall drop the ss.) The solution for the differential equation may then be formally stated by superposition as follows:

$$v_y(t) = v_{ytr}(t) + v_{yss}(t) \qquad (5.28)$$

Let us now turn to solving Eq. 5.27. v_{ytr} has already been found and is the form given in Eq. 5.22. All that remains is to find v_{yss}.

We note that the right-hand side $F(t)$ is a simple constant with no time variation. Thus, if Eq. 5.27 is to have a solution at all, dv_{yss}/dt must be 0 (this agrees with intuition, for if we apply a steady force, we know that ultimately Joe will reach a steady velocity wherein the drag force just balances the applied force). Let us assume a solution of the form

$$v_{yss} = C$$

This is simply solved as follows:

$$aC = g; \qquad C = \frac{g}{a} = \frac{32.2}{0.152} = 212$$

From Eq. 5.28 we then can write our complete solution.

$$v_y = Ae^{-at} + \frac{g}{a} = Ae^{-0.152t} + 212$$

As before, it is necessary to evaluate the constant A from initial conditions. This is done as follows: at $t = 0$:

$$v_y = 0$$

$$0 = Ae^0 + \frac{g}{a}$$

$$A = -\frac{g}{a} = -212$$

☆   You will find it worthwhile to memorize this result.

☆   Note that constant A is evaluated by substituting the initial conditions in the *complete* solution, i.e., the initial condition is:

$$v_y(0) = v_{ytr}(0) + v_{yss}(0) = 0$$

not

$$v_{ytr}(0) = 0$$

You had better memorize this too.

The final solution may be written numerically as follows:

$$v_y = \frac{g}{a}(1 - e^{-at}) = 212\,(1 - e^{-0.152})^t \tag{5.29}$$

It is convenient to plot Eq. 5.29 nondimensionally as we did in Fig. 5.11. This is shown in Fig. 5.15(b).

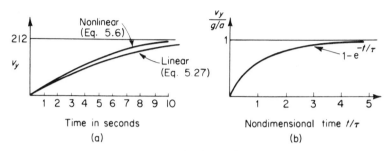

Fig. 5.15. Vertical velocity of paratrooper. (a) Linear and nonlinear equations solutions. (b) Nondimensional linear solution form.

The nondimensional plot of Fig. 5.15(b) represents the very general solution to a step input of the first order or single capacitance (since there is a single energy storage element) system. The curve is similar in form to the exponential response of Fig. 5.11 and thus, the numerical results of Fig. 5.12 are easily applicable.

It is seen that the linear solution differs rather markedly from the nonlinear solution. This result comes about because of our decision to match up the final velocity rather than the equal area approximation. In either case, we would not expect two different equations to produce identical results. It may be noted that the initial slopes are, in fact, almost identical and thus yield the same time constant and, of course, the final velocity has been made equal. As pointed out before, there really is a wide disparity between the drag as a function of velocity squared and the linear drag assumed in the linear equation. The disparity indicated in Fig. 5.15(a) is not to be interpreted as a weakness in the analytical solution in general. As stated before, there are a great many real situations where the drag (or damping) is accurately approximated by a linear term.

5.14 Other First Order System General Solutions

5.14-1 Ramp Input

Assume that the input to a first order system is zero until $t = 0$ and then suddenly begins to increase linearly with time. This is a situation comparable to an electric motor starting up suddenly and

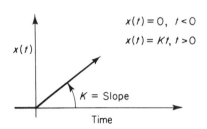

$$x(t) = 0, \ t < 0$$
$$x(t) = Kt, \ t > 0$$

K = Slope

Time

Fig. 5.16. Ramp input $x(t)$.

running at constant speed. The angle of rotation then increases linearly with time. Such an input may be characterized as in Fig. 5.16.

When we consider $x(t)$ as the input or right-hand side of an equation of the form of Eq. 5.26, Equation 5.30 results.

$$\tau \dot{v} + v = Kt$$

$$\dot{v} + \frac{1}{\tau} v = \frac{Kt}{\tau} \tag{5.30}$$

Its general solution is as before (see Eq. 5.28):

$$v = Ae^{-t/\tau} + v_{ss}$$

We must discover a solution for v_{ss} which satisfies the differential equation. A search for a possible form might lead us to try the following:

$$v_{ss} = C_1 + C_2 t$$

If $v(t)$ is to have the same general form of $x(t)$ for large time, it must be traveling with some rate C_2 and will in general lag behind $x(t)$ by an amount C_1. When substituted back into the original Eq. 5.30 we find that C_1 and C_2 can be determined; thus the original assumed solution form works.

$$C_2 + \frac{1}{\tau} C_1 + \frac{1}{\tau} C_2 t = \frac{Kt}{\tau}$$

$$C_2 = K$$

$$C_1 = -\tau K$$

Thus the final solution has the form of Eq. 5.31:

$$v = Ae^{-t/\tau} + K(t - \tau) \tag{5.31}$$

The constant A is to be evaluated from initial conditions at $t = 0$ as follows: at $t = 0$:

     With experience you will soon become adept at selecting the right form of solution. The type of input will usually give you a hint about what to choose and substitution in the original differential equation will show whether it works or not.

$$v = 0$$

$$0 = A - \tau K$$

$$A = \tau K$$

Thus,

$$v = K(\tau e^{-t/\tau} + t - \tau)$$

or

$$\frac{v}{K\tau} = e^{-t/\tau} + \frac{t}{\tau} - 1 \tag{5.32}$$

The final solution is given in Eq. 5.32 and is plotted in nondimensional terms in Fig. 5.17.

Note that Kt is the time integral of the constant K and may be thought of as the integral of a step of height K. Note also that the response indicated by Eq. 5.32 is the integral of the response obtained for the solution of the differential equation when the input was a step (see Eq. 5.29). Thus, another approach to finding a ramp response is to integrate the step response directly. This specific result is an example of the fact that in linear systems one may say that the response of a linear system due to the integral (or derivative) of an input function is identical to the integral (or derivative) of the output.

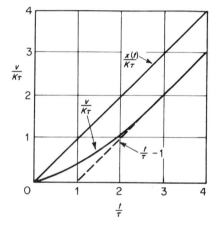

Fig. 5.17. Nondimensional response of first order system.

5.14-2   UNIT EXPONENTIAL INPUT

Let us assume the input $x(t)$ shown in Fig. 5.18 which is not unlike the exponential response shown in Fig. 5.11. The differential equation becomes that of Eq. 5.33 and its solution is of the form of Eq. 5.28.

$$\dot{v} + \frac{1}{\tau} v = \frac{Be^{-t/\tau_a}}{\tau} \tag{5.33}$$

As before, we must seek a solution which will satisfy Eq. 5.33. Let us try the exponential form itself, since the steady-state solution must have a form similar to the driving function.

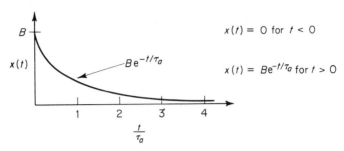

Fig. 5.18. Exponential "impulse" input.

$$v_{ss} = C_1 e^{-t/\tau_a} \tag{5.34}$$

Substituting Eq. 5.34 into Eq. 5.33 gives

$$-\frac{C_1}{\tau_a} + \frac{C_1}{\tau} = \frac{B}{\tau}$$

$$C_1 = \frac{B/\tau}{1/\tau - 1/\tau_a} = \frac{B\tau_a}{\tau_a - \tau}$$

Equation 5.35 shows the final result before initial conditions are included.

$$v = A e^{-t/\tau} + B\frac{\tau_a}{\tau_a - \tau} e^{-t/\tau_a} \tag{5.35}$$

As before, A may be determined from initial conditions. At $t = 0$:

$$v = 0$$

$$0 = A + B\frac{\tau_a}{\tau_a - \tau}$$

$$v = B\frac{\tau_a}{\tau_a - \tau}(e^{-t/\tau_a} - e^{-t/\tau})$$

$$\frac{v}{B\tau_a/(\tau_a - \tau)} = e^{-t/\tau_a} - e^{-t/\tau} \tag{5.36}$$

Equation 5.36 shows the final nondimensional results. A single case of this result is plotted in Fig. 5.19.

Let $\tau_a = 2\tau$ in Eq. 5.36, then

$$\frac{v}{2B} = e^{-t/2\tau} - e^{-t/\tau}$$

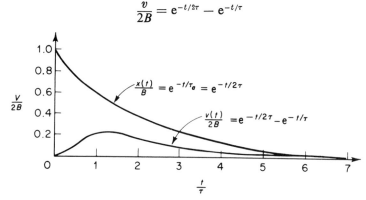

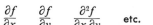

Fig. 5.19. Response of first order system of time constant τ to an exponential "impulse" input of time constant 2τ.

5.15   Lumped Parameter and Distributed Parameter Systems

The constant-coefficient-linear-differential equation is a member of a much larger class of differential equations. The larger class describes systems containing a finite set of elements which can be considered for modeling purposes. Systems of this type are called *lumped parameter systems*. Examples are systems composed of mass, spring, and damper elements or those composed of resistors, capacitors, and inductors. More generally, the elements can be described accurately enough by a relationship between their terminal variables and/or their total derivatives with respect to time without a detailed representation of their internal structure. On the other hand, you will find that most systems which involve thermodynamic, fluid, or electrodynamic phenomena require a consideration of the continuous space distributions of variables as well as time variations. Hence they generate a differential equation which involves partial derivatives, some with respect to space and others with respect to time. This class is called *distributed parameter systems*. Often a distributed parameter system can be described by a lumped parameter model simply by lumping the characteristics of part of the system. A total derivative expression can then be defined. A system described by a lumped parameter model can also be described by a distributed parameter model if its "fine grain" beha-

---

Partial derivatives are used whenever a problem involves more than one independent variable. They are defined using the Greek letter delta, ∂, e.g.

$$\frac{\partial f}{\partial x} \qquad \frac{\partial f}{\partial y} \qquad \frac{\partial^2 f}{\partial x \, \partial y} \qquad \text{etc.}$$

vior is to be examined. In general, it is much more difficult to solve a partial differential equation. In the interests of simplicity, the engineer often attempts to devise a lumped parameter model which approximates the system accurately enough.

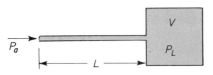

For example, consider the fluid system shown in Fig. 5.20. It consists of a long line of length L and area A connected to a volume V. It is desired to measure the pressure P_a. The line represents the connection between the pressure point and the transducer whose internal volume is V. A pressure in the volume is then converted to an electrical signal by the transducer. The differential equation relating P_a and P_L will tell us how well the transducer will reproduce changes in P_a. In both models we shall assume that pressure P_L is uniform inside the volume.

5.15–1   DISTRIBUTED PARAMETER MODEL

Consider a short segment of the fluid in the line of length Δx. A free body diagram in Fig. 5.21 shows the forces on this element.

$$A = \frac{\pi D^2}{4} = \text{area of end of element}$$

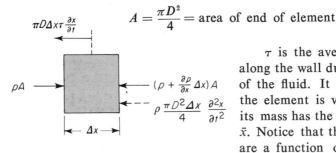

Fig. 5.21. Free body diagram for distributed parameter system.

τ is the average shear stress along the wall due to the viscosity of the fluid. It is assumed that the element is very small so all its mass has the same acceleration $\ddot{x}$. Notice that the fluid properties are a function of two variables, time and position. d'Alembert's principle yields

$$\left(p - p - \frac{\partial p}{\partial x}\Delta x\right)\frac{\pi D^2}{4} - \tau\pi\,D\Delta x\frac{\partial x}{\partial t} - \rho\frac{\pi D^2}{4}\Delta x\frac{\partial^2 x}{\partial t^2} = 0$$

which yields

$$+\frac{\partial p}{\partial x} + \frac{4\tau}{D}\frac{\partial x}{\partial t} + \rho\frac{\partial^2 x}{\partial t^2} = 0$$

In a similar way the flow of mass in and out of the element can be related to the buildup of fluid inside it to yield a second differential equation (continuity of mass).

$$\frac{\pi D^2}{4}\left[\rho\dot{x} - \rho\left(\dot{x} + \frac{\partial\dot{x}}{\partial x}\Delta x\right)\right] = -\frac{\partial}{\partial t}\left(\rho\frac{\pi D^2}{4}\right)\Delta x$$

We assume that the density ρ is uniform in the element. This expression yields

$$+\frac{\partial\dot{x}}{\partial x} = \frac{\partial\rho}{\partial t}$$

or

$$\frac{\partial}{\partial x}\left(\frac{\partial x}{\partial t}\right) = \frac{\partial\rho}{\partial t}$$

Then knowing p_a at the start of the line and the fact that the fluid leaving the line equals the buildup of mass inside the volume,

$$\rho(L, t)\frac{\pi D^2}{4}\frac{\partial x}{\partial t}(L, t) = V\frac{\partial\rho(L, t)}{\partial t}$$

allows us to determine $\rho(t)$ at $x = L$.

In this way the distributed parameter model for the system is

$$\frac{\partial p(x, t)}{\partial x} + \frac{4\tau}{D}\frac{\partial x}{\partial t} + \rho(x, t)\frac{\partial^2 x}{\partial t^2} = 0$$

$$\frac{\partial}{\partial x}\dot{x}(x, t) = \frac{\partial\rho(x, t)}{\partial t}$$

$$p(0, t) = p_a(t)$$

$$p(L, t) = p_L(t)$$

$$\frac{\pi D^2}{4}\rho(L, t)\dot{x}(L, t) = V\frac{\partial\rho(L, t)}{\partial t}$$

An additional equation is necessary for the solution which relates the pressure and density of the fluid in the line. This equation is called a state equation and depends on the fluid. If the state equation involves temperature, as would be the case with air, a process equation might also be required.

5.15-2   LUMPED PARAMETER MODEL

In the lumped parameter model we shall ignore changes in the system variables as a function of x. A new schematic of the system in Fig. 5.22 indicates how we *lump* the small element volumes into a

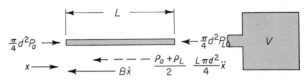

Fig. 5.22. Free body diagram for lumped parameter model.

single element. In the lumped model notice we assume that the fluid in the line moves with a uniform velocity. Hence velocity is a function of line length alone.

d'Alembert's principle yields

$$\frac{\pi D^2}{4}(p_a - p_L) - \tau \pi D L \dot{x} - \left(\frac{\rho_a + \rho_L}{2}\right)\left(\frac{L\pi D^2}{4}\right)\ddot{x} = 0$$

Then continuity of mass into the volume yields, as before,

$$\rho_L \dot{x} \frac{\pi D^2}{4} = V \frac{d\rho}{dt}$$

Notice that this model forces us to assume that pressure and density change suddenly at the edge of the lumps whereas in the distributed model this discontinuous change took place at the edge of a much smaller elementary volume.

Thus the model for the lumped system is

$$\frac{\pi D^2}{4}(p_a(t) - p_L(t)) - \tau \pi D L \frac{dx(t)}{dt} = \left(\frac{\rho_a + \rho_L}{2}\right)\left(\frac{\pi D^2 L}{4}\right)\frac{d^2 x(t)}{dt^2}$$

$$\frac{\pi D^2}{4}\rho_L(t)\frac{dx(t)}{dt} = V \frac{d\rho(t)}{dt}$$

An additional fluid state equation can provide a relation between $p(t)$ and $\rho(t)$. As before, if this relationship depends on temperature an additional process equation, determined by how heat flows in the pipe, would be necessary to eliminate the temperature variable introduced by the state equation. For example, if the fluid is a liquid we can write

$$\frac{d\rho(t)}{dt} = \frac{\rho(t)}{\beta}\frac{dp(t)}{dt}$$

where β = bulk modulus, which allows the second equation to be written as

$$\dot{x}\frac{\pi D^2}{4} = \frac{V}{\beta}\frac{dp(t)}{dt}$$

Comparing the two models that we have obtained yields the following observations:

(1) The distributed parameter model involves more simultaneous differential equations than the lumped parameter model. In the lumped parameter model we assumed that the fluid in the line behaved like a solid body, eliminating the need for a differential equation describing the relative motion of fluid in the line.

(2) The lumped parameter model is characterized by a set of linear-constant-coefficient-differential equations. This occurs because we assumed an average density $(\rho_a + \rho_L)/2$ for the fluid in the line. Of all the differential equations which we may encounter, solutions for this form will be the easiest to solve.

(3) The distributed parameter model variables depended on position x and time t, whereas the lumped parameter model variables were only time dependent.

(4) The two-variable dependency (time t, space x) of the distributed parameter model variables required additional equations known as *boundary values* whose role is the same as the initial conditions required for ordinary differential equations.

5.16 Differential Equation Classification

We have stated that differential Eqs. 5.3 and 5.4 were nonlinear "... because the variable appears in the equation as squared instead of to the first power only ...." At this point it would be well to consider a more general definition. Differential equations can be classified as being total derivative or partial derivative equations representing lumped or distributed parameter models, respectively. We might further arrange them according to the difficulty of obtaining solutions. In order of decreasing difficulty they may be classified as:

(1) nonlinear differential equations
(2) linear differential equations with nonconstant coefficients
(3) constant-coefficient-linear-differential equations

Nonlinear differential equations have terms are not a constant or a known function times a variable or its derivatives; that is,

$$x\frac{d^2x}{dt^2} + \frac{dx}{dt} + x = f(t) \tag{5.37}$$

Equation 5.37 is a nonlinear differential equation because one of its terms, $x\,dx^2/dt^2$, is not a constant or a known function times a variable or its derivatives. In the same manner, Eq. 5.38,

$$\frac{d^2 x}{dt^2} + \left(\frac{dx}{dt}\right)^2 + x = f(t) \tag{5.38}$$

is nonlinear because of the $(dx/dt)^2$ term and

$$A\frac{\partial x}{\partial y} + \left(\frac{\partial x}{\partial t}\right)^2 = f(t) \tag{5.39}$$

Equation 5.39 is a nonlinear partial differential equation because of the $(\partial x/\partial t)^2$ term.

In general a nonlinear differential equation is much more difficult to solve than a constant-coefficient-linear-differential equation Some attempt will usually be made to replace a nonlinear differential equation model by a simpler model for the same reasons that we preferred a lumped parameter model to a distributed one.

The second type of differential equation which may be generated to model a physical system is known as a linear differential equation with nonconstant coefficients. Equations of this form contain one or more terms which are a known function of time multiplied by a variable or its derivative. For example, Eq. 5.40,

$$\frac{d^2 x}{dt^2} + \cos t \frac{dx}{dt} = f(t) \tag{5.40}$$

is of this type because the term, $\cos t \, dx/dt$, is the product of a known function of time and a derivative of the dependent variable. Likewise, Eq. 5.41,

$$\frac{\partial^2 x}{\partial y^2} + t\frac{\partial x}{\partial t} = f(t) \tag{5.41}$$

is a linear differential equation with nonconstant coefficients. In general, these differential equations are about as difficult to solve as a nonlinear differential equation. To summarize, we can refer to Fig. 5.23.

We can construct a block diagram for all these differential equation models. However, in order to construct the diagram we shall need other operators besides the basic three used to represent a constant-coefficient-linear-differential equation. Often the block diagram for these more complicated differential equations will be useful in reducing them to the simplest form by linearizing or lumping the elements to produce a constant-coefficient-linear-differential equation. This simplest form is the only type which has a general solution. All the other differential equation types require a particular

	Lumped Parameter Systems	Distributed Parameter Systems
Linear Differential Equation with Constant Coefficients	**Example** $$2\frac{d^2x}{dt^2} + 3\frac{dx}{dt} + 4x = f(t)$$	**Example** $$7\frac{\partial x}{\partial y} + 8\frac{\partial x}{\partial t} + x = f(t)$$
	Differential equation in which all terms are composed of a variable times a constant.	
Linear Differential Equations with Nonconstant Coefficients	**Example** $$\frac{dx}{dt} + t^2x = f(t)$$	$$\frac{\partial^2 x}{\partial y^2} + e^{-t}\frac{\partial x}{\partial t} = f(t)$$
	Some terms contain a variable times a known function.	
Nonlinear Differential Equations	**Example** $$\frac{dx}{dt} + x^2 = f(t)$$	$$\frac{\partial^2 x}{\partial y^2} + \sqrt{\frac{\partial x}{\partial t}} = f(t)$$
	Some terms are not composed of a variable or its derivative times a constant or known function.	

Fig. 5.23.   Differential equation classification.

set of parameter values and initial conditions in order to obtain a particular solution. The problem of generalizing these solutions is a difficult one which has no good solution in most cases.

5.17 Summary

We have shown that differential equations in unknown functions can be solved by developing a set of discrete equations. These equations represent the system at discrete instants of time and provide a set of algebraic equations with constant unknowns. This set of equations is easily solved using the rules of elementary algebra. This approach is very similar to the numerical methods used for digital computer solutions of differential equations. The solution depends on the initial conditions, the system inputs, and the system parameter values, so that a separate calculation is required for every set of initial conditions and parameters.

If the differential equation can be simplified by linearization to obtain a constant-coefficient-linear-differential equation, then a more general solution can be obtained in the form of an exponential with unknown constants. The solution of the differential equation is then reduced to the solution of a set of algebraic equations with unknown constants. Thus a more general form results which allows us to select parameter values for a system response.

Problems

5-1. A free falling body is described by the simple equation and block diagram as follows: $M\ddot{x} = Mg$. The solution will be known:

$$v = gt + v_0; \quad x = \tfrac{1}{2}gt^2 + v_0 t + x_0.$$

Using numerical integration, find v versus t at one second intervals for first ten seconds of fall. Calculate x versus t and compare results.

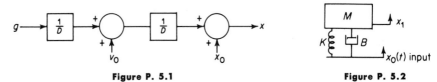

Figure P. 5.1   **Figure P. 5.2**

5-2. For the rough model of a car shown in Fig. P. 5.2, solve for $x_1(t)$ by numerical integration.

$$Mg = 6{,}400\,\text{lb} \qquad x_0(t) = 0 \quad \text{for} \quad t < 0$$
$$K = 800\,\text{lb/in.} \qquad\qquad\quad = 3t \quad \text{for} \quad t \geq 0$$
$$B = 400\,\frac{\text{lb-sec}}{\text{in.}}$$

5-3. For the two equations shown below, draw a block diagram (do not reduce) and write the necessary equations to solve by numerical integration (hand or computer calculation). Solve for first two time intervals.

$$\ddot{\theta}_1 + 2\dot{\theta}_2\,\dot{\theta}_1 + \cos\theta_1 = 0$$
$$\ddot{\theta}_2 + (\theta_1 - \pi/2)\theta_2 = 1$$

Initial conditions: $\theta_1(0) = 0 \qquad \theta_2(0) = 0$
                       $\dot{\theta}_1(0) = \pi/2 \qquad$ Time interval $= \pi/2$

5-4. Linearize the following equation about the operating point $\ddot{x}_0$, $\ddot{x}_0$, $\dot{x}_0$, x_0 for small changes in $\dddot{x}$, $\ddot{x}$, $\dot{x}$, x.

$$a\frac{d^3x}{dt^3} + bx^{1/2}\left(\frac{d^2x}{dt^2}\right)^2 + c\frac{dx}{dt} + gx^3 = f(t)$$

5-5. Linearize the following equations for a hydraulic servo valve.

(a) $q = K_1(u + e - d)\sqrt{2(p_c - p)/\rho} - K_1(u - e - d)\sqrt{2p/\rho}$
(b) $q = 2A\dot{x} + \dot{p}(V_0 + 2Ax)/B_s$
(c) $p = p_c/2 + K_2\ddot{x} + K_3\dot{x}x + K_4x^2$
Variables are: q, e, d, p, x.

5-6. Linearize the following equations.
(a) $f = M\ddot{x} + B\dot{x}^2 + Kx$
Variables are: f, x
(b) $q = \pi D(x - y)\sqrt{(P_1 - p)/\rho} + \pi D\dot{x}x\sqrt{y - x^2}$
Variables are: q, x, y, p

5-7. Make a time plot of the following functions.
(a) $5e^{-3t}$,
(b) $-3e^{-(1/2)t}$
(c) $4(1 - e^{-(1/4)t})$
(d) Find the slope at $t = 0$ of each. At what time does this slope cross the final value of the function if drawn from the initial value?
(e) What is the value of the function at this time? What percentage of the distance from initial to final value has the function gone?

5-8. Given the following second order differential equation with constant coefficients, solve completely for y as a function of time.

$$4\ddot{y} + 8\dot{y} = 12t^2 \qquad \text{At} \quad t = 0, \quad y = 4, \quad \dot{y} = 0$$

5-9. For system in Fig. P. 5.9, switch closes at $t = 0$. Initial voltage across capacitor is equal to zero [$v_c(0) = 0$]. Write an expression for $v_c(t)$ for all $t \geq 0$.
(a) Assume an exponential form for the solution of the equation and obtain an analytical expression for $v_c(t)$ given $e(t) = E$, a constant.
(b) What is the time constant of the solution?

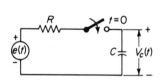

Figure P. 5.9

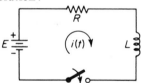

Figure P. 5.10

5-10. Write the differential equation for the circuit in Fig. P. 5.10 and solve for the current after the switch is closed at $t = 0$. What is the time constant?

5-11. The suspended carriage on the tire tester below moves with a constant velocity V_0. If there is initially no force between the tire and the ground, determine the vertical force upon the tire after $t = 0$. Assume the mass of the tire can be neglected. Consider the solution in two parts:
(a) The force during the time the tire is on the ramp.
(b) The force after the tire has reached the level track.
(1) Assume a solid tire.

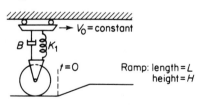

Figure P.5.11

(2) Assume the tire can be represented as a spring K_t.

5-12. Given the following block diagrams —(a), (b), (c), and (d)—, sketch the output y as a function of time for cases (a), (b), (c), and (d) for each of the following inputs x.

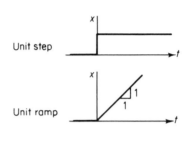

Unit step

Unit ramp

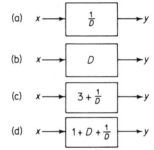

(a) $x \longrightarrow \boxed{\dfrac{1}{D}} \longrightarrow y$

(b) $x \longrightarrow \boxed{D} \longrightarrow y$

(c) $x \longrightarrow \boxed{3 + \dfrac{1}{D}} \longrightarrow y$

(d) $x \longrightarrow \boxed{1 + D + \dfrac{1}{D}} \longrightarrow y$

Figure P. 5.12

5-13. In the circuit in Fig. P.5.13, switches S_1 and S_2 are both switched at $t = 0$. For $t < 0$, S_2 has been closed a long time so that i_L is at steady state. Solve (analytically) for $i_L(t)$ for $t > 0$, i.e, determine the particular and complementary solution for $i_L(t)$. Sketch your solution approximately.

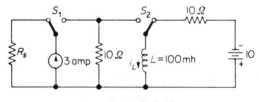

Figure P. 5.13

5-14. The circuit shown in Fig. P. 5.13 depicts a typical relay. This particular relay opens when the current through the inductive winding L_r reaches $\frac{1}{5}$ amp and closes when the current is $\frac{1}{10}$ amp. Design a circuit for an airplane wing light flasher so that a bulb will flash at a rate of 1/sec $\pm$ 10%. Use any resistors or capacitors you may need. The relay is supplied with a 24-volt D.C. source.

5-15. Lake Linear in the Melborp Mountains is a scene of much scientific

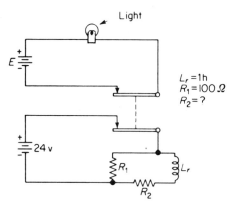

Figure P. 5.14

activity. The temperature of this lake on the night of the first full moon of summer decreases 1°F/ft below the surface. Professor Sink wanted to test this belief, so first he determined the time constant of his thermometer by lowering it into a pail of water held at 60°F. This he did so he could correct his temperature readings of the lake. The chart below shows the temperature response observed in the test. Professor Sink then lowered his thermometer into the lake at a constant velocity of 1 ft/sec. If the surface temperature was 80°F and the initial reading on the thermometer was 80°F, what was the error in the reading when the thermometer had descended 10 ft?

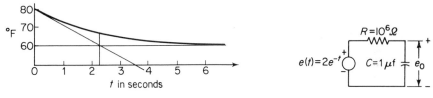

Figure P. 5.15   **Figure P. 5.16**

5-16. For the system in Fig. P. 5.16, find $e_0(t)$ by solving the differential equation, given an input voltage $e(t) = 2e^{-t}$. Initial condition: $e_0(0) = 0$.

5-17. For the circuit of Prob. 5-16, suppose $e(t)$ was $e(t) = t + e^{-2t}$. Find $e_0(t)$ for $e_0(0) = 0$.

5-18. For the circuit of Prob. 5-16, for $e(t) = \sin \omega t$, plot the $\log_{10}|e_{0_{ss}}|$ versus $\log_{10} \omega$ or plot $|e_{0_{ss}}|$ on log-log paper where $|e_0|$ is the magnitude of e_0. Find the phase difference ϕ between input and output, and plot that angle versus $\log_{10} \omega$. Hint: put $e_{0_{ss}}$ in form: $A \sin(\omega t + \phi)$.

5-19. For some reason, we obtained: $2\dot{x} + \frac{1}{2}x = \frac{1}{2}te^{-(1/4)t} + t$. Solve for $x(t)$, given $x(0) = 0$.

5-20. A temperature measuring device is immersed in a bath of oil. The relationship between the actual temperature of the oil and the reading on the scale of the measuring instrument can be represented as a first order differential equation with a time constant of 2 sec. If the temperature of the bath is increasing at a rate of $1°/\text{sec}$, what is the difference between the oil bath actual temperature and system scale reading as a function of time? At $t = 0$, temperature of oil and scale reading are $30°$.

5-21. Classify the following equations as linear or nonlinear differential equations. In each case state why it is linear or nonlinear.

(a) $d^2\theta/dt^2 + b\,d\theta/dt + e^\theta = 6$

(b) $d^2x/dt^2 + t\,dx/dt + 3x = 0$

(c) $d^2y/dt^2 + y = \sin \omega t$

6 *Approximate Transient Response*

6.1 Introduction

The transient response of electrical circuits following the closing or opening of a switch is often of interest to engineers. This response, for example, describes the change in the output voltage of a power supply when the power is suddenly turned on or off. It is possible that the form of these transients may have a very serious effect upon the equipment which is being connected to the power supply. In addition the transient response of electronic equipment such as hi-fi amplifiers and microphones can often provide insight into the response of this equipment to the more complicated wave forms which occur during the reproduction of voice or music. The transient response of a mechanical system is also of great interest to engineers who are trying to predict its performance. For example, the suspension system of an automobile is subjected to step, impulse, or ramplike inputs due to road surface irregularities. The subsequent motion of the vehicle is quite important to the comfort and safety of the passengers. In addition some types of equipment need to be protected from their environment during motion of that environment. For example, delicate electronic equipment is often protected by spring and damper arrangements which isolate this equipment from the shock and vibration inside an airplane or missile. Also, the transient response of measuring devices provides insight into the response of these devices to the more complicated signals they must measure. An accelerometer which is capable of measuring accelerations and producing an output signal proportional to these accelerations can be evaluated by subjecting it to a step or ramp change in acceleration. Its response to these kinds of transients provides a good deal of insight into its response for other types of signals. It will be shown, in a later chapter, that the response of a system to an arbitrary input can be determined from its response to an inpulse, providing the system can be characterized by a linear differential equation. Thus the transient response of a system has great engineering importance, and approximate methods for finding this transient response will have great utility in the dynamic analysis of engineering systems.

The general solution to any linear differential equation consists of the sum of the particular and the complementary solutions. The arbitrary constants of the complementary solution are evaluated from a set of initial conditions. The final behavior of a circuit when it reaches equilibrium can be used to find the form of the particular solution. Thus, one sees that the initial and final states of a circuit are important for obtaining a complete solution.

It is possible in many systems to learn a great deal about the nature of their transient response merely from a study of the initial and final values of variables in the system. It is the purpose of this chapter to discuss how one may predict the transient response knowing only the initial and final values without actually solving the differential equation. These techniques are important for the student in order to obtain a "first" solution to a problem without solving the mathematical equation, to aid in getting a "feel" for the nature of his answer, and to provide check points against which he can compare a later mathematical analysis.

6.2 Capacitor Circuits

Consider Eqs. 3.2 and 3.3 for the capacitor:

$$i = C\frac{de}{dt} \tag{3.2}$$

$$e = \frac{1}{C}\int_0^t i\,dt + \text{initial voltage} \tag{3.3}$$

A consequence of Eq. 3.3 is that the voltage across a capacitor cannot change in zero time for any finite current going through it. This means that *a capacitor acts like a voltage source for any sudden changes*

☆   This is another valuable technique to have at your disposal—you will be surprised how much you can learn about the system response without actually solving the differential equation.

in current going through it. Whatever voltage exists on a capacitor, whether it is zero or some finite value, will remain unchanged during a zero interval of time exemplified by the opening or closing of a switch. If we let $t = 0^-$ be the time just before switching, the capacitor will have the same voltage across it at $t = 0^+$, denoting a zero interval of time later.

Equation 3.2 shows that the current through a capacitor must be zero if the voltage applied to the capacitor does not change with time. That is, any DC voltage applied across the capacitor will produce no current flow. Thus, *a capacitor acts like an open circuit or as if it weren't even there when a circuit reaches an equilibrium state in which no voltages are varying.*

The implication of the two statements in italics may be illustrated in the following examples. Consider the circuit of Fig. 6.1. This is the familiar *RC* circuit made up of a battery with voltage *E* and a switch which may be instantaneously opened or closed. The voltage across the capacitor is considered as the output voltage *e*. Assume that there is no initial charge on the capacitor *C* and that the switch is open. Let us study the initial and final values following the closing of switch *S*. Switch *S* is closed in a zero interval of time represented by the time between $t = 0^-$

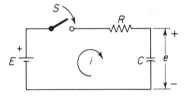

Fig. 6.1. Example 1: *RC* circuit. with switch and battery.

and $t = 0^+$. Let us draw two circuits, one for the initial value and one for the final value. In the initial value circuit, the capacitor is shown as a short circuit (a voltage source of zero volts is a short circuit) and in the final value circuit it is shown as an open circuit. These are illustrated in Fig. 6.2.

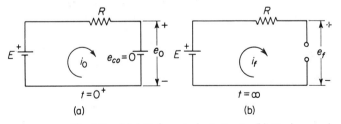

Fig.6.2. (a) Initial equivalent circuit. (b) Final equivalent circuit.

Inspection of Fig. 6.2(a) shows that e_0 must be zero since the voltage cannot change instantaneously across the capacitor. It shows

---

Remember voltage sources? We discussed them in Sec. 3.6. ☆

further that the initial value i_0 of current is limited only by the resistor R and is given then by Eq. 6.1.

$$i_0 = \frac{E}{R} \tag{6.1}$$

Equation 6.1 allows us to compute the rate of change of e_0 from Eq. 3.2.

$$\left.\frac{de}{dt}\right|_{t=0^+} = \frac{i_0}{C} = \frac{E}{RC} \tag{6.2}$$

The final value of e may be seen by inspection from Fig. 6.2(b) to be equal to E since i_f must be zero in the open circuit. All of these conclusions can be sketched as in Fig. 6.3.

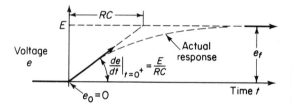

Fig. 6.3. Initial and final values of e following closure of switch.

It may be seen by inspection that we have almost completely defined the transient response of the voltage e in Fig. 6.1 following the closing of switch S. The actual response shown as a dotted line may be plotted from the solution of the differential equation or it may be sketched in, knowing the initial and final slopes and values. Thus we see that a great deal of information may be obtained by

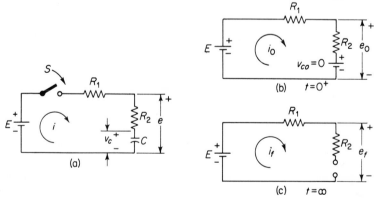

Fig. 6.4. Example 2: (a) Capacitor circuit. (b) Initial equivalent. (c) Final equivalent.

inspection without solving the differential equation. Some other examples follow. Consider the circuit shown in Fig. 6.4 with $e_c = 0$ at $t = 0^-$. The initial and final equivalent circuits are also shown. The initial value e_0 is given in Eq. 6.3 and the initial rate of change of e is shown in the derivation which leads to Eq. 6.4.

$$e_0 = \frac{R}{R_1 + R_2} E \tag{6.3}$$

$$\left. \begin{aligned} E &= i(R_1 + R_2) + \frac{1}{C} \int i\, dt \\ e &= iR_2 + \frac{1}{C} \int i\, dt \end{aligned} \right\}$$

These equations hold for all time after closing the switch.

$$0^+ \leq t \leq \infty$$

Differentiating both equations,

$$0 = (R_1 + R_2)\frac{di}{dt} + \frac{i}{C}$$

$$\frac{de}{dt} = R_2 \frac{di}{dt} + \frac{i}{C}$$

and, at time $i = 0^+$,

$$(R_1 + R_2)\frac{di}{dt}\Big|_{t=0^+} = -\frac{i_0}{C} \quad \text{or} \quad \frac{di}{dt}\Big|_{t=0^+} = -\frac{i_0}{(R_1 + R_2)C}$$

$$\frac{de}{dt}\Big|_{t=0^+} = R_2 \frac{di}{dt}\Big|_{t=0^+} + \frac{i_0}{C}$$

Now

$$i_0 = \frac{E}{R_1 + R_2}$$

Therefore,

$$\frac{de}{dt}\Big|_{t=0^+} = -\frac{R_2 E}{(R_1 + R_2)^2 C} + \frac{E}{(R_1 + R_2)C} = \frac{E}{(R_1 + R_2)C}\left(1 - \frac{R_2}{R_1 + R_2}\right) \tag{6.4}$$

The final value e_f may be seen from Fig. 6.4(c) to be just equal to E. The foregoing results are shown in Fig. 6.5. Note that e changes suddenly from zero at $t = 0^-$ to $e = R_2 E/(R_1 + R_2)$ at $t = 0^+$.

As a third example consider the circuit of Fig. 6.6 with its initial and final equivalent circuits, $e = 0$ at $t = 0^-$.

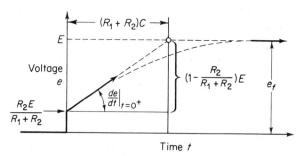

Fig. 6.5. Initial and final nature of transient response of circuit of Fig. 6.4.

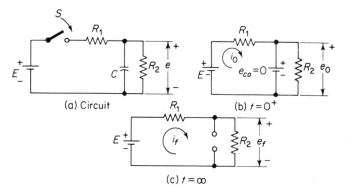

Fig. 6.6. Example 3: (a) Capacitor circuit. (b) Initial equivalent. (c) Final equivalent.

Inspection of the initial circuit shows that the initial value of e must be zero since the capacitor acts as a short circuit and all the initial current will go through the capacitor producing no voltage drop across R_2. Under these conditions, the initial rate of change of voltage e will be given by Eq. 6.5:

$$i_0 = \frac{E}{R_1}, \quad \frac{de}{dt}\bigg|_{t=0^+} = \frac{i_0}{C} = \frac{E}{R_1 C} \tag{6.5}$$

The response curve may be sketched as in Fig. 6.7, noting that the final value of e is that given by the drop due to final current i_f through R_2:

$$e_f = \frac{ER_2}{R_1 + R_2}$$

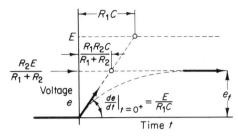

Fig. 6.7. Initial and final nature of transient response of circuit of Fig. 6.6.

6.3   Inductor Circuits

A second pair of statements apply to the initial and final values of variables in inductors. They may be deduced from Eqs. 3.5 and 3.6 which are rewritten here.

$$e = L \frac{di}{dt} \tag{3.5}$$

$$i = \frac{1}{L} \int_0^t e \, dt + \text{initial current} \tag{3.6}$$

For a finite voltage across an inductor, the current through an inductor cannot change in zero time. Therefore, *an inductor acts like a current source for a sudden change in voltage across it.* This means that, for all voltage changes involving inductors following a sudden closing or opening of a switch, the inductors act like a current source at $t = 0^+$. If an inductor has a current i flowing through it at time $t = 0^-$, then the same current will be flowing at $t = 0^+$.

     In steady state when all voltage and current changes are zero, the voltage drop across an inductor must be zero. Therefore *the inductor acts like a short circuit in the steady state when no voltages are varying.*

     The two foregoing italicized statements enable us to predict the nature of transient responses following sudden opening or closing of switches for circuits containing inductors in much the same way as previously shown for circuits containing capacitors. One may draw initial and final equivalent circuits. Some examples follow. Figure 6.8 shows a circuit containing an inductor which is essentially equivalent to the *RC* circuit shown in Fig. 6.1. Inspection of Fig. 6.8(b) shows

Look up Sec. 3.6 again if you are still unsure about current sources. ☆

the initial value of voltage e_0 will jump immediately to E on closing switch S. Figure 6.8(c) shows the final value e_f to be zero and the

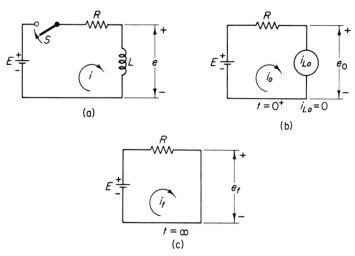

(a)

(b)

(c)

Fig. 6.8. Example 4: (a) Series RL circuit. (b) Initial equivalent. (c) Final equivalent.

final current to be limited by R. The initial slope of current is given by Eq. 6.6:

$$\frac{di}{dt}\bigg|_{t=0^+} = \frac{e_0}{L} = \frac{E}{L} = \frac{E/R}{L/R} \tag{6.6}$$

Figure 6.9(a) shows the current response and since $e = E - iR$, the voltage response may be sketched as shown in Fig. 6.9(b).

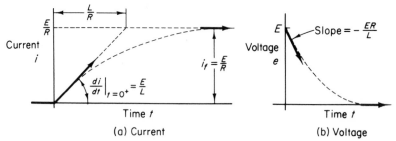

(a) Current

(b) Voltage

Fig. 6.9. Initial and final nature of transient response of circuit of Fig. 6.8.

6.4 Examples with Capacitors and Inductors

Figure 6.10 shows a somewhat more complicated circuit and the initial and final equivalents. Assume that

$$e_c = i_1 = i_2 = 0 \quad \text{at} \quad t = 0^-$$

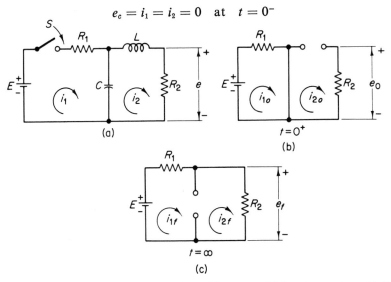

(a)

$t = 0^+$

(b)

$t = \infty$

(c)

Fig. 6.10. Example 5: (a) Circuit. (b) Initial equivalent. (c) Final equivalent. Note that the short circuit and open circuit in (b) can actually be considered as a zero voltage source and zero current source, respectively.

Inspection of Fig. 6.10(b) shows that e must be zero at $t = 0^+$. That the rate of change of e is also zero is shown by the following equations:

$$i_{10} = \frac{E}{R_1} \qquad i_{20} = 0$$

around loop 2

$$\frac{1}{C} \int (i_2 - i_1)\, dt + L\frac{di_2}{dt} + i_2 R_2 = 0$$

at $t = 0^+$

$$0 + L\frac{di_2}{dt}\bigg|_{t=0^+} + 0 = 0$$

therefore,

$$\frac{di_2}{dt}\bigg|_{t=0^+} = 0 \quad \text{and} \quad e = i_2 R_2$$

then

$$\frac{de}{dt} = R_2 \frac{di_2}{dt} \quad \text{and thus} \quad \frac{de}{dt}\bigg|_{t=0^+} = 0$$

The response may be sketched as in Fig. 6.11. The shape of the

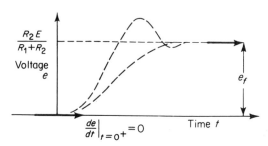

Fig. 6.11 Initial and final nature of transient response of circuit of Fig. 6.10.

response itself is determined by the actual solution of the differential equation. One may even predict the shape of the response, having knowledge of certain ratios of circuit parameters. This sort of knowledge shall be developed later in the book.

Another interesting question is raised if one asks "What happens when the switch is opened in the circuit of Fig. 6.10 after equilibrium has been reached?" Figure 6.10(c) shows that the final voltage across the capacitor is given by the voltage drop across the resistor R_2. When the switch is opened this voltage cannot change instantly. Thus for the purpose of an initial circuit, the capacitor may be shown

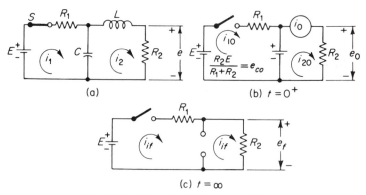

(a)

(b) $t = 0^+$

(c) $t = \infty$

Fig. 6.12. Example 6: (a) Circuit of Fig. 6.10 but with switch opening. (b) Initial equivalent. (c) Final equivalent.

as a battery. The final value of current i_2 derived from Fig. 6.10(c) is shown as a current source for initial value purposes for the response when the switch is opened since this current cannot change instantly in the inductor L. Figure 6.12 shows the circuit with initial and final value equivalents. Note that the voltage and current sources shown in Fig. 6.12(b) hold only for $t = 0^+$.

The initial and final values of e may be obtained from inspection of Fig. 6.12(b) and (c). The initial rate of change of e may be seen to be zero from the following equations:

around loop 2,

$$\frac{1}{C}\int(i_2 - i_1)dt + L\frac{di_2}{dt} + i_2 R_2 = 0$$

at $t = 0^+$,

$$-\frac{R_2 E}{R_1 + R_2} + L\frac{di_2}{dt}\bigg|_{t=0^+} + i_{20} R_2 = 0$$

$$L\frac{di_2}{dt}\bigg|_{t=0^+} = \frac{R_2 E}{R_1 + R_2} - \frac{ER_2}{R_1 + R_2} = 0$$

Thus the final response may be sketched as in Fig. 6.13.

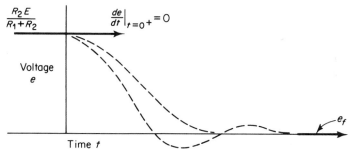

Fig. 6.13. Initial and final nature of transient response of circuit of Fig. 6.12.

While we are "opening switches," let us return to the circuit shown in Fig. 6.6 and sketch its response for the switch opening condition. The initial and final value circuits will then appear as in Fig. 6.14.

As before, the initial equivalent shows a voltage source equal to the initial voltage stored on capacitor C and the final equivalent shows that e_f must go to zero. Note that the intercept of the initial slope with the final value is the time constant of the circuit,

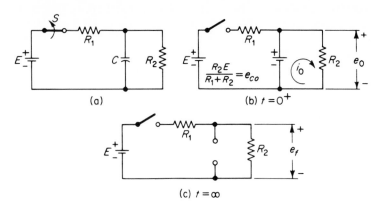

Fig. 6.14. Example: (a) Circuit of Fig. 6.6 but with switch opening. (b) Initial equivalent. (c) final equivalent.

$$\frac{R_1 R_2}{R_1 + R_2} C \text{ and } R_2 C,$$

respectively (see Figs. 6.6 and 6.15).

$$i_0 = \left(\frac{R_2 E}{R_1 + R_2}\right)\left(\frac{1}{R_2}\right) = \frac{E}{R_1 + R_2}$$

$$\left.\frac{de}{dt}\right|_{t=0^+} = -\frac{i_0}{C} = -\frac{E}{(R_1 + R_2)C}$$

The response may be sketched as in Fig. 6.15.

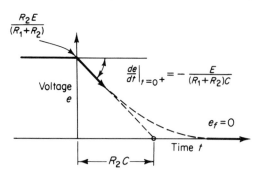

Fig. 6.15. Initial and final nature of transient response of Fig. 6.14.

6.5 Mechanical System Elements

It is possible to obtain the approximate transient response of mechanical systems by considering the physical properties of the system elements. By looking at the defining equations for the mass and dashpot, we can make analogous statements to those made for electrical elements. For example, (see Fig. 3.20)

$$F = M\frac{dv_1}{dt} \quad \text{where} \quad \frac{dv_2}{dt} = 0 \quad \text{defining equation for mass} \quad (3.38)$$

Equation 3.38 says that an infinite force is required to change the velocity of the mass in zero time. *Therefore, for finite forces, a mass must have the same velocity at* $t = 0^+$ *that it had at* $t = 0^-$. For the dashpot we have the defining equation, (see Fig. 2.6)

$$F = B\left(\frac{dx_2}{dt} - \frac{dx_1}{dt}\right)$$

$$= B\frac{d(x_2 - x_1)}{dt} \quad (2.23)$$

Equation 2.23 says that an infinite force is required to change the distance between the ends of the damper in zero time. *Thus for finite forces,* $x_2 - x_1$ *cannot change in the zero time interval from* $t = 0^-$ *to* $t = 0^+$.

To summarize, the velocity of a mass cannot change instantaneously and the length of a dashpot cannot change instantaneously.

6.6 Mechanical System Examples

As an example, consider the mechanical system in Fig. 6.16. It is assumed that the mass of the springs and damper support is negligible. In addition, mass M and the support are confined to move in one dimension.

First, consider the system at rest with x_1 and x_2 measured from equilibrium. If a step change in x_1 occurs, then

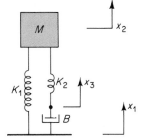

$$x_1 = 0 \quad \text{at} \quad t = 0^-$$

$$x_1 = X \quad \text{at} \quad t = 0^+$$

Fig. 6.16. Proposed suspension system.

when X is the magnitude of the step change in x_1. At $t = 0^+$, the length of the damper, $x_3 - x_1$, must be the

---

Mechanical systems are a little trickier to deal with than electrical systems because you need to have some "feel" for how mechanical elements react to a stimulus. Study this section carefully. ☆

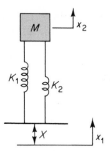

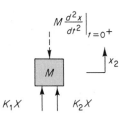

Fig. 6.17. Initial model at
$t = 0^+$. Following step
change in x_1.

Fig. 6.18. Free body diagram at $t = 0^+$.

same as it was at $t = 0^-$. In other words the damper acts as a solid
connection during the step input in x_1. We also know that the position of the mass cannot change instantaneously because this would
imply an infinite acceleration. The initial model of the system at $t = 0^+$
is shown in Fig. 6.17.

If we now examine the initial form of x_2 using this model, we
see from the free body diagram in Fig. 6.18 that

$$K_1 X + K_2 X - M \frac{d^2 x_2}{dt^2}\bigg|_{t=0^+} = 0$$

or

$$\frac{d^2 x_2}{dt^2}\bigg|_{t=0^+} = \frac{(K_1 + K_2)X}{M}$$

which is the initial acceleration of the mass at $t = 0^+$.

Thus the initial acceleration is constant and can be integrated
twice to obtain an expression for $x_2(t)$ at $t = 0^+$, i.e.,

$$x_2(t) = \int \left[\int \frac{(K_1 + K_2)}{M} X \, dt \right] dt$$

$$= \frac{(K_1 + K_2)X t^2}{2M}$$

Also,

$$x_2(0^+) = \frac{dx_2}{dt}\bigg|_{t=0^+} = 0$$

    Don't be put off by the double integral sign. It is quite straightforward as the
result shows.

since the body is at rest at $t = 0$ and it would require an infinite force to impart an initial velocity to mass M. Thus the initial response follows a parabolic curve as shown in Fig. 6.20.

After the transients have died out, the system comes to rest so we can write

$$\ddot{x}_1(\infty) = \ddot{x}_2(\infty) = \ddot{x}_3(\infty) = \dot{x}_1(\infty) = \dot{x}_2(\infty)$$
$$= \dot{x}_3(\infty) = 0$$

Since there is no relative velocity between the terminals of the damper it transmits no force. This means that only spring K_1 has any effect on the mass as indicated in Fig. 6.19. However, the force exerted by this spring on the mass must be zero in order to satisfy the requirement that $\ddot{x}_2(\infty) = 0$, i.e.,

Fig. 6.19. Simplified system at $t = \infty$.

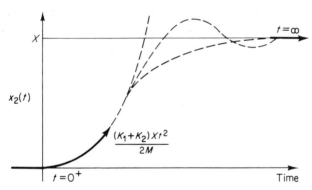

Fig. 6.20. Approximate transient response.

$$K_1[x_1(\infty) - x_2(\infty)] = 0$$

Therefore, $x_1(\infty) = x_2(\infty) = X$. This final condition is also shown in Fig. 6.20.

We have thus determined the initial and final form of the system response. Determining the exact form of the response for $0 < t \leq \infty$ requires solution of the differential equations. The only thing we can say now is that the exact response is dependent on the relative values of the parameters M, B, and K_1, K_2.

Figure 6.20 shows two possible responses (broken lines). These will be much more meaningful once you have read Chap. 7. ☆

6.7 Fluid System Response

The concepts that we have used to approximate the transient response
of mechanical and electrical systems are not restricted to systems of
this type. They can also be applied to other physical systems. For
example, consider the fluid system in Fig. 6.21 which represents the
model of a pressure transducer configuration introduced in Chap. 5.

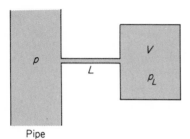

Pipe

Fig. 6.21. Pressure transducer model.

It is designed to measure a step change in pressure p in a pipe. If
the tubing connecting the transducer to the pipe has a very small
diameter and is relatively short, we can ignore the inertial effects of
the fluid moving down the tube and characterize it by a resistance
to flow. If we have a step change in p, then

$$p = 0 \quad \text{at} \quad t = 0^-$$

$$p = P \quad \text{at} \quad t = 0^+$$

assuming that the system is initially in equilibrium.

$$p(0) = p_L(0) = 0$$

then: (a) When p changes suddenly to P there will be a flow down
the tube. We have neglected inertial effects so that this causes a step
change in flow down the tube. That is, initially $q_{t=0^+} = P/R$ where
q is amount of fluid flowing into the volume V. R depends on the
characteristics of the tube fluid. (b) The fluid flowing down the tube
causes the fluid in the volume to compress. This raises the pressure
in the volume. Using the equation of state for a gas and assuming
that the heat transfer is of a particular form yields

$$q = \frac{V}{\beta} \frac{dp_L}{dt}$$

where β is the bulk modulus of the fluid. That is, the rate of change of pressure inside the volume is proportional to the flow into it. (c) Consequently since there is a step change in flow into the volume, the initial rate of change of pressure is constant. That is,

$$\frac{dp_L}{dt}\bigg|_{t=0^+} = \frac{\beta P}{VR}$$

Finally, as fluid flows into the volume, the pressure inside the volume increases until it equals the new value of pressure in the pipe. At this point no more fluid enters the volume and the rate of change of pressure is zero so that finally $p_{Lf} = P$. Thus on the basis of physical reasoning we can sketch $p_L(t)$.

Notice the similarity between this response in Fig. 6.22 and the response of an electrical network shown in Fig. 6.3. For this reason

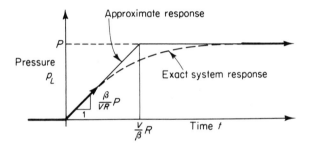

Fig. 6.22. Response of fluid system.

V/β is sometimes called the capacitance of a volume of fluid and R the resistance of a pipe. Also VR/β is known as the time constant of a fluid volume and resistance. Notice also that if we desired to measure a step change in p, we actually are in error by a rather large amount for a period of time VR/β. For this reason it is important to make R very small and V/β very small so that the dynamic response of the pressure measuring system can be as good as possible. This has led to the development of miniature pressure transducers which can be placed in the fluid with a configuration which has as small a value of VR/β as possible.

6.8 Summary of Approximate Transient Response Method

The approximate transient response of physical systems has been determined by finding the exact response initially $(t = 0^+)$ and at equilibrium $(t = \infty)$. This can be done by examining the system at $t = 0^-$ and representing it by a simpler system which has an identical response at $t = 0^+$. The response of the simpler system to the given set of initial conditions yields the initial form of the actual system response. The conditions for equilibrium at $t = \infty$ yield the final form of the response. The initial and final forms yield considerable insight into the total response.

6.9 Phase Plane Representation of a Single Degree of Freedom System Response

It has just been demonstrated that it is possible to obtain a clear picture of the transient response of a system without actually solving the system differential equations. An alternative method of achieving the same end is to draw a *phase plane* representation of the system response. This method is generally limited to single degree of freedom systems and is therefore not nearly so versatile as the approximate transient response method. Nevertheless, it is worthy of consideration because it can be used to determine the response of nonlinear as well as linear systems and is sometimes employed for this purpose in automatic control engineering, electrical engineering and in mechanics.

Suppose that we have a simple mechanical system such as that shown in Fig. 6.23. If position *and* velocity variables are assigned to

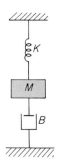

Fig. 6.23. A single degree of freedom system. Since the system differential equation was derived assuming $x = 0$, in the steady state, the system comes to rest at $x = 0$, as shown by the trajectory in Fig. 6.24.

the mass, the result will be a set of two first order differential equations and two dependent variables. We can obtain a representation of the system response to any initial values of position and velocity by plotting the velocity versus the position. The velocity-position plane is called the *phase plane*. The differential equation can be modified further to yield an algebraic equation which relates the

 This is a good example of how the mathematical model can be used to optimize the design of a system.

slope of the velocity versus position curves at any point in the velocity-position plane to the values of velocity and position at that point. Thus it becomes possible to quickly solve the system differential equation by plotting a path in the phase plane called a *trajectory* which starts from a given initial velocity and position. This plot has many interesting properties and a family of these trajectories can completely describe the system response to any initial conditions.

The utility of this approach diminishes rapidly as the number of degrees of freedom is increased beyond one because we are forced to represent a trajectory in a space of one less dimension than the highest order derivative in the differential equation. Since it is required to reduce the system differential equations into a set of first order differential equations to use the method, a $2n$ space for a system of n degrees of freedom results. There is some difficulty in visualizing behavior in three dimensions let alone in $2n$ dimensions, and so the utility of this method of solution is largely academic for $n > 1$.

The phase plane method can be illustrated by the example shown in Fig. 6.23. Using the free body diagram approach, we may write the system differential equation,

$$M\ddot{x} + B\dot{x} + Kx = 0 \tag{6.7}$$

Then, defining a velocity *and* a position variable for the mass yields

$$v = \dot{x} \tag{6.8}$$

$$M\dot{v} + Bv + Kx = 0 \tag{6.9}$$

These two equations have time as an independent variable. Time can be eliminated from the equations by noting that

$$\dot{v} = \frac{dv}{dt} = \frac{dv}{dx}\frac{dx}{dt}$$

$$= v\frac{dv}{dx} \tag{6.10}$$

Using this derived expression we may write

$$Mv\frac{dv}{dx} + Bv + Kx = 0 \tag{6.11}$$

This equation relates the slope of the velocity-position curves at any point to the value of the velocity and position at that point. That is,

$$\text{Curve slope} = \frac{dv}{dx} = \frac{-Bv - Kx}{Mv} \qquad (6.12)$$

Thus given the initial conditions $v(0)$, $x(0)$, we can compute dv/dx. Assuming that this slope is constant, we may approximate the velocity-position curve by a short straight line segment. At the end of the segment we have a new value of velocity and position which can be used to compute a new dv/dx. This value can also be averaged with the first value to obtain a more accurate approximation to the new velocity and position. The process may be continued until the system comes to rest ($v = 0$, $x = 0$ for this example). Often it is more convenient to draw lines of constant slope as shown in Fig. 6.24. In this example for the case where $B/M = K/M = 1$, we have

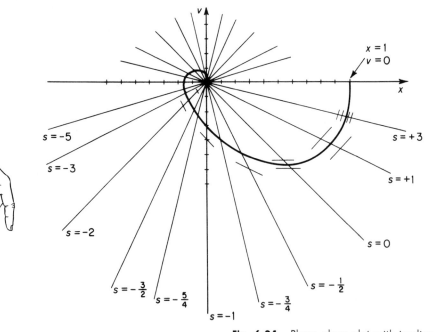

Fig. 6.24. Phase plane plot with isoclines.

$$\frac{dv}{dx} = -1 - \frac{x}{v} = s$$

or

☆   It is useless to draw a diagram like Fig. 6.24 if you don't make an effort to understand its physical significance. Think about it and then ask yourself what would happen if there were no damper—you should get an ellipse. What would that mean?

$$x = -(s + 1)v \qquad (6.13)$$

A response for $x = 1$, $v = 0$ is shown using these lines of constant slope, which are called *isoclines*. The isoclines enable us to plot a tangent to the curve at the point where it crosses the isocline. The resulting response of the system to an initial displacement $x = 1$ is sketched in Fig. 6.24.

Problems

6-1. Draw approximate responses for each of the following circuits, assuming $e(t)$ in each case is as shown.

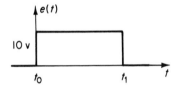

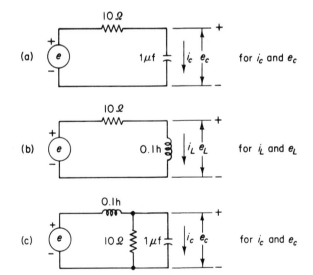

Figure **P. 6.1**

6-2. Draw the mass analogy for Prob. 6-1(c), using the mass-capacitance analogue.

$$M \longleftrightarrow C$$
$$B \longleftrightarrow 1/R$$
$$K \longleftrightarrow 1/L$$
$$v \longleftrightarrow e$$
$$f \longleftrightarrow i$$

What does this analogy indicate about masses, springs, and dampers for step inputs to mechanical systems?

6-3. Below are shown some electrical circuits. Think about and discuss what happens when the switch is closed and when it is opened. All

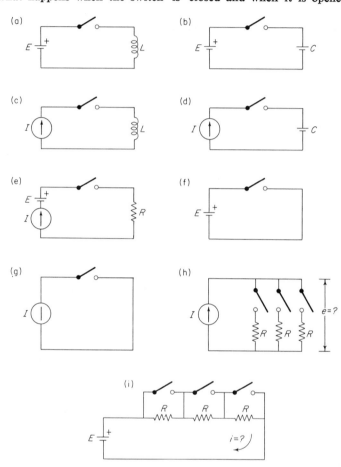

Figure P. 6.3

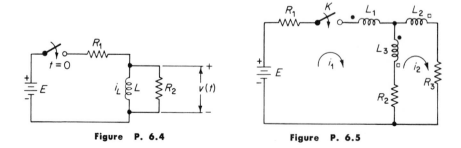

Figure P. 6.4   Figure P. 6.5

sources are constant. Assume closing switch indicates current source is turned on.

6-4. For the circuit shown in Fig. P. 6.4, $v(t) = 4e^{-t/2}$, $di_L/dt|_{t=0^+} = 20$ amps/sec, and $E = 10$ volts. Find R_1, R_2, and L.

6-5. In the network shown in Fig. P. 6.5, the switch K is closed at the instant $t = 0$, connecting an unenergized system to a voltage source. Let $M_{12} = 0$. Determine the values of di_1/dt and di_2/dt.

6-6. Part 1 of Fig. P. 6.6 shows a basic circuit used to drive an electronic key punch. The punch is controlled by the transistor in the circle which is in turn controlled by $e_2(t)$. This circuit is approximated in Part 2. $R_0(i)$ is a resistance which is a function of the current from b to e. Typically for e_2 large and positive and i large, $R_0(i) = 0.5$ ohms. For $e_2 \leq 0$, $R_0(i) = 10^6$ ohms. Thus the circuit can be modified (Part 3).

Switch S is connected to terminal 1 for e_2 large and positive, and to terminal 2 for $e_2 = 0$. Given $e_2(t)$ (Part 4), find the approximate transient response for e_{ce}.

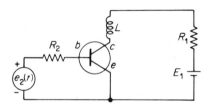

Figure P. 6.6 Part 1

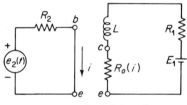

Figure P. 6.6 Part 2

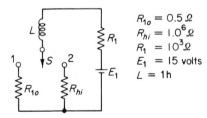

$R_{1o} = 0.5\ \Omega$
$R_{hi} = 1.0^6\ \Omega$
$R_1 = 10^3\ \Omega$
$E_1 = 15$ volts
$L = 1$h

Figure P. 6.6 Part 3

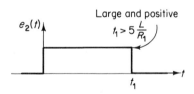

Figure P. 6.6 Part 4

6-7. (a) If $i(t)$ is as shown below, sketch the approximate transient response for the voltage across the capacitor C_2.

(b) For the same $i(t)$ used in (a) and with capacitor C_2 removed, sketch the approximate transient response for the voltage across the inductor L.

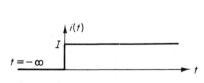

Figure P. 6.7(a)

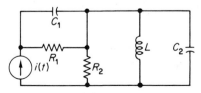

Figure P. 6.7(b)

6-8. For the light blinker shown, find the rate at which the light turns on and off, given:

   The relay coil energizes when current through it reaches 73.1% of its steady state value. When the coil energizes, S_2 closes and S_1 opens. When current through the relay coil decays to 26.7% of steady state value that would be achieved if S_1 were left closed, the relay de-energizes and S_1 closes and S_2 opens. What is the rate at which light goes on and off?

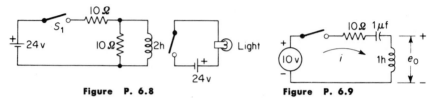

Figure   P. 6.8   Figure   P. 6.9

6-9. From Fig. P. 6.9 sketch the approximate transient response for both e_0 and i, when the switch is closed. Assume the capacitor is discharged at $t = 0$.

6-10. Assume the circuit shown below has been in the state shown for a long time. At $t = 0$, the switch is closed. Sketch the resulting approximate transient response for i_c and e_c. After a long time, the switch is opened; sketch the response.

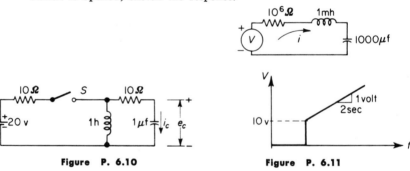

Figure   P. 6.10   Figure   P. 6.11

6-11. Sketch the approximate transient response of $i(t)$ for the circuit with the voltage source V as shown in Fig. P. 6.11.

6-12. Determine the transient response for the following circuits:

   (a) Switch S is opened at $t = 0$. Determine approximate transient response for $e_R(t)$.

   (b) Sketch approximate transient response for $i_L(t)$. Switch is closed at $t = 0$.

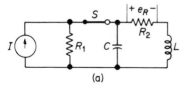
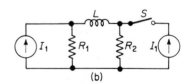

Figure   P. 6.12(a)   Figure   P. 6.12(b)

6-13. (a) Given the circuit shown below, with the initial voltage on one

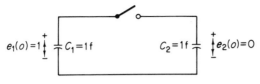

Figure P. 6.13(a)

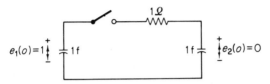

Figure　P. 6.13(b)

capacitor being 1 volt and 0 volts on the other, what is the transient response after the switch is closed? Does this system represent a physical system (check energy conservation)?

(b) If a resistor is inserted into the circuit, how does it change the response?

6-14. An experiment on a "Black Box" gave the results in the first diagram. This "Black Box" is now put into the second circuit. At time $t = 0^-$, S_1 has been open and S_2 closed for a *long* time. At $t = 0$, S_1 is closed.
(a) Find *initial* and *final* values of $i(t)$.

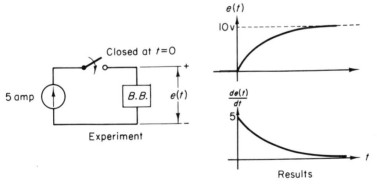

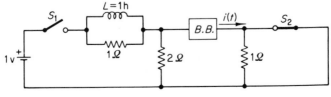

Figure　P. 6.14

After S_1 has closed for a *very* long time, S_2 is opened.
(b) Find *initial* and *final* values of $i(t)$ again.

6-15. Find the relationship between $e(t)$ and $i(t)$ for the first circuit. Note:
By finding the $e-i$ relationship,
you have specified an equivalent
"Black Box" behavior (second
figure). The "Black Box" is described by the $e-i$ relation that
you found.

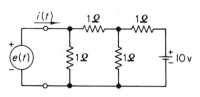

Now find the voltage $e_a(t)$ for
the third circuit, using the information you have just obtained.

Figure P. 6.15 Diagram 1

Diagram 2

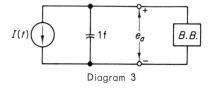

Diagram 3

7 *Second Order Differential Equation Transient Solution*

7.1 Introduction

The second order differential equation is characterized by terms containing first and second derivatives of the dependent variable. A large number of physical systems may be described by second order differential equations. Problems in heat transfer, pneumatic and hydraulic devices, and mechanical and electrical systems can be represented by second order differential equations (see Fig. 7.1). We shall proceed in this chapter to develop the mathematical solution of these equations and insights necessary to understand the behavior of many such systems.

In order that the results may be general and applicable to a wide variety of systems, equations and results will be nondimensionalized. We shall give physical reality to nondimensional parameters by carrying two representative systems through our analysis, one electrical and one mechanical. We shall also see that two nondimensional parameters characterize a second order system, and are sufficient to specify system response given the initial conditions and the inputs. Later on we shall examine examples of other systems which may be nondimensionalized to fall under the same governing equations.

We have already derived the differential equations for the systems to be studied. These systems are shown in Fig. 7.2.

In the following development the equations for both the mechanical

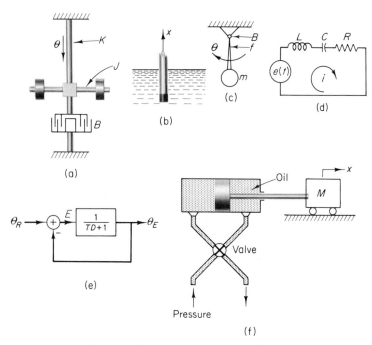

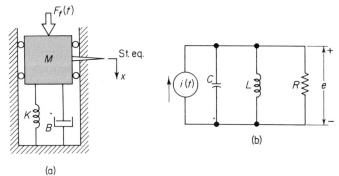

Fig. 7.1. Some examples of second order systems. (a) Torsional mechanical. (b) Weighted stick floating in water. (c) Simple pendulum (small angles). (d) Series "RLC" circuit. (e) Simple servomechanism. (f) Hydraulic piston and load mass.

Fig. 7.2. Mechanical and electrical systems to be studied in Chapter 7.

and electrical systems will be developed in parallel until the point is reached where they may be represented by the same nondimensional equation. Schematics of the systems shown in Fig. 7.1 are repeated in Fig. 7.3 in a somewhat more simplified form.

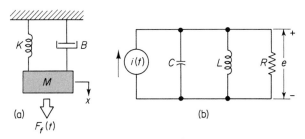

Fig. 7.3. (a) Mass-spring-dashpot system. (b) Parallel RLC circuit with current source.

The governing equations are shown in Eqs. 7.1 and 7.2. Note that the electrical system is described by an integro-differential equation. It may be differentiated once in order to bring it into the same second order form as that for the mechanical system. Remember that when differentiated, the input $i_f(t)$ also is differentiated with respect to time.

$$M\ddot{x} + B\dot{x} + Kx = f_f \qquad (7.1)$$

$$C\frac{de}{dt} + \frac{1}{R}e + \frac{1}{L}\int e\,dt = i_f \qquad (7.2)$$

7.2 Dimensionless Second Order Form

Equations 7.1 and 7.2 each involve three parameters M, B, K or C, R, and L. We may reduce the number of parameters required to specify the response of the systems described by these equations by combining these parameters into dimensionless groups. This is most easily accomplished by multiplying and dividing both sides of the equation by constants and redefining the time scale. For example in Eq. 7.1:
(a) Divide both sides by K to make coefficient of x unity.

$$\frac{M}{K}\ddot{x} + \frac{B}{K}\dot{x} + x = \frac{f_f}{K}$$

(b) Since $d^2x/dt^2 = \ddot{x}$ the coefficient of $\ddot{x}$ would be unity if we redefined the time scale so that $M/Kt^2 = 1/\tau^2$ or $\tau = \sqrt{K/M}\,t$. Then,

$$\frac{M}{K}\frac{d^2x}{dt^2} = \frac{M}{K}\frac{d}{d(\sqrt{M/K}\,\tau)}\left[\frac{dx}{d(\sqrt{M/K}\,\tau)}\right] = \frac{d^2x}{d\tau^2}$$

Likewise,

$$\frac{B}{K}\frac{dx}{dt} = \frac{B}{K}\sqrt{\frac{K}{M}}\frac{dx}{d\tau}$$

Thus we can rewrite Eq. 7.1 using this new time scale as:

$$\frac{d^2x}{d\tau^2} + \frac{B}{K}\sqrt{\frac{K}{M}}\frac{dx}{d\tau} + x = \frac{f_f}{K}$$

In the same way Eq. 7.2 can be reduced by differentation and algebraic manipulation to

$$\frac{d^2e}{d\tau^2} + \frac{L}{R\sqrt{LC}}\frac{de}{d\tau} + e = \frac{L}{\sqrt{LC}}\frac{di_f}{d\tau}$$

where

$$\frac{1}{\sqrt{LC}}t = \tau$$

Notice that:

(1) We have redefined the time scale using a parameter with the dimensions of time to make the scale dimensionless.

(2) The coefficient of each term in the new differential equation is unity except for the first order term. This result is not unique; we could have made the coefficient of the second order term non-unity by using $\tau = (K/B)t$ for Eq. 7.1, or $\tau = (R/L)t$ for Eq. 7.2. In either case the procedure above yields a single parameter in the left side of the equation and a time scale parameter.

(3) The right side of the reduced equation is a combination of the forcing function and some of the system parameters. If the forcing function has a simple form such as a step or impulse or a ramp, we may further reduce the equation by dividing both sides by the right-hand side and redefining the dependent variable. For example in Eq. 7.1 we could define $\bar{x} = Kx/F_f$ where F_f is the magnitude of a unit step input and in Eq. 7.2, $\bar{e} = \dot{I}_r e\sqrt{C/L}/(di_f/d\tau)$ where $\dot{I}_r$ is the magnitude of a ramp input i_f.

Thus we have shown that it requires two numbers to specify the response of a second order system to a given set of initial conditions or a given forcing function. It required one number to specify the

  Students usually have difficulty with this process because the logic of the method is not very obvious. Always ensure that the forcing function is isolated on the right side of the equation before you start. Then arrange the coefficient of one of the dependent variable terms on the left side to be unity. Now you can redefine the time scale using any one of the *other* dependent variable terms. It helps to use D notation.

response of the first order systems considered in Chap. 5. In general we can show that a system described by an nth order differential equation requires n numbers to specify its response to a given set of initial conditions and forcing functions.

The two numbers which define the response of a second order system need a special definition which is based on the following form for the left side of the dimensionless equation:

$$\frac{d^2y}{d\tau^2} + 2\zeta\frac{dy}{d\tau} + y = \text{forcing function}$$

where

$$\frac{t}{T} = \tau$$

The coefficient of the first order term in this form is known as twice the *damping ratio*, where the damping ratio is represented by the Greek letter zeta, ζ.

	Eq. 7.1	Eq. 7.2
	Mechanical	*Electrical*
Damping ratio:	$\zeta = \dfrac{B}{2\sqrt{KM}}$	$\zeta = \dfrac{1}{2R}\sqrt{\dfrac{L}{C}}$

The time scale factor T has the dimensions of time. It is called, logically, the *time constant*. Its inverse, which has the dimensions of frequency (time^{-1}), is called the *natural frequency* and is denoted by ω_n.

	Eq. 7.1	Eq. 7.2
	Mechanical	*Electrical*
Time constant:	$T = \sqrt{\dfrac{M}{K}}$	$T = \sqrt{CL}$
Natural frequency:	$\omega_n = \sqrt{\dfrac{K}{M}}$	$\omega_n = \dfrac{1}{\sqrt{CL}}$

It is interesting to note that if no damping were present, $B = 0$ in Eq. 7.1 or $R = \infty$ in Eq. 7.2, ω_n would be the frequency in radians per second at which each system would oscillate. Hence, the name *natural*

The natural frequency is often quoted in cycles per second instead of radians per second, i.e,

$$f_n = \frac{\omega_n}{2\pi} \quad \text{cycles per second}$$

frequency. Using these definitions we may write Eqs. 7.1 and 7.2 in several forms.

Time constant form:

$$\frac{T^2 d^2 x}{dt^2} + 2\zeta \frac{T\,dx}{dt} + x = \frac{f_f}{K}$$

where

$$\zeta = \frac{B}{2\sqrt{KM}} \quad \text{and} \quad T = \sqrt{\frac{M}{K}}$$

and

$$\frac{T^2 d^2 e}{dt^2} + 2\zeta T \frac{de}{dt} + e = L \frac{di_f}{dt}$$

where

$$\zeta = \frac{1}{2R}\sqrt{\frac{L}{C}} \quad \text{and} \quad T = \sqrt{CL}$$

or by multiplying both sides by $1/T^2$ we obtain *natural frequency form*

$$\frac{d^2 x}{dt^2} + 2\zeta \omega_n \frac{dx}{dt} + \omega_n^2 x = \frac{f_f}{M} \tag{7.3}$$

where

$$\zeta = \frac{B}{2\sqrt{KM}} \quad \text{and} \quad \omega_n = \sqrt{\frac{K}{M}}$$

and

$$\frac{d^2 e}{dt^2} + 2\zeta \omega_n \frac{de}{dt} + \omega_n^2 e = \frac{1}{C}\frac{di_f}{dt} \tag{7.4}$$

where

$$\zeta = \frac{1}{2R}\sqrt{\frac{L}{C}} \quad \text{and} \quad \omega_n = \frac{1}{\sqrt{CL}}$$

The equivalents in the natural frequency form using the D notation are

------

We shall be using ζ and ω_n very extensively from now on so try to keep in mind what they mean and how they are derived.

$$[D^2 + 2\zeta\omega_n D + \omega_n^2]x = \frac{f_f}{M} \tag{7.5}$$

$$[D^2 + 2\zeta\omega_n D + \omega_n^2]e = \frac{1}{C}Di_f \tag{7.6}$$

A common block diagram applies to each system. It is shown in Fig. 7.4. While Fig. 7.4 does apply to both the mechanical and electrical

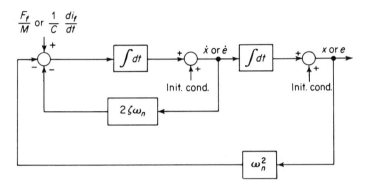

Fig. 7.4. Block diagram for second order system.

systems, note that it is required that i_f be differentiated as an input. It may be more convenient when studying the circuit on an analogue computer to feed in i_f without requiring its derivative. An alternate block diagram may be derived directly from Eq. 7.2 by solving it for the highest derivative. This is shown in Fig. 7.5. It simply shows each variable integrated once. The block diagram remains unchanged; one merely interprets each variable as the integral of its corresponding term in Fig. 7.4. The disadvantage of Fig. 7.5 is that the second derivative or acceleration of voltage does not appear. However, this parameter may not be of interest in the electrical circuits.

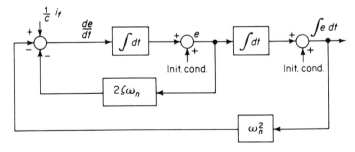

Fig. 7.5. Block diagram for Eq. 7.2 in integro-differential form.

We shall now proceed with the solution of Eqs. 7.3 and 7.4. As in the case of the first order system, the general solution of these differential equations may be divided into the sum of a transient and steady state solution. The transient solution results when the right-hand side is zero. In mathematical terms, the transient solution is called the complementary solution and the equation, when its right-hand side is zero, is termed a homogeneous equation. First we shall study the transient solution alone. Let us use the equation written in the mechanical form with x_t as a variable, recognizing that x_t may be replaced by e_t to apply immediately in the electrical case. The equation for which we seek a solution is then shown as Eq. 7.7. In fact when we obtain a solution for Eq. 7.7, it will also be the solution to any second order differential equation which we can make into the form of Eq. 7.7. We need only to evaluate the magnitude of ω_n and ζ for the particular case in which we are interested.

$$\ddot{x}_t + 2\zeta\omega_n\dot{x}_t + \omega_n^2 x_t = 0 \qquad (7.7)$$

In general ζ can take on any value from $-\infty$ to $+\infty$. We shall see however that the form of the solution to Eq. 7.7 depends heavily on the value of ζ. This was shown in the dimensionless time form for the second order differential equation which we obtained earlier, when $f_f = 0$,

$$\frac{d^2x}{d\tau^2} + 2\zeta\frac{dx}{d\tau} + x = 0$$

There are three ranges for the values of ζ which define three quite different types of response. These ranges are defined as follows:

$$1 < \zeta \qquad \text{overdamped response}$$

$$0 < \zeta < 1 \qquad \text{underdamped response}$$

$$0 > \zeta \qquad \text{unstable response}$$

At the transition values of ζ in these equations ($\zeta = 1$ and $\zeta = 0$), unusual response forms result. They are defined:

$$1 = \zeta \qquad \text{critically damped response}$$

$$0 = \zeta \qquad \text{undamped natural oscillatory response}$$

We shall consider the overdamped response first.

☆   We are not dealing with mathematical abstractions. These ranges have an important practical significance because the system response varies dramatically for each range.

7.3 The Overdamped Transient Solution; $\zeta > 1$

We learned before that the exponential function is a powerful solution to guess. Let us assume, therefore, x_t given in Eq. 7.8.

$$x_t = Ae^{\lambda t} \tag{7.8}$$

When this is substituted back into Eq. 7.7, we obtain Eq. 7.9. Equation 7.9 is a quadratic algebraic equation with roots, λ_1, λ_2 given in Eq. 7.10.

$$\lambda^2 + 2\zeta\omega_n\lambda + \omega_n^2 = 0 \tag{7.9}$$

$$\lambda_1, \lambda_2 = -\zeta\omega_n \pm \omega_n \sqrt{\zeta^2 - 1} \tag{7.10}$$

Equation 7.9 is often called the *characteristic equation* of the second order system and the roots, λ_1 and λ_2, shown in Eq. 7.10 are called the *roots of the characteristic equation*. We shall see later when we become familiar with the nature of the solutions to Eq. 7.7, that the system and its responses may be identified either with the characteristic equation or with the roots of the characteristic equation.

We have now obtained a solution for Eq. 7.7. We see that there are two values of λ which satisfy the assumed solution and we must conclude, therefore, that the solution contains two terms of the form shown in Eq. 7.8. This result is fortunate since we know that a second order differential equation must have two arbitrary constants in its solution to account for two integrations. The solution can then be written as in Eq. 7.11.

$$x_t = A_1 e^{(-\omega_n\zeta + \omega_n\sqrt{\zeta^2-1})t} + A_2 e^{(-\omega_n\zeta - \omega_n\sqrt{\zeta^2-1})t} \tag{7.11}$$

So far, we have not restricted the magnitude of ζ. We see that Eq. 7.11 may be used with no difficulty providing ζ is greater than 1. Thus this expression yields a solution for the overdamped case. Trouble arises if ζ is equal to or less than 1.

If $\zeta = 1$, the two terms of Eq. 7.11 must become one term and we are left with the solution with only one arbitrary constant. This solution cannot be valid. In the case where $\zeta < 1$, we find the necessity of extracting the square root of a negative number. This leads to complications which must be dealt with later. Therefore, a solution form of Eq. 7.11 will be restricted at this point to the case where $\zeta > 1$. Equation 7.11 may be rewritten as in Eq. 7.12.

$$x_t = e^{-\zeta \omega_n t}(A_1 e^{+(\omega_n \sqrt{\zeta^2-1})t} + A_2 e^{(-\omega_r \sqrt{\zeta^2-1})t}) \tag{7.12}$$

To illustrate the nature of the solutions derived, let us examine a particular set of data applicable to the mechanical system of Fig. 7.3(a). Assume data as follows: Let

$$W = 38.6 \text{ lb}$$

$$K = 10 \text{ lb/in.}$$

$$B = 4 \text{ lb-sec/in.}$$

then ω_n and ζ will be defined below.

$$\omega_n = \sqrt{\frac{K}{M}} = \sqrt{\frac{10 \times 12 \times 32.2}{38.6}} = 10 \text{ rad/sec}$$

$$\zeta = \frac{B}{2\sqrt{KM}} = \frac{4}{2\sqrt{10 \times 38.6/386}} = \frac{4}{2} = 2$$

Equation 7.11 becomes Eq. 7.13,

$$x_t = A_1 e^{(-20+10\sqrt{3})t} + A_2 e^{(-20-10\sqrt{3})t}$$

$$x_t = A_1 e^{-2.7t} + A_2 e^{-37.3t} \tag{7.13}$$

If we assure that $f_f = 0$ in Eq. 7.3, then, as before, we evaluate the arbitrary constants through use of initial conditions. We must assume some sort of initial displacement and velocity for the system. Suppose we pull the mass down a distance of ten inches, hold it still, and let it go. The initial condition holding for $t = 0$ will then be as follows: At $t = 0$,

$$x_0 = 10 \text{ in.} \quad [\text{assume } x(t) \text{ positive down}]$$

$$\dot{x}_0 = 0$$

We form two equations to solve for the unknowns A_1 and A_2 using these initial conditions as follows:

$$\text{At } t = 0 \quad \begin{cases} 10 = A_1 + A_2 \\ 0 = -2.7A_1 - 37.3A_2 \end{cases}$$

$$A_1 = -\frac{37.3}{2.7} A_2 = -13.8A_2$$

   W is quoted here as a weight—remember our equations are written for the mass M, i.e., $W = Mg$

$$A_2 = -\frac{10}{12.8} = -0.78$$

$$A_1 = 10.78$$

The final transient solution for the assumed parameters and initial conditions is then given by Eq. 7.14.

$$x_t = 10.78e^{-2.7t} - 0.78e^{-37.3t} \qquad (7.14)$$

This solution is plotted in Fig. 7.6 wherein both the individual terms and their sum are shown. Also shown is a time scale nondimensionalized in terms of ω_n. With such a time scale the result becomes general for all systems having $\zeta = 2$. The ordinate is also nondimensionalized in terms of the original displacement.

A number of transient response solution forms are possible with the sum of two exponential terms. Some of these are indicated in the sketches in Fig. 7.7. They depend entirely on initial conditions.

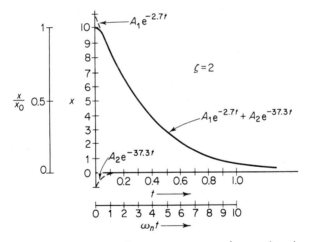

Fig. 7.6. Transient response of second order system; $\zeta = 2$; $\omega_n = 10$; $\dot{x}_0 = 10$ in. and $\dot{x} = 0$.

It is a good idea to do what we have done in Fig. 7.6, namely to plot the individual terms as well as their sum. With this method, an apparently complex function can be sketched very quickly. Try it and see.

Note the physical significance of Fig. 7.6, namely that the mass returns to its static equilibrium position within a couple of seconds of being released. It does *not* overshoot the equilibrium position. This behavior is characteristic of overdamped systems.

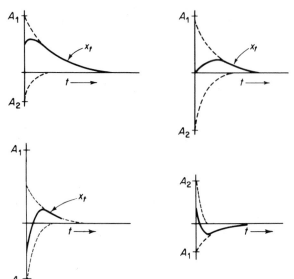

Fig. 7.7. Some possible transient responses for equations of the form of Eq. 7.11.

In the overdamped case a different form for Eq. 7.7 is sometimes used. That is,

$$\omega_n^2 [T_1 T_2 \ddot{x}_t + (T_1 + T_2)\dot{x}_t + x_t] = 0$$

or

$$\omega_n^2 (T_1 D + 1)(T_2 D + 1)x_t = 0$$

where T_1 and T_2 have the units of time and are known as *time constants*. Since Eq. 7.7 and the expression above are equivalent,

$$T_1 T_2 \omega_n^2 = 1$$

$$\omega_n^2 (T_1 + T_2) = 2\zeta\omega_n$$

or

$$\omega_n = \frac{1}{\sqrt{T_1 T_2}} \qquad \zeta = \frac{1}{2}(T_1 + T_2)\frac{1}{\sqrt{T_1 T_2}}$$

Using these two equations, Eq. 7.11 can be rewritten as

$$x_1 = A_1 \exp\left[-\left(\frac{T_1 + T_2}{2T_1 T_2}\right) + \frac{1}{\sqrt{T_1 T_2}}\sqrt{\frac{1}{4}\frac{(T_1 + T_2)^2}{T_1 T_2} - 1}\right]t$$

$$+ A_2 \exp\left[-\frac{T_1 + T_2}{2T_1 T_2} - \frac{1}{\sqrt{T_1 T_2}}\sqrt{\frac{1}{4}\frac{(T_1 + T_2)^2}{T_1 T_2} - 1}\right]t$$

$$= A_1 e^{-t/T_1} + A_2 e^{-t/T_2}$$

which yields a much simpler expression for the exponents.

7.4 Critically Damped Response; $\zeta = 1$

The special case for the damping ratio ζ exactly equal to 1 cannot really occur in nature. ζ is defined from system parameters which include damping and no matter how accurately these parameters are measured there will always be some degree of inaccuracy so that the ratio is not precisely 1. A parameter such as damping is often subject to temperature and other effects. Thus, even if for a fleeting second the damping ratio were exactly unity, it would not remain so. All systems in reality have a damping ratio greater or less than one. However, there is a mathematical usefulness for the case $\zeta = 1$ as a reference. For this reason, the value of damping B_c which makes $\zeta = 1$ is called the *critical damping constant* and ζ_c is called the *critical damping ratio*. Equation 7.15 shows this.

$$\zeta_c = \frac{B_c}{2\sqrt{KM}} = 1 \qquad B_c = 2\sqrt{KM} \qquad (7.15)$$

We noted before that Eq. 7.11 degenerates for the case of $\zeta = 1$ into a form having only one arbitrary constant of integration and therefore could not stand as a solution. This means that the assumed form of solution in Eq. 7.8 was not sufficiently general to work. Let us try another solution which appears somewhat similar but where the constant is replaced by a function. Since we have experience with the nature of λ, Eq. 7.10 tells us that it is equal to $-\zeta\omega_n$. Thus, our assumed solution for the critically damped case will have the form of Eq. 7.16. Assume that

$$x_t = u(t)e^{-\zeta\omega_n t} \qquad (7.16)$$

where $u(t)$ is an unknown function of time.

We shall need the higher derivatives to substitute back into the original differential equation. They are given in Eqs. 7.17 and 7.18:

$$\dot{x}_t = -\zeta\omega_n u(t)e^{-\zeta\omega_n t} + \dot{u}(t)e^{-\zeta\omega_n t} \qquad (7.17)$$

$$\ddot{x}_t = (\zeta\omega_n)^2 u(t)e^{-\zeta\omega_n t} - 2\zeta\omega_n \dot{u}(t)e^{-\zeta\omega_n t} + \ddot{u}(t)e^{-\zeta\omega_n t} \qquad (7.18)$$

When we substitute Eqs. 7.16, 7.17, and 7.18 back into the original differential Eq. 7.7, we obtain the desired form for $u(t)$ which will produce a correct solution for this critically damped case. This is given in Eq. 7.19, and Eq. 7.20 is the complete solution form.

$$[\ddot{u}(t) - 2\zeta\omega_n\dot{u}(t) + (\zeta\omega_n)^2 u(t) - 2(\zeta\omega_n)^2 u(t)$$
$$+ 2\zeta\omega_n\dot{u}(t) + \omega_n^2 u(t)]e^{-\zeta\omega_n t} = 0$$

$$\ddot{u}(t) + \omega_n^2 u(t) - (\zeta\omega_n)^2 u(t) = 0 \qquad (7.19)$$

For $\zeta = 1$:

$$\ddot{u}(t) = 0$$

$$\dot{u}(t) = C_1$$

$$u(t) = C_1 t + C_2$$

Thus,

$$x_t = (C_1 t + C_2)e^{-\omega_n t} \qquad (7.20)$$

The nature of the response shown in Eq. 7.20 may be seen using the mechanical system in the previous example with ζ set equal to 1 instead of 2. ω_n is 10 rad/sec as before. When $f_f = 0$ in Eq. 7.3, we evaluate initial conditions in the same way. At $t = 0$:

$$x_0 = 10 = C_2, \qquad \dot{x}_0 = 0$$

$$\frac{dx_t}{dt} = -\omega_n(C_1 t + C_2)e^{-\omega_n t} + C_1 e^{-\omega_n t}$$

$$0 = -\omega_n C_2 + C_1$$

$$C_1 = \omega_n C_2 = 100$$

Hence,

$$x_t = 10(10t + 1)e^{-10t} \qquad (7.21)$$

Equation 7.21 gives the transient solution for the assumed displacement and is plotted in Fig. 7.8. We can obtain further insight into the critically damped case by noting that the *time constant* expression for the overdamped case takes on a particular form. That is,

$$\omega_n^2(T_1 D + 1)(T_2 D + 1)x_t = 0$$

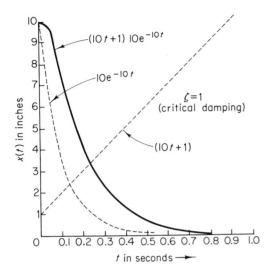

Fig. 7.8. Transient response of second order system. $\zeta = 1$; $\omega_n = 10$; $x_0 = 10$ inches; and $\dot{x}_0 = 0$.

where

$$\omega_n = \frac{1}{\sqrt{T_1 T_2}}$$

and

$$\zeta = \frac{1}{2}(T_1 + T_2)\sqrt{\frac{1}{T_1 T_2}}$$

When $\zeta = 1$, from the second of these two equations we have:

$$2\sqrt{T_1 T_2} = T_1 + T_2$$

or

$$4T_1 T_2 = T_1^2 + T_2^2 + 2T_1 T_2$$

Solving for T_1 yields

$$T_1^2 - 2T_2 T_1 + T_2^2 = 0$$

The response of Fig. 7.8 is similar to that of Fig. 7.6 but the process is speeded up because the damping ratio is smaller (1 instead of 2). If we made the damping ratio a fraction smaller than 1 the mass would again return to the equilibrium position but it would *overshoot* it first. This is why we use the term *critical damping* when $\zeta = 1$.

$$T_1 = \frac{+2T_2 \pm \sqrt{4T_2^2 - 4T_2^2}}{2}$$

$$= T_2$$

Thus our time constant form for $\delta = 1$ in D notation becomes $x_t(T_1 D + 1)^2 = 0$. This leads to a solution of the form $x_t = (C_1 t + C_2)e^{-t/T_1}$, and usually whenever the differential equation can be expressed in D notation in the form

$$x_t(T_1 D + 1)^n = 0 \tag{7.22}$$

the solution is of the form

$$x_t = (C_1 t^{n-1} + C_2 t^{n-2} + \cdots + C_n)e^{-t/T_1} \tag{7.23}$$

7.5   Undamped Natural Oscillations; $\zeta = 0$

We shall now study a case with which you are probably already familiar. This is the situation represented by zero damping in the second order system. For most real systems this is a hypothetical situation since for a system to have zero damping it must have frictionless bearings or resistanceless components and would exhibit a kind of perpetual motion. Exceptions may be mentioned wherein oscillations may go on forever. For example, interplanetary bodies moving in frictionless space, feedback systems wherein energy is added in just the right amount to balance that which is normally dissipated, molecular and electron motions, and current flow in wires at absolute zero represent zero damped systems.

Many examples of second order systems behave almost as if they had zero damping. A clock pendulum, a vibrating string, a tuning fork, and a tuning circuit in a radio are examples of systems where oscillations die off slowly. If one examines such a vibrating system for only two or three vibrations, one finds very little difference between the observed dynamics and that predicted by equations having zero damping. Thus the *natural frequency* of an oscillating system, which may be calculated as if there were no damping, can be observed to high accuracy in systems with very little damping. For the case of zero damping, Eq. 7.7 may be rewritten as Eq. 7.24.

$$\ddot{x}_t + \omega_n^2 x_t = 0 \tag{7.24}$$

It may be seen that the solution of Eq. 7.24 must be of such a form that when differentiated twice, the same function appears. It must also contain two arbitrary constants of integration. We may choose, on the basis of our knowledge of the sine and cosine functions, a solution of the form of Eq. 7.25 since we know in advance that it must work.

$$x_t = A_1 \sin \omega_n t + A_2 \cos \omega_n t \tag{7.25}$$

That Eq. 7.25 is truly a solution may be checked by substituting x_t back into Eq. 7.24. The result is below:

$$-\omega_n^2 A_1 \sin \omega_n t - \omega_n^2 A_2 \cos \omega_n t + \omega_n^2 A_1 \sin \omega_n t + \omega_n^2 A_2 \cos \omega_n t = 0$$

Equation 7.25 represents the sum of two *sine waves* which itself is also a sine wave. ω_n is now seen to be the circular frequency in radians per second for these sine waves. It is the natural frequency of oscillation of a system without damping.

Let us illustrate the form of Eq. 7.25 by means of the mechanical system previously looked at. We shall assume that $\zeta = 0$ (0 damping) and that ω_n, the natural frequency, is 10 rad/sec. The constants in Eq. 7.25 are determined by initial conditions as in Examples 7.A, 7.B and 7.C.

Example 7.A:

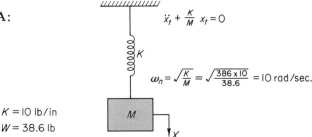

$$\ddot{x}_t + \frac{K}{M} x_t = 0$$

$$\omega_n = \sqrt{\frac{K}{M}} = \sqrt{\frac{386 \times 10}{38.6}} = 10 \text{ rad/sec.}$$

$K = 10$ lb/in
$W = 38.6$ lb

If at $t = 0$

$x = 10$ in.

$\dot{x} = 0$

$10 = B$

$0 = 10 A$

$\therefore x = 10 \cos 10 t$

Period $= \frac{2\pi}{\omega_n} = 0.628$ sec.

Frequency $= \frac{\omega_n}{2\pi} = 1.61$ cycles per sec.

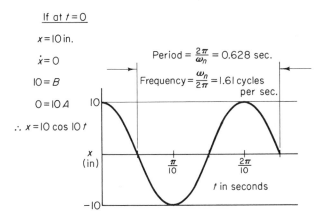

We shall use the words *sine wave* to refer to any sinusoidally varying quantity as well as to the sine wave itself which is zero at $t = 0$.

Example 7.B:

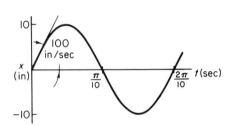

If at $t = 0$

$x = 0$ and $\dot{x} = 100$ in/sec.

$$0 = B$$

$$100 = 10\,A; \quad A = 10$$

$$\therefore x = 10 \sin 10t$$

Example 7.C:

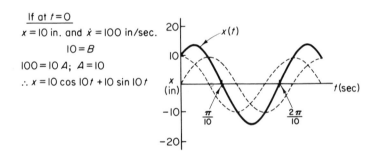

If at $t = 0$

$x = 10$ in. and $\dot{x} = 100$ in/sec.

$$10 = B$$

$$100 = 10\,A; \quad A = 10$$

$$\therefore x = 10 \cos 10t + 10 \sin 10t$$

The foregoing examples show that either the sine or the cosine or the sum of both terms form the solution depending upon the particular set of initial conditions. It is an important result that the sum of a cosine and a sine having the same frequency may be represented by a single cosine or sine term involving an appropriate phase angle. This identity is given in Eq. 7.28 and illustrated in Fig. 7.9.

In order to add and subtract sines and cosines, we may use the trigonometric identities found in tables, or we may employ a geo-

☆   Compare this result for an undamped system with the *critically* damped system, Fig. 7.8.

metrical addition method. In this second approach we use the following geometrical representation of a sine or cosine. Consider a plane divided into four quadrants by a pair of perpendicular x- and y-axes. Then consider a line segment of length W beginning at the origin as shown in Fig. 7.10. The counterclockwise angle that the line segment makes with the x-axis is called theta, θ. Now the projection of W on the x-

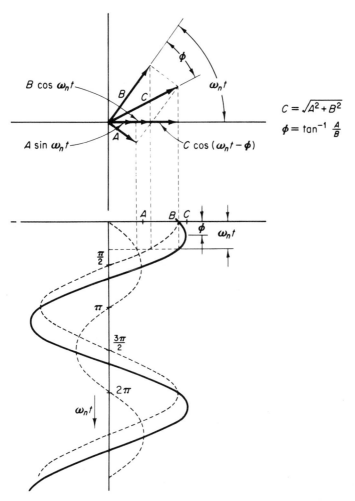

$$C = \sqrt{A^2 + B^2}$$
$$\phi = \tan^{-1} \frac{A}{B}$$

Fig. 7.9. Construction to illustrate that $A_1 \sin \omega_n t + b \cos \omega_n t = C \cos (\omega_n t - \Phi)$ where $C = \sqrt{A_1^2 + b^2}$ and $\Phi = \tan^{-1}(A_1/A_2)$.

Such line segments have some vector properties, but do not follow the rules of vector multiplication which will be used in developing complex algebra. We shall avoid the use of the word vector.

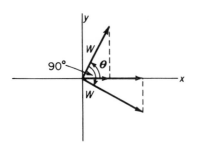

Fig. 7.10. Vector addition of sines and cosines.

axis is

$$W \cos \theta$$

If we draw a line segment of length W perpendicular to the original line with a direction 90° clockwise to it, its projection on the x-axis is

$$W \sin \theta$$

We can represent the addition and subtraction of sine and cosine terms by vectorially adding their corresponding line segments to obtain a resultant. The projection of this resultant on the x-axis has the cosine form and is equal to the sum or difference of the original sine and cosine terms. For example, consider

$$\cos \frac{\pi}{4} - \sin \frac{\pi}{4} = ?$$

Cos $\pi/4$ is the projection on the x-axis of a line of length unity directed at a counterclockwise angle of $\pi/4$ from the x-axis. Sin $\pi/4$ is the projection on the x-axis of a line of length unity directed at a clockwise angle of $\pi/4$ from the x-axis. The line whose projection is $-\sin \pi/4$ is directed 180° from the line whose projection is $\sin \pi/4$. The resultant is a line segment of length $\sqrt{2}$ at an angle $\pi/2$. Its projection on the x-axis is zero.

Hence, refering to Fig. 7.11,

$$\cos \frac{\pi}{4} - \sin \frac{\pi}{4} = 0$$

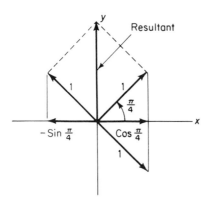

Fig. 7.11. Example of vector addition.

This approach can be used to represent $A_1 \sin \omega_n t + A_2 \cos \omega_n t$ in a different form as illustrated in Fig. 7.9. The line A_2 at an angle $\omega_n t$ has a projection on the x-axis, $A_2 \cos \omega_n t$. The line whose projection on the x-axis is $A_1 \sin \omega_n t$ is located 90° clockwise from A_2: the resultant vector sum of these two is C.

$$C = \sqrt{A_1^2 + A_2^2} \tag{7.26}$$

It is located at an angle $\omega_n t - \Phi$ where

$$\Phi = \tan^{-1} \frac{A_1}{A_2} \tag{7.27}$$

The projection of this line segment on the x-axis is

$$C \cos(\omega_n t - \Phi) = \sqrt{A_1^2 + A_2^2}\, \cos\left[\omega_n t - \tan^{-1}\frac{A_1}{A_2}\right]$$

$$= A_1 \sin \omega_n t + A_2 \sin \omega_n t \tag{7.28}$$

Figure 7.9 therefore illustrates the very important concept that *sine and cosine terms may be thought of as projections of rotating line segments on an axis.* You've probably seen this concept before, but it is italicized here because it forms the basis of a very powerful analytical approach to dynamic systems. The mathematical representation of the line segment which rotates in a plane and whose projection on an arbitrary axis represents the time varying sine or cosine function has many advantages over the sine and cosine representation. The line segment is of constant length and for a fixed ω_n rotates at a fixed angular velocity. Its angle relative to a zero reference line is given at any time by $\omega_n t$.

We shall find it very useful to draw attention away from the sine and cosine variations themselves and deal instead with rotating lines. We shall learn to use the line segment itself rather than its projection to represent the solution of a differential equation. Since a rotating line segment is located in a plane, a mathematical system to locate it and to perform algebraic manipulation is required. Such means exist in the concept of complex numbers and the reader is urged to study the treatment of complex numbers presented in the Appendix which has been especially developed for engineers.

7.6 Underdamped Transient Response of the Second Order System; $\zeta < 1$

We now return to Eq. 7.7 to study its transient solutions when ζ is less than 1. Figure 7.12 repeats some of the information presented earlier for the mechanical and electrical system examples. We shall proceed to the solution of the transient response for Eq. 7.7 along two paths. The first will be analogous to that used to solve for the critically damped case and is essentially algebraic. The second path will employ the newly presented complex number representations. Let us assume the same form of solution as we did in a critically damped case as in Eq. 7.16 which is repeated below.

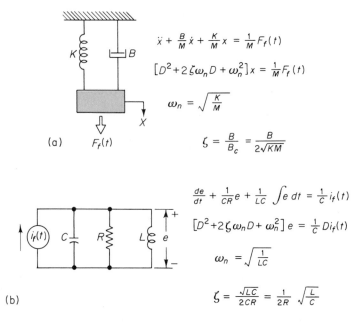

$$\ddot{x} + \frac{B}{M}\dot{x} + \frac{K}{M}x = \frac{1}{M}F_f(t)$$

$$[D^2 + 2\zeta\omega_n D + \omega_n^2]x = \frac{1}{M}F_f(t)$$

$$\omega_n = \sqrt{\frac{K}{M}}$$

(a) $F_f(t)$

$$\zeta = \frac{B}{B_c} = \frac{B}{2\sqrt{KM}}$$

$$\frac{de}{dt} + \frac{1}{CR}e + \frac{1}{LC}\int e\, dt = \frac{1}{C}i_f(t)$$

$$[D^2 + 2\zeta\omega_n D + \omega_n^2]e = \frac{1}{C}Di_f(t)$$

$$\omega_n = \sqrt{\frac{1}{LC}}$$

(b)

$$\zeta = \frac{\sqrt{LC}}{2CR} = \frac{1}{2R}\sqrt{\frac{L}{C}}$$

Fig. 7.12. Summary of mechanical and electrical example system parameters.

$$x_t = u(t)e^{-\zeta\omega_n t} \qquad \text{where } u(t) \text{ is a function of time} \qquad (7.16)$$

When Eq. 7.16 is substituted into the original Eq. 7.7, Eq. 7.19 results (repeated below).

$$\ddot{u}(t) + \omega_n^2 u(t) - (\zeta\omega_n)^2 u(t) = 0$$

or $$\ddot{u}(t) + (1 - \zeta^2)\omega_n^2 u(t) = 0 \qquad (7.19)$$

Equation 7.19 is seen to be identical in form to Eq. 7.24 and thus the solution for $u(t)$ will be as in Eq. 7.29:

$$u(t) = A_1 \sin \omega t + A_2 \cos \omega t \qquad (7.29)$$

where $$\omega = \sqrt{1 - \zeta^2}\,\omega_n \qquad (7.30)$$

ω as defined in Eq. 7.30 is called the *damped natural frequency* and is related to ω_n as shown. When damping is zero, ω is precisely equal to ω_n and when the damping ratio is unity, ω is equal to zero, i.e., there is no frequency of oscillation for the critical or overdamped case. The critical and overdamped transient response have therefore no period of oscillation and are termed *aperiodic*. Equation 7.29 may also be written in the form of Eq. 7.28 as shown in Eq. 7.31 wherein the arbitrary constants A_1 and A_2 are replaced by arbitrary constants C and Φ.

$$u(t) = C \cos (\omega t - \phi) \qquad (7.31)$$

The final transient solution can then be written as in Eq. 7.32.

204

$$x_t = Ce^{-\zeta\omega_n t} \cos\left(\sqrt{1 - \zeta^2}\,\omega_n t - \phi\right) \tag{7.32}$$

Let us return to the mechanical example in Sec. 7.2 in which a mass was pulled down a distance of ten inches and released with zero initial velocity. We now assume a damping ratio, $\zeta = 0.5$. This data is summarized below.

$$W = 38.6\,\text{lb}$$

$$K = 10\,\text{lb/in.}$$

$$\zeta = 0.5 \quad \therefore B = (0.5)(2)\sqrt{\frac{10 \times 38.6}{386}} = 1\,\text{lb-sec/in.}$$

$$\omega_n = \sqrt{\frac{K}{M}} = \sqrt{\frac{386 \times 10}{38.6}} = 10\,\text{rad/sec}$$

$$\text{at } t = 0 \qquad x_0 = 10\,\text{in.} \quad \text{and} \quad \dot{x}_0 = 0$$

We must introduce the initial conditions in order to evaluate the constants of Eq. 7.32 when $f(t) = 0$ in Eq. 7.1. Two equations result. The second equation involves the time derivative of Eq. 7.32 and is shown in Eq. 7.33. For the two initial conditions we obtain

$$\dot{x}_t = -\zeta\omega_n Ce^{-\zeta\omega_n t} \cos\left(\sqrt{1 - \zeta^2}\,\omega_n t - \phi\right)$$
$$- \sqrt{1 - \zeta^2}\,\omega_n Ce^{-\zeta\omega_n t} \sin\left(\sqrt{1 - \zeta^2}\,\omega_n t - \phi\right) \tag{7.33}$$

$$\text{at } t = 0 \quad \begin{cases} 10 = C\cos(-\phi) \\ 0 = -\zeta\omega_n C\cos(-\phi) - \sqrt{1 - \zeta^2}\,\omega_n C\sin(-\phi) \end{cases}$$

These equations may be solved as follows:

$$\frac{\sin(-\phi)}{\cos(-\phi)} = -\tan\phi = -\frac{\zeta\omega_n C}{(\sqrt{1 - \zeta^2})\,\omega_n C} = -\frac{\zeta}{\sqrt{1 - \zeta^2}}$$

for $\zeta = 0.5 \qquad \tan\phi = \frac{0.5}{\sqrt{0.75}} = 0.578 \qquad \phi = 30° \quad \text{or} \quad \frac{\pi}{6}\,\text{rad}$

$$C = \frac{10}{\cos\phi} = \frac{10}{0.867} = 11.5$$

The response following given initial conditions will then appear as

$$x_t = 11.5e^{-5t} \cos\left(8.67t - \frac{\pi}{6}\right) \tag{7.34}$$

Equation 7.34 is plotted in Fig. 7.13. The response is arbitrarily shown as the product of an exponential and a cosine curve. Note that the cosine curve has an amplitude greater than ten in order that its initial slope will compensate for the initial negative slope of the exponential to produce the zero initial slope required by the initial conditions.

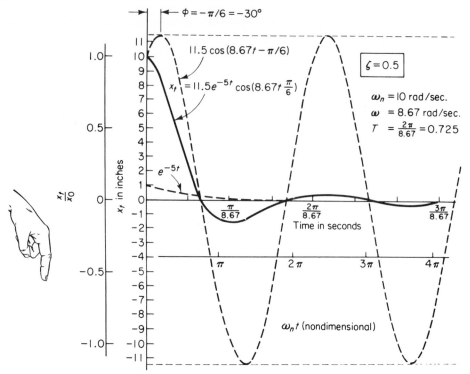

Fig. 7.13. Transient response of second order system following initial displacement $\zeta = 0.5$.

Note also that if ordinate and abscissa are plotted as nondimensional ratios, the resulting curve will be applicable to all systems having a damping ratio $\zeta = 0.5$.

We shall now return to Eq. 7.7 and follow the second path discussed earlier. Let us assume a solution more like the early solution forms as in Eq. 7.35 where the coefficient of the exponential is seen to be a complex number. Assume

$$x_t = Be^{\lambda t} \tag{7.35}$$

As in Sec. 7.2, we obtain Eq. 7.9, a characteristic equation in λ, shown below.

$$\lambda^2 + 2\zeta\omega_n\lambda + \omega_n^2 = 0 \tag{7.9}$$

which has roots, λ_1 and λ_2, given in Eq. 7.10 repeated below.

☆   Fig. 6.24 shows the behavior of the same kind of system plotted in a different way. Compare it with Fig. 7.13.

Fig. 7.13 illustrates the point we raised in connection with Fig. 7.8, namely that when the damping ratio is made less than unity (but greater than zero) the mass will still return to the static equilibrium position but it will oscillate in the process. How long it oscillates depends on the value of ζ. As ζ approaches zero the oscillations take longer to die out.

$$\lambda_1, \lambda_2 = -\zeta\omega_n \pm \omega_n\sqrt{\zeta_2 - 1} \tag{7.10}$$

from which Eq. 7.36 results:

$$x_t = \mathbf{B}_1 e^{(-\zeta\omega_n + j\omega_n\sqrt{1-\zeta^2})t} + \mathbf{B}_2 e^{(-\zeta\omega_n - j\omega_n\sqrt{1-\zeta^2})t} \tag{7.36}$$

We eliminate the square root of a negative number by factoring out the square root of minus one in the form of j. Remembering that $\omega = \sqrt{1 - \zeta^2}\,\omega_n$ and that we may factor exponentials, we obtain Eq. 7.37.

$$x_t = e^{-\zeta\omega_n t}(\mathbf{B}_1 e^{j\omega t} + \mathbf{B}_2 e^{-j\omega t}) \tag{7.37}$$

At this point we must do some mathematical reasoning. The term $e^{-\zeta\omega_n t}$ in Eq. 7.37 is familiar and we recognize it as a simple exponential which approaches zero in time. The second factor in Eq. 7.37 is not so familiar but may be reminiscent of the Euler equation form for sinusoidal functions (see Appendix, Eq. A.18). The trouble is that $\mathbf{B}_1$ and $\mathbf{B}_2$ appear to be two arbitrary complex numbers. If we reflect, however, that x_t must be a real quantity, we shall discover that for the form presented in Eq. 7.37, $\mathbf{B}_1$ and $\mathbf{B}_2$ must be complex conjugates. There are no other arbitrary complex numbers occupying positions of $\mathbf{B}_1$ and $\mathbf{B}_2$ in Eq. 7.37 which would produce a real quantity x_t at all times. We may then deduce a situation pictured in Fig. 7.14. Equation

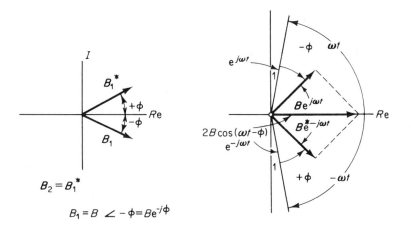

Fig. 7.14. To show that $\mathbf{B}_2 = \mathbf{B}_1^*$ in Eq. 7.37.

7.37 then becomes Eq. 7.38 which may be written as in the real form of Eq. 7.39 which is seen to be identical to Eq. 7.32, previously derived, with the exception that B, the magnitude of a pair of rotating vectors in Eq. 7.39, is seen to be just one-half the magnitude C which resulted in Eq. 7.32.

$$x_t = e^{-\zeta\omega_n t}(B_1 e^{j\omega t} + B_1^* e^{-j\omega t}) \tag{7.38}$$

or from Eq. A.26 (Appendix),

$$x_t = 2Be^{-\zeta\omega_n t}\cos{(\omega t - \phi)}$$

or

$$x_t = 2Be^{-\zeta\omega_n t}\cos{(\sqrt{1 - \zeta^2}\,\omega_n t - \phi)} \tag{7.39}$$

7.7 Determination of ζ and ω_n Experimentally

It is often desirable to test a recorder, or oscillograph, or other instruments to determine ζ and ω_n. The system may be disturbed by any convenient input as the exact initial conditions are not important. A record like that shown in Fig. 7.15 should be obtained. The period of oscillation T can be measured directly from crossing points on the

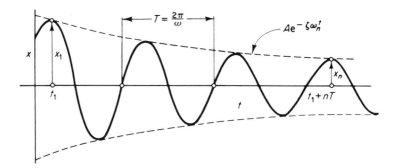

Fig. 7.15. An experimentally recorded transient.

zero axis; ω is then given by Eq. 7.40.

$$\omega = \frac{2\pi}{T} \quad [\text{rad/sec}] \tag{7.40}$$

At a time t_1, measure an amplitude x_1. At a later time $t_1 + nT$, measure an amplitude x_n. Choose n large enough so that x_1/x_n is not too near unity. Note that x_1/x_n is given by Eq. 7.41.

$$\frac{x_1}{x_n} = \frac{Ae^{-\zeta\omega_n t_1}}{Ae^{-\zeta\omega_n(t_1 + nT)}} = e^{+n\zeta\omega_n T} \tag{7.41}$$

and

$$\ln \frac{x_1}{x_n} = n\zeta\omega_n T = \text{logarithmic decrement } \delta \tag{7.42}$$

The logarithm of the ratio of succeeding amplitudes is given the name *logarithmic decrement* and the symbol δ as shown in Eq. 7.42. Equation 7.42 can be simplified as follows:

$$\delta = n\zeta\omega_n T = n\zeta\omega_n\frac{2\pi}{\omega} = \frac{n\zeta 2\pi}{\sqrt{1-\zeta^2}} \tag{7.43}$$

Equation 7.43 permits the direct calculation of ζ from δ. ω_n can then be formed from $\omega_n = \omega/\sqrt{1-\zeta^2}$. Note that, for ζ less than $\frac{1}{4}$ or so, Eq. 7.43 can be written approximately as in Eq. 7.44.

$$\delta \cong n\zeta 2\pi \quad \text{or} \quad \zeta \cong \frac{\delta}{2\pi n} \tag{7.44}$$

7.8 Roots of the Second Order Characteristic Equation

We have now completed the study of the transient responses of the second order system. We have derived solutions for systems with damping. We could even obtain solutions for systems with negative damping ratios. The negative damping ratio causes a response which tends toward ∞ as $t \to \infty$. It is characteristic of so-called *unstable* systems. In Sec. 7.3 we derived the characteristic Eq. 7.9 for the second order systems in terms of the damping ratio ζ and the natural frequency ω_n. The roots λ_1 and λ_2 of this characteristic equation were defined by Eq. 7.10. It is of interest to relate the transient solutions studied with the nature and location of the roots λ_1 and λ_2 in the complex plane. Equations 7.9 and 7.10 are repeated below.

$$\lambda^2 + 2\zeta\omega_n + \omega_n^2 = 0 \tag{7.9}$$

$$\lambda_1, \lambda_2 = -\zeta\omega_n \pm \omega_n\sqrt{\zeta^2 - 1} \tag{7.10}$$

or

$$\lambda_1, \lambda_2 = -\zeta\omega_n \pm j\omega_n\sqrt{1 - \zeta^2}$$

While the transient responses vary according to initial conditions, we see by now that if the damping and natural frequency are set, all responses for a system have much in common. The systems are either oscillatory or they are not; and if oscillatory, the rate of decay of

---

An unstable response will be oscillatory when $-1 < \zeta < 0$ or aperiodic (no oscillation) when $\zeta < -1$. You can prove this for yourself using the method just discussed.

oscillation is independent of the initial condition. Consider the case when ω_n is constant and ζ varies from $-\infty$ to $+\infty$. For $\zeta \geq 1$ we see that the roots are real and that as ζ decreases from infinity toward 1,

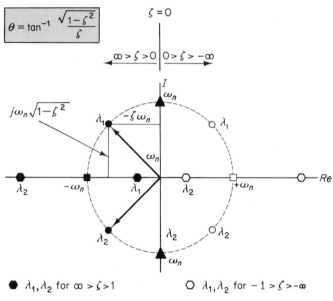

Fig. 7.16. Possible locations for roots of second order characteristic equations in complex plane when $\omega_n = $ constant.

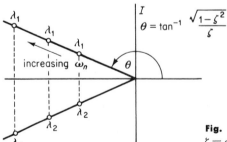

Fig. 7.17. Locus of roots λ_1 and λ_2 for $\zeta = $ constant; where $0 < \zeta < 1$.

 Fig. 7.16 looks very complex but is really quite simple. In a nutshell: roots lying in the left half of the diagram yield a stable response and those in the right half an unstable response. Roots lying on the circle means that the system will oscillate while roots on the R_e axis correspond to a nonoscillating response.

the roots approach the value ω_n. When $\zeta < 1$ the roots are complex and are seen to be represented by a pair of conjugate complex numbers of magnitude ω_n and angle $\theta = \tan^{-1}(\sqrt{1 - \zeta^2}/\zeta)$. This is shown in Fig. 7.16.

For a constant damping ratio and varying ω_n, the roots are seen to lie on a straight line whose angle is defined by ζ in the complex plane as shown in Fig. 7.17. Here ζ is chosen greater than zero and less than one.

7.9 Step and Impulse Response of Second Order Systems

The response of mechanical systems to step and impulse changes in force is representative of their response to so-called shock loading. For example, an automobile suspension system receives an impulse displacement input when the car goes over a bump in the road. The subsequent motion of the chassis is important to the comfort of the passengers. A wind gust may apply a steplike input to a missile just leaving the launching pad. Its subsequent motion must be specified by the guidance and control system inside the missile. Hence, much can be learned from the response of a mechanical system to a step input. The exact solution of the second order differential equations may be obtained by methods similar to those used in Chap. 5.

7.9–1 STEP RESPONSE

So far we have confined our study to the transient response or the complementary solution of the homogeneous differential equation, i.e., when the right-hand side is zero or when there is no external disturbance on the system. A transient response results, of course, from a set of initial conditions which are different from the equilibrium position or equilibrium state of the system. In this section we shall study the particular solution of Eqs. 7.5 and 7.6 when the right-hand side is either a step or an impulse.

Consider that the inputs to the systems shown in Fig. 7.3 or Fig. 7.12 are step changes. A step change in force can result on the mechanical system when the applied force is suddenly increased or decreased to a new value. In the case of the electrical system in Fig. 7.3 or 7.12 a step change input does not result from a step change in current source. This is because in the second order form of the differential equation the current is differentiated when considered as an input. Thus, a sudden continuous increase in current ("ramp input") will produce effectively a step input. These inputs are shown in Fig. 7.18 where Eqs. 7.5 and 7.6 are repeated.

The general solution to Eqs. 7.5 and 7.6 is as before, the sum of transient and steady state solutions as shown in Eq. 7.45.

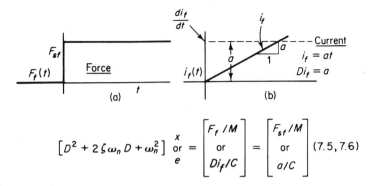

$$\left[D^2 + 2\zeta\omega_n D + \omega_n^2\right] \begin{matrix} x \\ \text{or} \\ e \end{matrix} = \begin{bmatrix} F_f/M \\ \text{or} \\ Di_f/C \end{bmatrix} = \begin{bmatrix} F_{sf}/M \\ \text{or} \\ a/C \end{bmatrix} \quad (7.5, 7.6)$$

Fig. 7.18. Step inputs to mechanical and electrical systems of Figs. 7.2 and 7.12.

$$x = x_{\text{tr}} + x_{\text{ss}} \tag{7.45}$$

The transient solution has been derived in its various forms in previous sections. The steady state solution can be written almost by inspection since if the input is a constant, the higher derivative terms must all be zero. Thus, we may write the steady state solution in Eq. 7.46:

$$\omega_n^2 x_{\text{ss}} = \frac{F_{\text{sf}}}{M} \quad \text{and} \quad \omega_n^2 e_{\text{ss}} = \frac{a}{C} \tag{7.46}$$

$$x_{\text{ss}} = \frac{F_{\text{sf}}}{M\omega_n^2} = \frac{F_{\text{sf}}}{K} \qquad e_{\text{ss}} = \frac{a}{C\omega_n^2} = aL$$

The general solutions may be summarized as follows:

$$\begin{matrix} x \\ \text{or} \\ e \end{matrix} = \begin{matrix} (a) \\ (b) \\ (c) \\ (d) \end{matrix} \left\{ \begin{matrix} A_1 e^{\omega_n(-\zeta+\sqrt{\zeta^2-1})t} + A_2 e^{\omega_n(-\zeta-\sqrt{\zeta^2-1})t} \\ (C_1 t + C_2)e^{-\omega_n t} \\ Ce^{-\zeta\omega_n t}\cos(\sqrt{1-\zeta^2}\,\omega_n t - \phi) \\ C\cos(\omega_n t - \phi) \end{matrix} \right\} + \left\{ \begin{matrix} \dfrac{F_{sf}}{K} \\ \text{or} \\ aL \end{matrix} \right. \tag{7.47}$$

(a) $\zeta > 1$ (b) $\zeta = 1$ (c) $\zeta < 1$ (d) $\zeta = 0$

The coefficient in the transient terms of Eq. 7.47 may be evaluated from initial conditions. We shall do this for the oscillatory case of the mechanical system only as follows: if at $t = 0$,

$$x = 0 \quad \text{and} \quad \dot{x} = 0$$

$$x = 0 = C \cos(-\phi) + \frac{F_{sf}}{K}$$

$$\dot{x} = 0 = -\zeta\omega_n C \cos(-\phi) - \sqrt{1 - \zeta^2}\, \omega_n C \sin(-\phi)$$

The equations above are similar to those which led to Eq. 7.33. Let us assume a damping ratio, $\zeta = 0.5$. This results in the same phase angle calculated in Eq. 7.33 but a different coefficient C. Assume $\zeta = 0.5$:

$$\tan \phi = \frac{\zeta}{\sqrt{1 - \zeta^2}} = 0.578 \qquad \phi = 30° \quad \text{or} \quad \frac{\pi}{6}$$

$$C = -\frac{F_{sf}}{K}\left[\frac{1}{\cos \phi}\right] = -1.15\frac{F_{sf}}{K}$$

The general solution for the mechanical system with damping ratio, $\zeta = 0.5$, is then given in Eq. 7.48 and if one defines F_{sf}/K as x_{ss}, the steady state value of x, Eq. 7.48 may be nondimensionalized as in Eq. 7.49.

$$x = \frac{F_{sf}}{K}\left[1 - 1.15e^{-0.5\omega_n t}\cos\left(0.86\omega_n t - \frac{\pi}{6}\right)\right] \qquad (7.48)$$

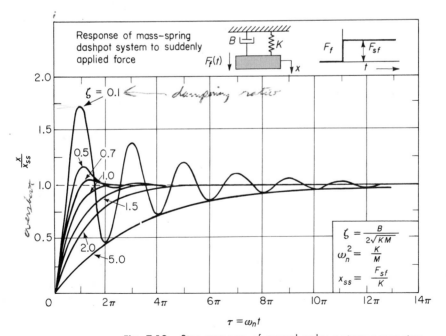

Fig. 7.19. Step response of second order systems parameters.

$$\frac{x}{x_{ss}} = \left[1 - 1.15e^{-0.5\omega_n t} \cos\left(0.86\omega_n t - \frac{\pi}{6}\right)\right] \qquad (7.49)$$

A family of curves, of which Eq. 7.49 is one, is plotted in Fig. 7.19 which is reminiscent of Figs. 7.6, 7.8, and 7.13.

A further comment about Fig. 7.19 should be made. Note that the nondimensional time parameter is $\omega_n t$. This allows us to represent x/x_{ss} versus time as a function of only one parameter, ζ. It results from the process of making the differential equation dimensionless. It is developed as follows from the system differential equation:

$$\frac{d^2 x}{dt^2} + 2\zeta\omega_n \frac{dx}{dt} + \omega_n^2 x = \frac{F_{sf}}{M} \qquad (7.50)$$

(a) Dividing both sides by ω_n^2 to make the coefficient of x equal unity yields

$$\frac{1}{\omega_n^2}\frac{d^2 x}{dt^2} + \frac{2\zeta}{\omega_n}\frac{dx}{dt} + x = \frac{F_{sf}}{M\omega_n^2} = \frac{F_{sf}}{K} = x_{ss} \qquad (7.51)$$

(b) The time scale can be changed to make the coefficient of the second order term unity by letting $1/\omega_n^2 t^2 = 1/\tau^2$ or

$$\tau = \omega_n t \qquad (7.52)$$

This yields

$$\frac{d^2 x}{d\tau^2} + 2\zeta \frac{dx}{d\tau} + x = x_{ss} \qquad (7.53)$$

(c) Making both sides dimensionless by dividing by x_{ss} provides a reduced form of the differential equation which depends only on one parameter 2ζ, that is,

$$\frac{d^2(x/x_{ss})}{d\tau^2} + 2\zeta\, d\frac{(x/x_{ss})}{d\tau} + \frac{x}{x_{ss}} = 1 \qquad (7.54)$$

This is plotted in Fig. 7.19 for several values of ζ.

7.9-2　Impulse Response

Suppose in Fig. 7.2 the current source is provided with a switch

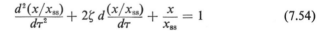

 Fig. 7.19 shows (as you would expect) that the mass settles down in a new equilibrium position distance x_{ss} from the old one. How it arrives there depends on the values of ζ and ω_n as indicated.

 Impulse responses often occur in practice and are rather tricky to deal with—study this section carefully.

and the switch is suddenly closed so that the circuit "sees" a sudden change in current; or suppose that a bullet of mass m is fired vertically into the mass in the mechanical system in Fig. 7.3. What would be the resulting responses? In each of these cases, an *impulse* in the input quantity is applied to the system. The mechanical impulse is one of force and in the electrical case it is a rate of change of current.

The true impulse exists only in the realm of mathematics. It is a force or input which has a magnitude of infinity but has zero duration in time. It is sometimes pictured as in Fig. 7.20(a). The quantity used

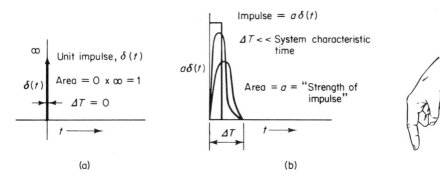

Fig. 7.20. (a) Unit impulse or delta function. (b) Realizable impulse functions, $a\delta(t)$.

to define an impulse is the area under its curve (which according to the previous definition must be zero times infinity). While the foregoing statement seems a bit ludicrous, the impulse cannot be dismissed so quickly for in actual practice many real situations can be represented by such an impulse. A practical impulse is one which has indeed a large magnitude but exists over a finite period of time. To be called an impulse this period of time must be small compared to a period of time which is significant in the response of the system. For example, if the system is oscillatory, it has a period of oscillation T and if the time duration of an imput quantity is less than say $T/100$, it appears to the system as a pure impulse. The magnitude or *strength* of an input impulse is the area under the curve. In the case of the mechanical force input it is $\int F\,dt$. The shape of the impulse curve does not matter if its time duration is so small that it may be considered as an impulse. Thus in Fig. 7.20(b) all of the shapes shown could be approximated by an impulse and are really what we are taking about when we refer to the impulse. A unit impulse has unity area in the system of units being considered.

The product of zero and infinity can be unity—don't ponder it, just accept it.   ☆

The unit impulse of Fig. 7.20(a) with area unity is sometimes given the symbol $\delta(t)$ and is also called a *delta function*. Any other impulse of different strength or area may then be written as $[a\delta(t)]$ where a represents the area of the impulse.

The solution of a differential equation having an input impulse is done classically by examination of the initial conditions using a knowledge of physics. The unit impulse or delta function has special significance in operational methods for the solution of differential equations with which the student shall become familiar in later courses.

Consider again the example of a bullet being shot into a suspended mass. There is a force on the bullet which is equal to the rate of change of bullet momentum. That is,

$$F = \frac{dmv}{dt} = m\frac{dv}{dt}$$

The bullet has an initial velocity, and if the main mass is very large compared to the bullet mass, its velocity after it becomes imbedded in the main mass is very low. Consequently bullet velocity changes suddenly. We may thus approximate v and dv/dt by the method shown in Fig. 7.21. Notice as the duration of bullet velocity change ΔT approaches zero, dv/dt approaches infinity and has the form of an impulse. The mass and bullet then move as a combined mass due to bullet impact. Initally, the main mass is at rest and if x is measured from the rest position, the spring force is balanced by the main mass. Consequently at the instant of impact, the only unbalanced force on the two masses is the impulse due to the rate of change of bullet momentum. This force is opposed by the inertia reaction force.

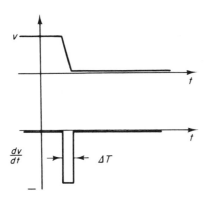

Fig. 7.21. Approximation of v and dv/dt.

$$-M\frac{dv}{dt} = (M + m)\ddot{x}$$

where m is the mass of bullet and
M is the main mass

This equation states that the initial acceleration has the same impulsive form as dv/dt. This expression can be integrated over a very short interval before and after impact and shows that a step change velocity occurs; that is, if $t = 0$ at impact, integrate from $t = 0^-$ to $t = 0^+$.

$$-m\,[v(0^+) - v(0^-)] = (M + m)\,[\dot{x}(0^+) - \dot{x}(0^-)]$$

$$v(0^-) \gg v(0^+) \quad \text{and} \quad \dot{x}(0^-) = 0$$

thus

$$mv(0^-) = (M + m)\,\dot{x}(0^+) \quad \text{or} \quad \dot{x}(0^+) = \left(\frac{m}{M + m}\right) v(0^-)$$

If we assume a damping ratio, $\zeta = 0.5$, and $\omega_n = 10$ rad/sec based on the parameters as shown, we may derive the general solution from the known initial conditions and note that the steady state solution is zero; i.e., equilibrium position remains unchanged if we neglect the slight change due to the increase in mass from the imbedded bullet. Equation 7.55 results as follows and Fig. 7.22 shows this impulse response.

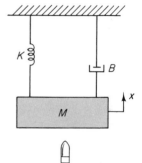

$$W = 3.86\ \text{lb}$$

$$K = 10\ \text{lb/in.}$$

$$B = 1\ \text{lb-sec/in.}$$

$$\zeta = 0.5$$

$$\omega_n = 10\ \text{rad/sec}$$

A 30–30 bullet that weighs 170 grains $= \dfrac{170}{7{,}000} = 0.024$ lb;

$$m = \frac{0.024}{32.2} = 7.55 \times 10^{-4}\ \frac{\text{lb-sec}^2}{\text{ft}}$$

$v(0^-) = 2{,}500$ ft/sec $\quad \therefore\ mv(0^-) = 7.55 \times 10^{-4}(2.500 \times 10^3) = 1.89$ lb-sec

$$= \int F\,dt$$

$$mv(0^-) = (m + M)\dot{x}(0^+) \approx M\dot{x}(0^+)$$

$$\dot{x}_0 = \frac{mv}{M}(0^-) = \frac{1.89}{38.6/32.2} = 1.58\ \text{ft/sec} = 19\ \text{in./sec}$$

$$x = Ce^{-5t}\cos(8.6t - \phi) + 0$$

At $t = 0 \qquad x_0 = 0 \qquad \dot{x}_0 = 19$ in./sec

$$\begin{cases} 0 = C \cos(-\phi) \\ 19 = -5C \cos(-\phi) - 8.6C \sin(-\phi) \end{cases}$$

$$\cos(-\phi) = 0 \quad \therefore \ \phi = -\frac{\pi}{2}$$

$$19 = -8.6C$$

$$C = -2.21$$

$$x = -2.21 e^{-5t} \cos\left(8.6 t + \frac{\pi}{2}\right) = 2.21 e^{-5t} \sin 8.6t \qquad (7.55)$$

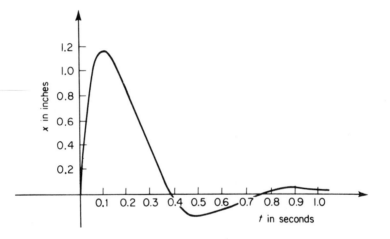

Fig. 7.22. Impulse response of a mass-spring-dashpot system ($W = 38.6$ lb., $K = 10$ lb/in., $B = 1$ lb-sec/in.) with $\zeta = 0.5$ and $\omega_n = 10$ rad/sec following impact of 30 cal bullet weighing 0.024 lb and velocity, 2500 ft/sec.

Let us return to the electrical system shown in Fig. 7.12(b). We shall assume that a current source $i_f(t)$ can deliver a constant current I_0 immediately upon closing the switch S shown in Fig. 7.23 which is a repeat of Fig. 7.12(b). Figure 7.23(b) and (c) show that in the initial value case the capacitor acts as a short circuit for all the current and in the final value case the inductor acts as a short circuit for all the current. The initial value of the rate of change of current is limited however by the capacitor so that the initial rate of change of voltage is given by Eq. 7.56.

$$\left.\frac{de}{dt}\right|_{t=0^+} = \frac{I_0}{C} \qquad (7.56)$$

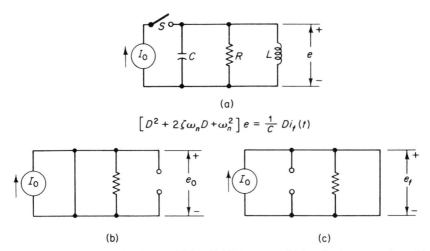

$$\left[D^2 + 2\zeta\omega_n D + \omega_n^2\right] e = \frac{1}{C} D i_f(t)$$

(b)   (c)

Fig. 7.23. (a) Parallel RLC circuit. (b) Initial value equivalent. (c) Final value equivalent.

Knowing the initial conditions at $t = 0$ and the final value, we may proceed to solve for the general solution of the equation shown in Fig. 7.23 in exactly the same way we did for the mechanical system. The voltage variation e following the closing of switch S will appear very similar to the response in Fig. 7.22 if the damping ratio ζ of the system is 0.5. The response will not be worked out numerically but its form will appear as in Fig. 7.24.

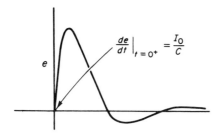

Fig. 7.24. Form of response of system of Fig. 7.23(a) following closing of switch with $i_F(t) = I_0$ a constant current source.

The best way to determine if an input is truly impulselike in nature is to try several different time durations. If the form of the response is the same, you can be sure that the time duration of the impulse is sufficiently short. But it is important that sufficient energy be associated with the impulse to bring about a measurable response of the system. This means that for finite amplitude of input, one should use as large a time duration for the impulse as possible. Note also that the *strength* of the impulse is equal to the area under the magnitude versus time curve. If one is comparing a response to a series of impulses of different time durations, one must alter the magnitude to keep the area constant.

7.10   The Convolution or Duhamel Integral*

In Sec. 7.9 the response of a second order system to an impulse was derived. The shape of an impulse response (its time duration, the ratio of amplitude of oscillations, etc.) is independent of the strength of the impulse. It depends only on the system parameters. Thus, the impulse response may be viewed as characteristic of a dynamic system and in a way may be considered as a description. *This is true of all linear dynamic systems, whatever the order of their differential equations.* Most dynamic systems of first and second or higher order are stable in the sense that they contain some degree of dissipative damping and tend to return to their equilibrium positions when displaced. There are exceptions including, for example, systems which have an output which is the integral of the input; however, in these cases we see that the derivative of the output reaches some equilibrium value if the system is stable.

In this section we shall attempt to present a different and powerful approach to the analysis of dynamic systems. We propose to do this with a minimum of mathematical complexity so that the basic idea may be understood. We shall deal with functions of time in the form of a discrete series of numbers as we did in Chap. 5. This will involve approximations of continuous functions. The numerical representation of the functions to be considered are conceptually easier to handle than the functions themselves and lead directly to digital computer analysis.

The fact that the impulse response of a dynamic system is characteristic of the system and that the superposition theorem holds for linear systems permits us to calculate the response of a linear system due to an arbitrary input knowing only the nature of the system impulse response. The superposition theorem for linear systems states that the response due to the sum of a number of arbitrary inputs is equivalent to the sum of the responses if each input were to act separately.

Consider an arbitrary input to a dynamic system of the form $F(t)$ as shown in Fig. 7.25(a). We replace this continuous function by an

---

*Also called "superposition integral," "folding integral," and "faltung integral."

approximately equivalent series of impulses as in Fig. 7.25(b). At this point we must choose a reasonable ΔT or width of each impulse. Consistent with the remarks in Sec. 7.9 about impulses, let us choose ΔT only so small that were it to be made any smaller the impulse response resulting would not differ substantially in form. In actual problems, this decision involves engineering judgement and a quantitative evaluation of the errors likely to result. Often common sense will produce a correct decision. The overall criterion for the impulses in Fig. 7.25(b) is that the total area of the impulses equals the area under the continuous function as in Fig. 7.25(a). Note that the first impulse at $t = 0$ represents only half the area of an impulse at the full ordinate height. This was done to account for the fact that the zeroth impulse occurred for time $\Delta T/2$ before t_0 whereas $F(t)$ was zero at that time. By making the amplitude of this pulse $F(0)/2$ we are insured that the area of $\int F(t)$ is equal to the area under the impulse approximation.

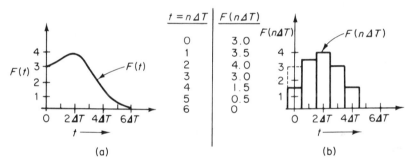

Figure 7.25

Now that we have replaced the continuous input by a series of impulses displaced in time, we are in a position to apply the superposition theorem. It states that the response of the system to all the impulses is equal to the sum of the responses of the system to each of the impulses acting separately.

Let us assume a system having an *impulse response* like that of Fig. 7.22. The *impulse response* $h(t)$ is literally the response of a system to an impulse of strength unity. A possible set of values for $h(t)$ are listed in Fig. 7.26(a). In an actual problem appropriate units of time and response variables would be applied. The response of a system may now be determined as in Fig. 7.26(b) where the responses due to each of the impulses comprised of $F(n\Delta T)$ are added graphically to produce the total response $x(t)$. The process indicated in Fig. 7.26(b) may be written mathematically as in Eq. 7.57.

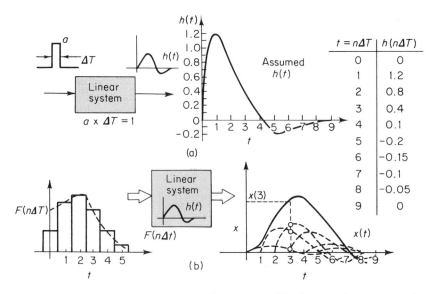

Fig. 7.26. (a) Impulse response, *h*(*t*), of system due to unit impulse. Values are assumed for representation. (b) Superposition of impulse responses to find total response, *x*(*t*), due to input, *F*(*n*Δ*T*).

$$x(t) = \sum_{n=0}^{k} h(n\Delta T)F(t - n\Delta T) \qquad (7.57)$$

The symbol *k* represents the number of intervals of time Δ*T* required to completely characterize the impulse response. $h(n\Delta T)$ is the ordinate value of the impulse response at the time point *n*Δ*T*. We note that the table in Fig. 7.26(a) shows that eight intervals of time Δ*T* in length are required to characterize the assumed *h*(*t*). Equation 7.57 may perhaps be better understood by considering the evaluation of *x* in Fig. 7.26(b) at $t = t_3$. Equation 7.58 shows the terms which make up *x* at $t = 3$.

$$x(3) = h(0)F(3) + h(1)F(2) + h(2)F(1) + h(3)F(0) + \cdots$$
$$= (1.2)(4) + (0.8)(3.5) + (0.4)(3) + \cdots$$
$$= 8.8 \qquad (7.58)$$

Equation 7.58 may be interpreted in a different way than indicated in Fig. 7.26(b). The evaluation of *x*(3) may be visualized as in Fig. 7.27 where the impulse response is shown plotted backward in time parallel with the input starting at $t = 3$ on the time axis.

To compute the response $x(t_4)$ at t_4 one could visualize the impulse response in Fig. 7.27 moved one increment Δ*T* to the right with respect

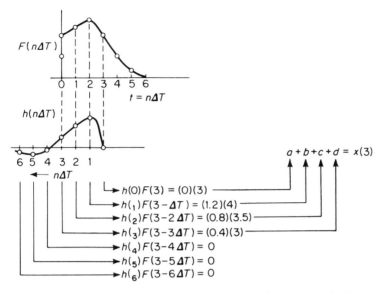

Fig. 7.27. Showing how the terms of Eqs. 7.57 and 7.58 may be obtained by "folding" the impulse response "against" the input.

to the input $F(n\Delta T)$ and a new set of terms computed for the series of Eq. 7.57. Thus one may visualize the complete process of computing the output response to an input $F(n\Delta T)$ as one of sliding the "backward plotted impulse response" along the input, stopping at each increment of time to compute a series of terms. This process may be easily done in numerical terms using a technique proposed by Professor Henry M. Paynter. Professor Paynter suggests plotting the ordinates of the impulse response on a strip of paper tape. A computation sheet is then arranged so this tape may be placed beside a series of numerical values representing the input function. As the tape is moved downward, values of output are successively computed. For the example being considered the output values up until time $t = 3$ might be computed as shown in Fig. 7.28. The continuous form of Eq. 7.57 may be derived by letting ΔT approach zero, the summation then becomes an integration which leads to the superposition integral which may be written as in Eq. 7.59.

$$x_t = \int_{-\infty}^{\infty} h(\sigma)F(t - \sigma)\, d\sigma \qquad (7.59)$$

In Eq. 7.59 the impulse response is a continuous function of time as are the inputs and outputs. This equation has been called variously the "convolution integral" or the "duhamel integral" and because of

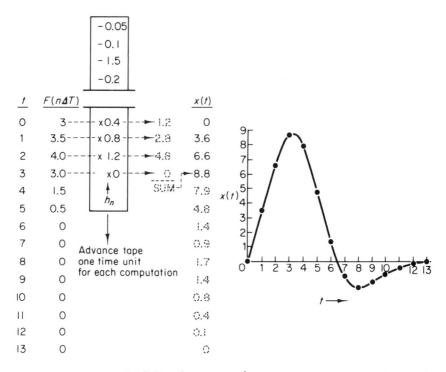

Fig. 7.28. Computation of system response using paper tape method of Henry Paynter. Tape is in position for computation at t_3.

the way in which the impulse response may be viewed as "folded in time" as in Fig. 7.27, it has been called the "folding" or "faltung integral." The computing process indicated in Figs. 7.27 and 7.28 may be viewed as a convolution of the impulse response on the input function, thus the name "convolution integral."

It is not our desire to study the application of the convolution integral in continuous form in this course. Our purpose is merely to help the student obtain some insight into its origin and theory in light of having studied the impulse response in Sec. 7.9. It is hoped that the student will not only have gained understanding of the convolution approach but also will have gained a practical method for numerical computation as demonstrated in Fig. 7.28.

7.11 Summary

Many physical systems can be described by linear-constant-coefficient-differential equations. Equations of this form can be algebraically manipulated and the time scale changed to rewrite them in one of several standard forms. The most common form is

$$f(t) = \frac{d^2x}{d\tau^2} + 2\zeta \frac{dx}{d\tau} + x$$

where

$$\tau = \frac{t}{T} = \omega_n t$$

The solution of this differential equation for a given set of initial conditions and $f(t)$ depends only on the damping ratio ζ and the time scale depends on the natural frequency ω_n. The damping ratio ζ can take on values from $-\infty$ to $+\infty$, however the form of the system response changes drastically at two specific values.

(a) When $\zeta < 0$, the system is unstable; when $\zeta > 0$, it is stable but oscillatory until $\zeta = 1$. Consequently, $\zeta = 0$ marks the transition between stable and unstable response.

(b) When $\zeta < 1$, the system is oscillatory; when $\zeta > 1$, it does not oscillate in response to an $f(t)$ or set of initial conditions. Consequently, $\zeta = 1$ is the transition between oscillatory (periodic) and nonoscillatory (aperiodic) response.

The classical methods of solution of this differential equation depend on the value of ζ. Since the solution is nonoscillatory for $\zeta > 1$, we find that methods used for first order systems can be used. Using these approaches we obtain the solution to the homogeneous equation. For $\zeta > 1$, $x(t) = Ae^{-t/T_1} + Be^{-t/T_2}$ where A and B depend on the initial conditions and T_1 and T_2 are functions of ω_n and ζ. For $\zeta = 1$,

$$x(t) = (C_1 t + C_2) e^{-\omega_n t}$$

If $\zeta < 1$, then the solution is most conveniently expressed in terms of complex numbers. In this case the concept of representing $A \sin \omega_n t$ as the projection of a rotating line segment on a fixed line is introduced as an aid to visualizing the combination of sinusoids in the solution of this form of the differential equation. This concept is widely used in the study of AC circuits and mechanical vibrations. This leads to the solution for this range of damping ratio. That is, for $\zeta < 1$,

$$x_t = Ce^{-\zeta \omega_n t} \cos(\sqrt{1 - \zeta^2}\, \omega_n t - \phi)$$

where C and ϕ are determined by the initial conditions.

This transient solution to the homogeneous equation is added to the steady state solution due to $f(t)$ to provide the total solution. Often for a given $f(t)$ form such as a step or ramp and a given set of initial conditions, plots of system response are developed for various values of damping ratio ζ with a time scale which is a function of the natural frequency ω_n. This allows us to predict the response without computing the solution simply by manipulating the differential equation into the standard form to obtain values for ζ and ω_n, and using the plots. This same approach can be extended to higher order systems where in general for an nth order system, $n - 1$ system parameters and a time scale parameter are required to specify the response for a given input and set of n initial conditions.

The impulse response of second order systems and, in general, linear systems of any order has special utility. With this solution to the differential equation we can generate the solution for any input using the convolution integral.

Problems

7-1. (a) For the given differential equation, determine ζ and ω_n.

(b) Find the solution for the following second order linear differential equation.

$$2\frac{d^2x}{dt^2} + 3\frac{dx}{dt} + x = 0$$

Initial conditions: $x(0) = 1$, $\dot{x}(0) = 0$.

(c) Is the equation critically damped, overdamped, etc.?

7-2. Solve the given differential equation.

$$\ddot{x} + 8\dot{x} + 16 = 0$$

Initial conditions: $x(0) = 1$, $\dot{x}(0) = 1$

7-3. (a) Given the circuit in Fig. P.7.3, determine $i(t)$ with the switch closed at $t = 0$. The initial conditions are $\left.\dfrac{di}{dt}\right|_0 = 0$ and $i(0) = 5$.

(b) What are ζ and ω_n?

7-4. Consider the electrical system in Fig. P. 7.4 with the indicated initial conditions and parameter values.

(a) Write the differential equation for $e(t)$ and determine ζ and ω_n.

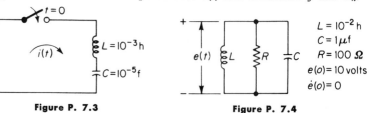

Figure P. 7.3   Figure P. 7.4

(b) Find $e(t)$ as a function of time.

7-5. Given the circuit shown in Fig. P. 7.5, find e as a function of time after the switch S is closed. Assume there was no energy stored in the system prior to the closing of the switch.

(a) $L = lh$, $C = 100f$, and $R = 50$.

(b) $L = lh$, $C = 100f$, and $R = 30$.

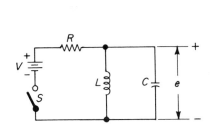

Figure P. 7.5   Figure P. 7.6

7-6. Given the system shown in Fig. P. 7.6

(a) If $B = 0$ and $K = 10$ lb/in., find ω_n and ζ.

(b) Find B and K for $\omega_n = 10$ and $\zeta = 2$.

(c) For $y(0) = 1$ ft and $\dot{y}(0) = -70.3$ ft/sec, derive $y(t)$ for $B = 0.59$ lb-sec/ft and $K = 82$ lb/ft.

(d) For $K = 10$ lb/ft, choose B so that the system is critically damped.

7-7. The circuit shown in Fig. P. 7.7 is in equilibrium at $t = 0$ with no initial change on the capacitor. Switch S is suddenly closed at $t = 0$. The resulting equations are concerned with the transient response following $t = 0^+$.

(a) Using initial and final value circuits, sketch the shape of the transient response.

(b) Derive the differential equation for e in terms of system parameters and the differential operator D.

(c) Assuming that the initial value of e at $t = 0^+$ is E, that de/dt at $t = 0^+$ is zero, and that e_{ss} is zero, write the equation for the transient response where $R(\text{ohms}) = C(\text{farads}) = L(\text{henries})$.

Note: Only the solution to the homogeneous equation is required here.

7-8. In the circuit shown in Fig. P. 7.8, the switch 2 is initially in position A, and switch 1 is open. At $t = 0$, switch 1 is closed. Find C so that a damping ratio of $\frac{1}{2}$ occurs.

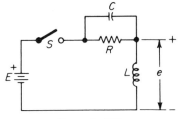
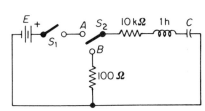

Figure P. 7.7   Figure P. 7.8

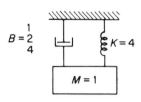

Figure P. 7.9

7-9. The system shown is initially in equilibrium. It is then displaced a distance $x_0 = 2$ ft in the downward direction and released. With what velocity does it pass through its original equilibrium position on its first upward pass for each value of B given?

7-10. A piston of mass M fits in a closed cylinder of cross-sectional area A. When the piston is in the central position ($x_0 = 0$), it is in equilibrium, and the pressure on each side is P. The gas in the cylinder follows Boyle's law. The piston is moved a distance x' from x_0 and then released. Assume a viscous friction exists between the piston and the cylinder. (Friction force is proportional to piston velocity.)
(a) Write the differential equation.
(b) Draw the functional block diagram for the equation.
(c) Linearize if necessary and solve for (1) damping ratio and (2) natural frequency.

7-11. (a) For the system shown in Fig. P. 7.11 used to measure the difference in velocity $v_1 - v_2$ between two tapes, find the response of x to a step change in $v_1 - v_2$ and show that as $t \to \infty$, x becomes proportional to $v_1 - v_2$.

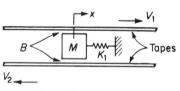

Figure P. 7.11

(b) What conditions are necessary for the response to be (1) over damped, (2) under damped, or (3) critically damped?
(c) How could you speed up the response (have transient die out faster)?
(d) How could you increase sensitivity $\Delta x / \Delta(v_1 - v_2)$

7-12. Given a second order system, $(D^2 + 3D + 9)x = 3t$, what must the initial conditions be so that the transient response is zero?

7-13. Solve $\ddot{x} + 6\dot{x} + 9x = te^{-3t}$.
Conditions: $x(0) = 0$, $\dot{x}(0) = 2$

7-14. Sketch a plot of the roots of the characteristic equation in the complex plane and then sketch the approximate transient response for the following differential equations:
(a) $\sqrt{2}\, D^2 x - 6Dx + \sqrt{2}\, x = 0$; $x(0) = 10$, $\dot{x}(0) = 0$.
(b) $8D^2 x + \sqrt{2}\, x = 0$; $x(0) = 3$, $\dot{x}(0) = 0$.
(c) $2D^2 x - 2\sqrt{2}\, Dx + x = 0$; $x(0) = 4$, $\dot{x}(0) = 0$.
(d) $2D^2 x + 6Dx + x = 0$; $x(0) = \frac{1}{2}$, $\dot{x}(0) = 0$.
(e) $2D^2 x + 2Dx + x = 0$; $x(0) = 10$, $\dot{x}(0) = 0$.
(f) $2D^2 x + 2\sqrt{2}\, Dx + x = 0$; $x(0) = 5$, $\dot{x}(0) = 0$.
(g) $3D^2 x - \sqrt{2} \sqrt{3}\, Dx + x = 0$; $x(0) = \sqrt{3}$, $\dot{x}(0) = 0$.
(h) $D^3 x + D^2 x - Dx + 2x = 0$; $x(0) = 9$, $\dot{x}(0) = 0$, $\ddot{x}(0) = 0$.

7-15. When we begin interplanetary trips, it will be necessary to maintain our weight (mass really) constant. Thus, though "weightless" we will be during the flight, we must weigh ourselves regularly. The basic bathroom scale form will serve quite well if the mass of our ship is much greater than that of the people on board (assume this is true). Our "scale" may be modeled as shown in Fig. P. 7.15.

A device will be used that will measure the time between 2 zero crossings of the scale pointer. Minimum time that may be measured is $\frac{1}{2}$ sec.

Further restrictions:

(1) B (internal damping) is expensive to reduce and cannot be made zero.

(2) "Weights" of all people shall remain within 120 to 180 lb.

(3) The damped frequency ω_d compared to ω_n for any person on the scale must satisfy $(\omega_n - \omega_d)/\omega_n \leq 0.01$.

(a) Explain how this system can be used to weigh people.

(b) Does a person's "weight" as measured depend on how the scale is set in motion?

(c) Select K and B. What is the maximum B that may be used?

(d) What is the maximum period of time the timer must measure?

(e) Plot a calibration curve for our use of the scale in space.

Scale pan on which a man will sit
and be fastened to (wt of pan: 0.32 lb)

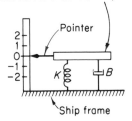

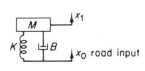

Ship frame

Figure P. 7.15   **Figure P. 7.16**

7-16. For the rough model of a car shown in Fig. P. 7.16 that has $B = 1600$ lb-sec/ft, 800 lb-sec/ft, and 400 lb-sec/ft, what is the motion of the car if it suddenly starts up a ramp after traveling on a level road for a long time?

7-17. For the system shown, given $L = 1$ henry, what values of R and C are needed to make $\omega_n = 10$ rad/sec and the damped frequency $= 5\sqrt{3}$ rad/sec for e_0?

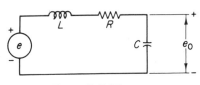

Figure P. 7.17

7-18. For some system, the following differential equation was derived: $8\dot{x} + \ddot{x} + 5\ddot{x} + 4 = 0$. Solve for $x(t)$, given $x = 1$, $\dot{x} = 0$ and $\ddot{x} = 0$ at $t = 0$.

7-19. The roots of the characteristic equation of a system are shown on the complex plane in Fig. P. 7.19.

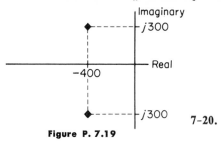

Figure P. 7.19

(a) Determine ω_n and ζ and the damped frequency ω.

(b) If the damping is reduced 25% but ω_n remains the same, show the effect on the root locations in the complex plane.

7-20.   (a) Using d'Alembert's principle, determine the equations of motion of M_0 in Fig. P. 7.20.

(b) For small values of θ, linearize these equations and solve for $\theta(t)$.

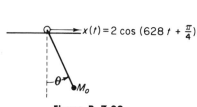

Figure P. 7.20

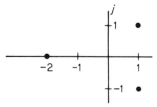

Figure P. 7.21

7-21.   Given the root locations shown in Fig. P. 7.21, what was the transient response for $x(0) = 1$, $\dot{x}(0) = 0$, $\ddot{x}(0) = 0$, and $x_{ss} = 0$?

7-22.   Given $x(t)(D + 1)(D^2 + 2\zeta\omega_n D + \omega_n^2) = 0$.
(a) Show roots of the characteristic equation for the differential equation above in complex root plane for $\zeta = 0.2$.
(b) Show roots of the characteristic equation for the differential equation above in complex root plane for $\zeta = 2.0$.
(c) Sketch the form of $x(t)$ for $\zeta = 0.2$ without computing any values for $x(t)$. The following conditions are given: $x(0) = a$ and $\dot{x}(0) = \ddot{x}(0) = 0$.
(d) Sketch the form of $x(t)$ for $\zeta = 2.0$ without computing any values for $x(t)$. The following conditions are given: $x(0) = a$ and $\dot{x}(0) = \ddot{x}(0) = 0$.

7-23.   The input to a recorder is a 10-volt battery with switch S. When switch S is closed at $t = 0$ (point 1 on chart), the record in Fig. P. 7.23(b) is produced.
(a) Assuming the recorder is a second order system, find ζ and ω_n.
(b) Assume that the correct answer to (a) is $\zeta = 0.4$ and $\omega_n = 2\pi$ rad/sec (they may or may not be correct). Find the values for A and θ in the equation which describes the voltage recorded by the recorder. It will have the following form: $e = Ae^{-\zeta\omega_n t} \cos(\omega_n\sqrt{1 - \zeta^2}\, t - \theta)$.
(c) Using the same "correct" values for ζ and ω_n given in (b), plot the roots of the characteristic equation for the recorder in the complex plane.
(d) It is desired to assemble an electric circuit (analogue) that will show a voltage variation on an oscilloscope that matches exactly the move-

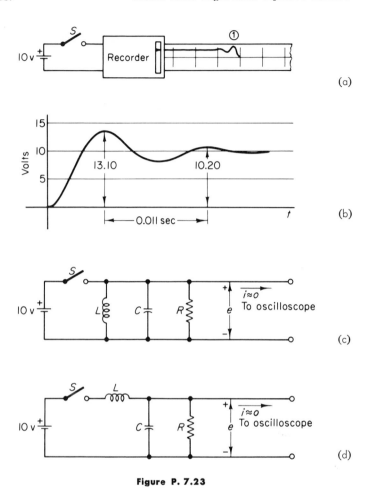

Figure P. 7.23

ment of the recorder pen. A student proposed the circuit shown in
Fig. P. 7.23(c). Will it work? Explain your answer.

(e) Another student suggested the circuit in Fig. P. 7.23(d); and derived
its equation as follows: $[D^2 + (1/RC)D + 1/LC]e = (1/LC)E$. What
values of L, C, and R should be used in the circuit to give the pseudo-
correct answers of (b)? Note: 1,000 farads is about as high in capacity
as it is feasible to use.

7-24.   An impulse response is taken for a pen-type recorder of the form
shown in Fig. P. 7.24(a). The response is that of the second order
system as shown in Fig. P. 7.24(c). The system differential equation
is given in Fig. P. 7.24(b).

(a) Find ζ and ω_n of the second order system.

(b) Find the step response by numerical convolution.

(c) Compute by numerical convolution the response to the input shown in Fig. P. 7.24(d) use the values for $y(t)$ given in the accompanying table.

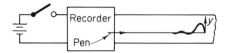

$$\ddot{y} + 2\xi\omega_n \dot{y} + \omega_n^2 y = Ke(t); \quad K = 100\,\frac{\text{in.}}{\text{sec}^2\,\text{volt}}$$

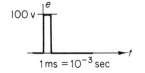

100 v

e

An impulse test pulse

$1\,\text{ms} = 10^{-3}\,\text{sec}$

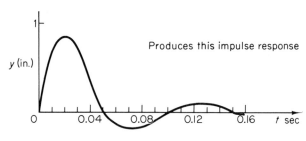

y (in.)

Produces this impulse response

0.04   0.08   0.12   0.16   *t* sec

See table of values below

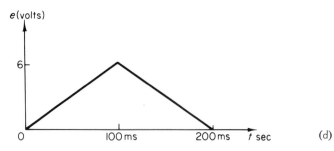

e(volts)

6

0   100 ms   200 ms   *t* sec   (d)

Figure   P. 7.24.

Impulse response

t(sec)	y(in.)
0.00	0.00
0.01	0.70
0.02	0.85
0.03	0.64

Impulse response (cont.)

t(sec)	y(in.)
0.04	0.32
0.05	0.00
0.06	−0.17
0.07	−0.20
0.08	−0.15
0.09	−0.07
0.10	0.00
0.11	0.04
0.12	0.05
0.13	0.04
0.14	0.02
0.15	0.00

8   Sinusoidal Frequency Response of First and Second Order Systems

8.1   Introduction

In this chapter we shall study the steady state response of systems which can be described by first and second order constant-coefficient-linear-differential equations when a sinusoidal input is applied. Such solutions are of far more importance and significance than may be indicated by the fact that they are just another specific solution of the complete differential equation. *It will be shown that when a sinusoidal input is applied to a linear system, the response in steady state is also sinusoidal at the same frequency as the input.* We shall find that the *output* differs from the *input* only in the *amplitude* of its sinusoidal response and the *phase angle* of the response when measured with respect to the input. Thus, the ratio of the output to input amplitude and the phase angle between the output and input sinusoid are the only two parameters required to predict the output of a linear system when the input is sinusoidal at a given frequency (see Fig. 8.1).

From another point of view we may say that a linear system alters (amplifies or attenuates) the amplitude of an input sinusoid and shifts its phase (either ahead or behind). In general the amplitude ratio B/A and the phase angle Φ involved are different for different input sinusoidal frequencies ω. It will be shown that a system characterized by a constant-coefficient-linear-differential equation may

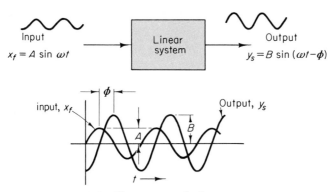

Fig. 8.1. The response of a linear system to an input sinusoid is a sinusoid of a different amplitude and phase.

be *defined* in terms of its amplitude and phase characteristics, i.e., how it affects a sinusoidally varying input at various frequencies.

The importance of sinusoidal frequency analysis is even greater than indicated in the foregoing. Not only does a complex dynamic relationship reduce to one which involves only two simple parameters for a large class of differential equations, but the methods of analysis for such systems are capable of being generalized to handle many other kinds of input-output situations. Any periodic input may be represented by means of a Fourier series as the sum of a number of different input sinusoids. Thus, the response of a linear system to any periodic function may be calculated as the sum of its responses to each of the sinusoids of which the periodic input is composed (called *harmonic components*). Also, the student will become aware in later courses that the important Fourier and Laplace transformations which greatly simplify the analysis of dynamic systems are built on the techniques of the sinusoidal frequency response method. Finally, the student may later learn that any time varying function including ones which are completely random may be represented statistically by combinations of sinusoids. These facts are mentioned with the hope that the student will pay particular attention to the methods of analysis which are to be developed in this chapter and which underlie the general methods of frequency response analysis.

8.2 Sinusoidal Frequency Response of First Order Systems

Consider the *RC* circuit shown in Fig. 8.2.

$$\tau \frac{de_2}{dt} + e_2 = e_1 \quad \text{where} \quad \tau = RC \tag{8.1}$$

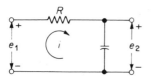

Fig. 8.2.   RC circuit.

or using the D notation,

$$e_2 = \left(\frac{1}{\tau D + 1}\right) e_1 \qquad (8.2)$$

It was shown in Ex. 3.11–1 that Eq. 8.1 relates the output voltage e_2 to the input voltage e_1.

8.2–1   First Order System Sinusoidal Solutions (positive ω)

We shall now proceed to obtain a steady state solution for Eq. 8.1 when e_1 is a sinusoidal input of the form shown in Eq. 8.3. Equations 8.4 and 8.5 show complex number representations of Eq. 8.3 and are complete equivalents, as shown in the Appendix .

$$e_1 = E_1 \cos \omega t \qquad (8.3)$$

$$e_1 = \operatorname{Re} E_1 e^{j\omega t} \qquad (8.4)$$

$$e_1 = \frac{E_1}{2}(e^{j\omega t} + e^{-j\omega t}) \qquad (8.5)$$

Note that ω is the input frequency parameter which may have any value. For purposes of convenience no subscript is used with ω in this chapter (e.g., forcing frequency might be denoted ω_f). However, the student is urged to avoid confusion with ω, the input driving frequency used in Chap. 8, and ω, the circular frequency for transient oscillation used in Chap. 7.

We may proceed with the solution of Eq. 8.1 using either Eq. 8.4 or Eq. 8.5. The paths resulting from either of these choices are somewhat different but lead to the same conclusion. We shall first solve the differential equation using Eq. 8.4 as an input. As before, we assume the form of solution which satisfies the differential equation and solve for the unknown constants; thus e_{2ss} may be represented by Eq. 8.6. In this chapter we are concerned only with steady state solutions. We shall therefore drop the *ss* subscript, keeping in mind that the results apply only to the steady state.

$$e_{2ss} = e_2 = \operatorname{Re} \mathbf{A}e^{j\omega t} \qquad (8.6)$$

Equation 8.6 essentially states that the result can be considered as a sinusoid represented by the real part of a rotating line segment

---

 Remember that x_{ss}, the steady state solution, is only part of the general solution, $x_{tr} + x_{ss}$. When a sinusoid is suddenly applied, there is a transient solution x_{tr} which usually dies away.

or complex number with amplitude and phase different from the input sinusoid. We shall proceed from this point, dealing not with the projection of the rotating line segment but with the line itself. The inherent assumption is that if the rotating line segment can be shown to be a solution of the differential equation, then its real part must also be a solution. We shall find that the complex number so designated is defined by an amplitude and phase with respect to the input and that these quantities are functions of the input frequency.

Let us define the complex number assumed for the solution as a function of its frequency of rotation using the notation of Eq. 8.7. The significance of $j\omega$ will become apparent later. The input as given in Eq. 8.4 may also be defined as a function of $j\omega$, i.e., represented by the rotating line segment itself, rather than just the real part.

$$e_2(j\omega) = \mathbf{A}e^{j\omega t} \quad \text{and} \quad e_1(j\omega) = E_1 e^{j\omega t} \tag{8.7}$$

When Eq. 8.7 is substituted back into Eq. 8.1, we obtain the unknown complex number $\mathbf{A}$ as in Eq. 8.8:

$$\tau j\omega \mathbf{A}e^{j\omega t} + \mathbf{A}e^{j\omega t} = E_1 e^{j\omega t}$$

$$\mathbf{A} = \left(\frac{1}{\tau j\omega + 1}\right) E_1 \tag{8.8}$$

Replacing the complex number by its magnitude and phase angle, Eq. 8.8 becomes Eq. 8.9. Remember that the magnitude is the square root of the sum of the squares of the real part and the imaginary part, and the phase angle is the arctangent of the imaginary part over the real part.

$$\mathbf{A} = \left[\frac{1}{(\sqrt{(\omega\tau)^2 + 1})\,e^{j\Phi}}\right] E_1 = \left[\frac{1}{\sqrt{(\omega\tau)^2 + 1}}\right] e^{-j\Phi} E_1 \tag{8.9}$$

where

$$\Phi = \tan^{-1}\frac{\omega\tau}{1}$$

$e_2(j\omega)$ is then as given in Eq. 8.10 and $e_2(t)$ as a function of time is as given in Eq. 8.11.

$$e_2(j\omega) = E_1\left[\frac{1}{\sqrt{(\omega\tau)^2 + 1}}\right] e^{-j\Phi} e^{j\omega\tau} = E_1\left[\frac{1}{\sqrt{(\omega\tau)^2 + 1}}\right] e^{j(\omega\tau - \Phi)} \tag{8.10}$$

$$e_2(t) = \operatorname{Re} E_1\left[\frac{1}{\sqrt{(\omega\tau)^2 + 1}}\right] e^{j(\omega\tau - \Phi)} = E_1\left[\frac{1}{\sqrt{(\omega\tau)^2 + 1}}\right] \cos(\omega\tau - \Phi) \tag{8.11}$$

The final result is then seen to be a sinusoid at the same frequency but with a different amplitude and phase angle as defined in Eq. 8.12.

$$e_2(t) = E_2 \cos(\omega t - \Phi) \tag{8.12}$$

where

$$E_2 = \frac{E_1}{\sqrt{(\omega\tau)^2 + 1}} \quad \text{and} \quad \Phi = \tan^{-1} \omega\tau$$

The ratio of amplitudes $|e_2/e_1|$ is seen to be nondimensional. This amplitude ratio, symbolized AR, and phase angle Φ, which for a given time constant τ are functions of frequency only, are plotted in Fig. 8.3.

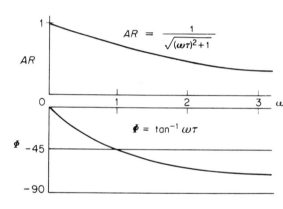

Fig. 8.3. Amplitude ratio, AR, and phase angle, Φ, for first order system versus nondimensional frequency parameter, $\omega\tau$.

The amplitude ratio AR and the phase angle Φ for a first order system are seldom presented as in Fig. 8.3. It is common practice, rather, to plot the logarithm of the amplitude ratio as a function of the logarithm of frequency parameter and to plot the phase angle also versus logarithm of $\omega\tau$. A linear-appearing scale for logarithm of amplitude ratio, log AR, may be obtained through use of the *decibel*. The decibel is defined as in Eq. 8.13.

$$\text{Amplitude Ratio in decibels (db)} = 20 \log_{10} AR \tag{8.13}$$

Using the logarithm and decibel scales, the data of Fig. 8.3 would then appear as in Fig. 8.4. The information contained in Fig. 8.4 is also plotted in greater detail in Figs. 8.16 and 8.17.

Figure 8.4 reveals some interesting facts about the frequency

---

The decibel is also used to define the logarithm of power ratios in acoustics. In such cases 1 db = 10 $\log_{10}$ (power ratio), not 20 $\log_{10}$ (voltage ratio).

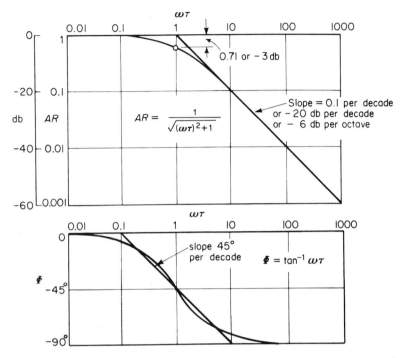

Fig. 8.4. Log *AR* (*AR* in db) and phase angle versus nondimensional frequency parameter, $\omega\tau$, for first order system.

response for the first order system. When $\omega\tau$ is less than one, the amplitude ratio is almost unity. When $\omega\tau$ is somewhat larger than one, we see the amplitude ratio decreases or "falls off" at a uniform rate. These facts are indicated in Eq. 8.14: for

$$\omega\tau < 1 \quad AR \approx 1 \qquad \omega\tau > 1 \quad AR \approx \frac{1}{\omega\tau} \tag{8.14}$$

Equation 8.14 and Fig. 8.4 show that the plot of amplitude ratio versus frequency on log-log paper may be approximated by two straight lines: one horizontal at an amplitude ratio of unity, and one "falling off" at the rate of $\frac{1}{10}$ for each increase in $\omega\tau$ by a factor of 10. These two straight lines intersect at a value $\omega\tau = 1$. This point of intersection is called the *break frequency*. Note that actual amplitude ratio at $\omega\tau = 1$ as calculated from Eq. 8.15 is 0.71 or is "down" 3 db, and one may sketch the amplitude ratio curve almost by inspection. Note also that the response falls off at the rate of 20 db/decade or 6 db/octave. Note also that the phase curve in Fig. 8.4 exhibits a rather odd symmetry about the $\omega\tau = 1$ ordinate. This means that this curve also may be readily sketched from only a few remembered points derived from Eq. 8.12 as

DB = 20 (log of ratio)

ratio = input / output

follows,

$$\Phi = 0 \quad \text{for} \quad \omega = 0$$

$$\Phi = 45° \quad \text{for} \quad \omega = \frac{1}{\tau}$$

$$\Phi = 90° \quad \text{for} \quad \omega = \infty$$

In addition, we note that a line of slope

$$\frac{d\Phi}{d(\log_{10}\omega\tau)} = -45°$$

passing through the point $\omega\tau = 1$ and $\Phi = 45°$ is a good approximation to the phase angle as shown in Fig. 8.4.

8.3 Frequency Response Function

The information in Figs. 8.3 and 8.4 may also be expressed in a different way. Basically these figures represent magnitude and phase data for a complex number. This complex number can be derived directly from Eqs. 8.7 and 8.8 using the complex number forms $e_2(j\omega)$ and $e_1(j\omega)$ as follows:

$$\frac{e_2(j\omega)}{e_1(j\omega)} = \frac{\mathbf{A}e^{j\omega t}}{E_1 e^{j\omega t}} = \frac{\mathbf{A}}{E_1} = \frac{1}{\tau j\omega + 1} = G(j\omega) \qquad (8.15)$$

Equation 8.15 can be interpreted in an important special way. If we consider $e_1(j\omega)$ as an input quantity and $e_2(j\omega)$ as an output quantity, their ratio may be used to define the first order system in block diagram form as in Fig. 8.5.

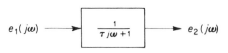

$$e_1(j\omega) \longrightarrow \boxed{\frac{1}{\tau j\omega + 1}} \longrightarrow e_2(j\omega)$$

Fig. 8.5. First order system frequency response function.

The function of frequency which is a complex number and the ratio of the rotating complex numbers whose real parts are the sinusoidal input and output $e_2(j\omega)/e_1(j\omega)$, is given the special name, *frequency response function* of a system, and may be symbolized by $G(j\omega)$. This is an appropriate name since when the input rotating complex number is multiplied by the stationary complex number or frequency response function, the rotating complex number

---

 Beware! $G(j\omega)$ is *not* equal to $e_2(t) = E_2 \cos \omega t$ divided by $e_1(t) = E_1 \cos \omega t$. We shall use the notation $e_2(j\omega)/e_1(j\omega) \equiv e_2/e_1(j\omega) = G(j\omega)$ to signify this.

whose real part is the output results.

It is common practice to plot the frequency response function of Eq. 8.15 in the complex plane as a function of frequency (see Fig. 8.6). When so done, the result is sometimes called a *complex frequency locus*. Both the magnitude and phase data of Figs. 8.3 and 8.4 are contained in Fig. 8.6 but note, however, that frequency must be

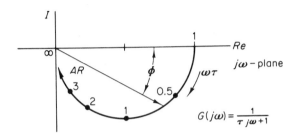

Fig. 8.6.   Complex locus for first order system.

marked on the plot. Note also that the complex locus or transfer locus of the first order system is a semicircle.

The information in Fig. 8.6 is also repeated in Fig. 8.19 which was prepared for both first and second order systems.

8.4   Steady State Solution Without Using Complex Number Representation

An alternate way of obtaining a steady state solution for Eq. 8.1 using e_1 in the form shown in Eq. 8.3,

$$e_1(t) = E_1 \cos \omega t \qquad (8.3)$$

can be developed without using rotating complex numbers. In Chap. 5 we showed that the steady state solution to a linear-constant-coefficient-differential equation must have the form

$$e_{2ss}(t) = \sum_{n=0}^{\infty} C_n \frac{d^n e_1(t)}{dt^n} \qquad (8.16)$$

That is, the steady state solution to this class of differential equations must be equal to a constant times the input, plus a constant times

This is a generalized way of writing the results of our search for steady state solutions in Chap. 5. You should verify this result. It works! Also note that $C_0 \, d^0 e_1(t)/dt^0 = C_0 e_1(t)$.

the first derivative of the input, plus a constant times the second derivative of the input, etc.

When $e_1(t)$ is given by Eq. 8.3 we can then assume that $e_{2ss}(t)$ will have the form

$$e_{2ss}(t) = C_0 E_1 \cos \omega t - C_1 \omega E_1 \sin \omega t$$

$$-C_2 \omega^2 E_1 \cos \omega t + C_2 \omega^3 E_1 \sin \omega t + \cdots \qquad (8.17)$$

Since for a given input amplitude E_1 and frequency ω, the higher order derivatives are just constants times $\cos \omega t$ or $\sin \omega t$, we can write $e_{2ss}(t)$ in a much simpler form:

$$e_{2ss}(t) = A_1 \cos \omega t + A_2 \sin \omega t \qquad (8.18)$$

We also showed in Chap. 5 that by substituting the steady state solution form $e_{2ss}(t)$ into the differential Eq. 8.1 we could obtain values for the unknown constants in this solution form. That is,

$$\tau \frac{de_{2ss}}{dt} + e_{2ss} = e_1 \qquad (8.19)$$

Using the assumed steady state solution form,

$$\frac{de_{2ss}}{dt} = -A_1 \omega \sin \omega t + A_2 \omega \cos \omega t \qquad (8.20)$$

Substituting Eqs. 8.18 and 8.20 into Eq. 8.19 yields

$$\tau(-A_1 \omega \sin \omega t + A_2 \omega \cos \omega t) + A_1 \cos \omega t + A_2 \sin \omega t = E_1 \cos \omega t$$
$$(8.21)$$

This equation must be true for all values of time t including $t = 0$. Substituting $t = 0$ in Eq. 8.21 we find, since $\sin(0) = 0$,

$$\tau A_2 \omega + A_1 = E_1 \qquad (8.22)$$

Likewise, the equation is also true for $t = \pi/2\omega$ where $\cos \omega t = 0$. Hence,

$$-\tau A_1 \omega + A_2 = 0 \qquad (8.23)$$

Solving these two equations for the constants A_1 and A_2 yields

$$A_1 = \frac{E_1}{\tau^2 \omega^2 + 1} \qquad (8.24a)$$

and

$$A_2 = \frac{E_1 \tau \omega}{\tau^2 \omega^2 + 1} \tag{8.24b}$$

Substituting these values into Eq. 8.18 yields the steady state solution.

$$e_{2ss}(t) = \frac{E_1}{\tau^2 \omega^2 + 1} (\cos \omega t + \tau \omega \sin \omega t) \tag{8.25}$$

However, it would be more convenient to have the solution in the form

$$e_{2ss}(t) = CE_1 \cos (\omega t + \Phi) \tag{8.26}$$

where C is the ratio of the output and input amplitudes and Φ is the phase angle between the output and input. The constants C and Φ determined by the correspondence between Eqs. 8.25 and 8.26 can be found in several ways. In Chap. 7 we showed this correspondence in Fig. 7.9. Referring to this figure we may write

$$C = \frac{\sqrt{1 + \tau^2 \omega^2}}{\tau^2 \omega^2 + 1} = \frac{1}{\sqrt{\tau^2 \omega^2 + 1}} \tag{8.27a}$$

and

$$\Phi = -\tan^{-1} \frac{\tau \omega}{1} \tag{8.27b}$$

Thus the steady state solution can be written as

$$e_{2ss}(t) = \frac{E_1}{\sqrt{(\omega \tau)^2 + 1}} \cos (\omega t - \tan^{-1} \omega \tau) \tag{8.28}$$

This is the same result as that obtained in Sec. 8.2.

8.5　The $j\omega$ Operator

The student has perhaps noticed the similarity between Eq. 8.15 which defines the frequency response function for a first order system and Eq. 8.2 which represents basically the differential equation using the D notation. When the D notation was introduced in Chap. 3, it was pointed out that it enabled the variables to be factored out and solved for explicitly. In Chap. 7 we noticed that the characteristic equation of the second order system (Eq. 7.9) was similar in form to the second order equation when written in D notation. All of this is a logical result of assuming a solution of exponential form as in Eq. 8.7. The

$j\omega$ in the exponent comes into the coefficient in algebraic form in exactly the way the D notation appears in the characteristic equation. This leads to the general conclusion that one may obtain the frequency response function in $j\omega$ directly from the differential equation when written in D notation by simply substituting $j\omega$ wherever D appears. Thus we could have derived Eq. 8.15 and the block diagram of Fig. 8.5 directly from Eq. 8.2 by substituting $j\omega$ for D. In other words, we *transformed* the *time domain* Eq. 8.2 into the *frequency domain* Eq. 8.15. This sort of transformation is a powerful analytical tool since it permits us to bypass the classical steady state solution of the differential equation and proceed immediately to the answer! The time domain differential equation is transformed into an algebraic equation in complex numbers or, in other words, into the complex frequency domain. This sort of transformation forms basis for the more general Fourier and Laplace transforms which will be studied in later courses. It is important for the student to recognize that the apparent simplicity of "plugging in" $j\omega$ wherever a D appears in the differential equation, has behind it the classical sinusoidal steady state solution theory.

8.6   Sinors and Phasors

The numerator and denominator of Eq. 8.15 each represent rotating complex numbers. Such complex numbers which rotate at constant speed and whose real and/or imaginary parts are used to represent sinusoidally varying functions are often called *sinors*. The ratio complex number which has been defined as the frequency response function and which is essentially a line segment fixed in space with magnitude and phase is called a *phasor*. Thus one may interpret Eq. 8.15 as follows: The sinor representing the output may be determined by multiplying the sinor of the input by the phasor which is a function of the system itself.

It is common practice in electrical engineering to deal almost exclusively with sinors and phasors rather than the real or imaginary parts which represent the time varying functions. It even becomes monotonous when dealing with sinors to carry the $e^{j\omega t}$ in every term. Thus, we sometimes find a sinor represented only by its amplitude vector. This can lead to considerable confusion because there is then no way to tell the fixed amplitude vector of a sinor from a phasor. We do not mean to confuse the student at this time, but rather to alert him to the need for referring all of the specially developed sinusoidal notations to basic time functions. Equation 8.29 repeats what has just been presented.

$$e_2(j\omega) = G(j\omega)e_1(j\omega) = \left(\frac{1}{\tau j\omega + 1}\right)E_1 e^{j\omega t} = E_2 e^{j\omega t} \qquad (8.29)$$

Phasor　Sinor　　　Sinor

8.7 Sinusoidal Solution by Means of Complex Conjugates (plus and minus ω)

We shall complete our analysis of the sinusoidal frequency response of the first order system by going back to Eq. 8.5 and assuming a solution of the form given in Eq. 8.30.

$$e_2 = \tfrac{1}{2}Ae^{j\omega t} + \tfrac{1}{2}A^* e^{-j\omega t} \qquad (8.30)$$

Substituting Eqs. 8.30 and 8.5 into Eq. 8.1 gives the following:

$$\tfrac{1}{2}j\omega\tau Ae^{j\omega t} - \tfrac{1}{2}j\omega\tau A^* e^{-j\omega t} + \tfrac{1}{2}Ae^{j\omega t} + \tfrac{1}{2}A^* e^{-j\omega t} = \tfrac{1}{2}E_1 e^{j\omega t} + \tfrac{1}{2}E_1 e^{-j\omega t}$$

or

$$(j\omega\tau A + A - E_1)e^{j\omega t} + [-j\omega\tau A^* + A^* - E_1]e^{-j\omega t} = 0 \qquad (8.31)$$

A with its conjugate A* is then defined from Eq. 8.31 by noting that since the equation is true for all time t, the coefficients of $e^{j\omega t}$ and $e^{-j\omega t}$ must each be zero, i.e.,

$$A = \left(\frac{1}{j\omega\tau + 1}\right)E_1 \qquad (8.32)$$

$$A^* = \left(\frac{1}{-j\omega\tau + 1}\right)E_1 \qquad (8.33)$$

We note that **A** is the same complex number assigned previously and the final results may be written as in Eq. 8.34.

$$e_2 = \left(\frac{E_1}{2}\right)\frac{1}{\sqrt{(\omega\tau)^2 + 1}}(e^{j(\omega t - \Phi)} + e^{-j(\omega t - \Phi)}) \qquad (8.34)$$

Thus, by assuming a solution which is the sum of two rotating conjugate complex numbers, we bypass the necessity of dealing with the real part of a single rotating line segment. On the other hand, we introduce further mathematical complexity and the notation of a complex number rotating at a negative frequency as well as one at a positive frequency. The frequency response function based on this point of view involves both the complex ratio contained in Eq. 8.32 and the ratio contained in Eq. 8.33 which involves negative frequency.

We shall restrict our analysis in this course to the previous type of analysis (Sec. 8.2–1) using a single rotating line segment and its real part. The latter analysis using positive and negative frequencies is introduced for information purposes only. A student may encounter the use of negative as well as positive frequencies in sinusoidal analysis in more advanced control and information theory and in circuit analysis. Equation 8.34 may be interpreted graphically as in Fig. 8.7.

Some of the concepts developed in this section will now be applied in a few examples.

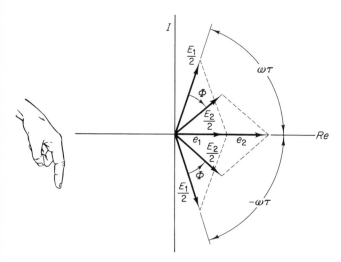

Fig. 8.7. Graphical interpretation of Eq. 8.34.

8.8 Examples of Frequency Response Solutions in First Order Systems

8.8–1 Audio Amplifier Coupling Circuit

Two *stages* in an audio amplifier are to be coupled by means of an *RC* circuit as shown in Fig. 8.8. $R = 10^6$ ohms. What value should *C* have to "pass" all frequencies above 10 cps? (Assume "pass" means

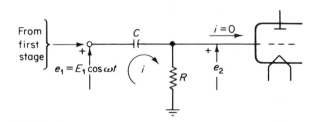

Fig. 8.8. Capacitor coupling circuit.

The figure shows that the real parts of the positive and negative frequency terms are equal while the imaginary parts are of opposite signs. The sum is then a real number as shown in Eq. 8.34.

that the amplitude ratio will be > 0.71.)

1) $$\left(\frac{1}{CD} + R\right) i = e_1$$

2) $$e_2 = iR = \frac{R}{1/CD + R} e_1 = \left(\frac{RCD}{1 + RCD}\right) e_1$$

3) $$\frac{e_2}{e_1}(j\omega) = \frac{RCj\omega}{1 + RCj\omega} = \frac{\omega RC e^{j\pi/2}}{\sqrt{1 + (RC\omega)^2}\, e^{j\Phi}} = \frac{\omega RC}{\sqrt{1 + (RC\omega)^2}} e^{j(\pi/2 - \Phi)}$$

where $\Phi = \tan^{-1} RC\omega$.

The design requirement is

4) $$\left|\frac{e_2}{e_1}\right| = \frac{\omega RC}{\sqrt{1 + (RC\omega)^2}} \geq 0.71 \qquad \begin{array}{l} \text{for } \omega > \omega_c \text{ where} \\ 10 \text{ cps} = 20\pi \text{ rad/sec} = \omega_c \end{array}$$

$R = 10^6$ ohms; thus, for $\omega = \omega_c$

$$\omega_c 10^6 C \geq 0.71 \sqrt{1 + (10^6 C \omega_c)^2}$$

$$\omega_c^2 10^{12} C^2 \geq 0.5(1 + 10^{12} C^2 \omega_c^2)$$

$$\omega_c^2 10^{12} C^2 = 1$$

5) $$C \geq \frac{10^{-6}}{\omega} = \frac{1}{20\pi} 10^{-6} \cong 0.016 \ \mu f$$

8.8-2 Two *RC* Circuits in Series

Figure 8.9 shows two *RC* circuits *coupled* by means of an *impedance changer* which serves only to accept an input voltage e_2 without draw-

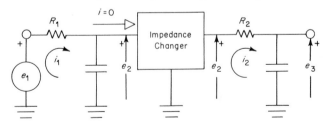

Fig. 8.9. Two RC circuits in series.

ing any current and applying e_2 as an input to the second *RC* circuit with whatever current i_2 is required. If $R_1 = 10^6$ ohms $= 1$ megohm, $R_2 = 0.5 \times 10^6$ ohms $= 0.5$ megohm, $C_1 = 100 \ \mu\mu f$ and $C_2 = 500 \ \mu\mu f$, what is the *frequency response* of e_3 (i.e., find e_3 when $e_1 = E_1 \cos \omega t$)?

From Eq. 8.15,

1) $$\frac{e_2}{e_1}(j\omega) = \frac{1}{\tau_1 j\omega + 1} \quad \text{and} \quad \frac{e_3}{e_2}(j\omega) = \frac{1}{\tau_2 j\omega + 1}$$

where

2) $$\tau_1 = (10^6)(100 \times 10^{-12}) = 10^{-4} \text{ sec}$$

$$\tau_2 = (0.5 \times 10^6)(500 \times 10^{-12}) = 2.50 \times 10^{-4} \text{ sec}$$

Note that

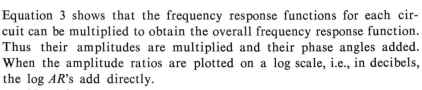

3) $$\frac{e_3}{e_1}(j\omega) = \frac{e_2}{e_1}(j\omega) \cdot \frac{e_3}{e_2}(j\omega) = \left(\frac{1}{\tau_1 j\omega + 1}\right)\left(\frac{1}{\tau_2 j\omega + 1}\right)$$

$$= \left[\frac{1}{\sqrt{(\tau_1 \omega)^2}}\right]\left[\frac{1}{\sqrt{(\tau_2 \omega)^2}}\right] e^{-j(\Phi_1 + \Phi_2)}$$

where

$$\Phi_1 = \tan^{-1} \omega\tau_1 \quad \text{and} \quad \Phi_2 = \tan^{-1} \omega\tau_2$$

Equation 3 shows that the frequency response functions for each circuit can be multiplied to obtain the overall frequency response function. Thus their amplitudes are multiplied and their phase angles added. When the amplitude ratios are plotted on a log scale, i.e., in decibels, the log *AR*'s add directly.

Note that

$$\tau_2 = 2.5 \, \tau_1$$

Using $\omega\tau_2$ as a reference we can sketch the overall frequency response as a function of the dimensionless frequency $\omega\tau_2$ directly from Fig. 8.4 as shown in Fig. 8.10.

8.8–3 DC Shunt Motor, Gears and Inertia

Figure 8.11 shows a DC shunt-wound motor loaded with an inertia J and a viscous damping B through a set of gears. Assuming the field current i_f is constant, neglecting the inductance of the armature, and assuming an armature resistance R_a, we may write the following somewhat simplified equations:

 Thus if we can factor $G(j\omega)$ into simple first order terms the log amplitude ratio and log frequency scales allow us to plot log *AR* and Φ for $G(j\omega)$ versus log ω by addition, using Fig. 8.4.

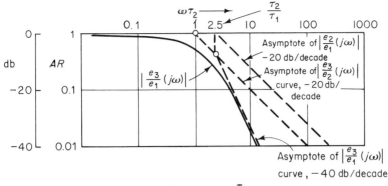

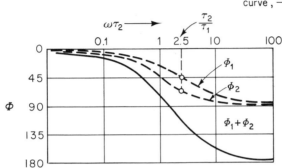

Fig. 8.10. Amplitude and phase plots for $(e_3/e_1)(j\omega)$ of Example 8.8–2.

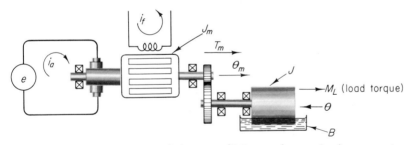

Fig. 8.11. A shunt wound DC motor driving a load inertia, J, through gear ratio, r.

(1) $e = i_a R_a + k_m \dot\theta_m$ where k_m is the back emf voltage constant

(2)   Torque on armature due to motor stator $= T_m = k_T i_a$

k_T is called the *torque constant*

(3) $\theta_m = r\theta$ $r = $ gear ratio $= \dfrac{\theta_m}{\theta} = \dfrac{D_{\text{gear}}}{D_{\text{pinion}}} = \dfrac{\text{teeth on gear}}{\text{teeth on pinion}}$

   We would like to determine the frequency response ratio between the output speed $\dot\theta$ and the input voltage e. Isolate the mechanical system as in Fig. 8.12.

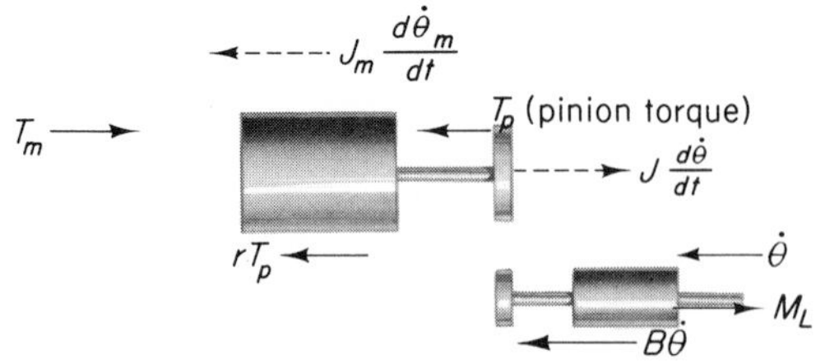

Fig. 8.12. Rigid body isolation of DC motor-gear-inertia system.

(4)
$$T_m = \frac{k_T}{R_a}(e - k_m\dot\theta_m) = \frac{k_T e}{R_a} - \frac{k_T k_m}{R_a}\dot\theta_m = T_p + J_m\frac{d\dot\theta_m}{dt}$$

(5)
$$J_m\frac{d\dot\theta_m}{dt} + \frac{k_T k_m}{R_a}\dot\theta_m + T_p = \frac{k_T e}{R_a}$$

(6)
$$J\frac{d\dot\theta}{dt} + B\dot\theta - rT_p = -M_L$$

Equations 5 and 6 yield

(7)
$$J\frac{d\dot\theta}{dt} + B\dot\theta + rJ_m\frac{d\dot\theta_m}{dt} + \frac{rk_T k_m}{R_a}\dot\theta_m = \frac{rk_T}{R_a}e - M_L$$

and remembering Eq. 3 we find

(8)
$$\underbrace{(J + r^2 J_m)}_{J_{eq}}\frac{d\dot\theta}{dt} + \underbrace{\left(B + \frac{r^2 k_T k_m}{R_a}\right)}_{B_{eq}}\dot\theta = \frac{rk_T}{R_a}e - M_L$$

Using D notation, we can write

(9)
$$(J_{eq}D + B_{eq})\dot\theta = \frac{rk_T}{R_a}e - M_L$$

or

(10)
$$(\tau D + 1)\dot\theta = \left(\frac{rk_T}{B_{eq}R_a}\right)e - \frac{M_L}{B_{eq}} \quad \text{where } \tau = \frac{J_{eq}}{B_{eq}}$$

If $e = E_1\cos\omega t$ and $M_L = 0$

(11)
$$\frac{\dot\theta}{e}(j\omega) = \left(\frac{rk_T}{B_{eq}R_a}\right)\left(\frac{1}{j\omega\tau + 1}\right) = \left|\frac{\dot\theta}{e}(j\omega)\right|e^{j\Phi}$$

(12) $\qquad \left| \dfrac{\dot{\theta}}{e}(j\omega) \right| = \left(\dfrac{rk_T}{B_{eq}R_a} \right) \dfrac{1}{\sqrt{(\omega\tau)^2 + 1}}, \qquad \Phi = -\tan^{-1}\omega\tau$

We see that Eq. 11 has turned out to be the familiar frequency response function for a first order system. Equation 12 gives the actual ratio of the amplitude of sinusoidal variation in speed $\dot{\theta}$ resulting from a sinusoidal variation in applied voltage e. Data for Eq. 12 could be read directly from Fig. 8.4 or easily calculated.

Some concluding remarks may be appropriate for this example. It is a typical example of how a rather complex engineering situation may be reduced to a form for which information already studied may be applied. It was probably not obvious at first glance that the system in Fig. 8.11 was really a simple first order system of the type studied in this chapter.

Equation 8 reveals some interesting facts. We note that the equivalent inertia J_{eq} includes the inertia of the motor multiplied by the square of the gear ratio. In many real systems where gear ratios may be large, say on the order of 100, it is apparent that the motor inertia, while it may be very much smaller than the inertia being driven, still may govern the dynamics of the system. Sometimes a term such as r^2J_m is referred to as a *reflected inertia*, i.e., it is the inertia as "seen" by the load through the gear train. We also see in Eq. 8 that while the motor was assumed to have no viscous damping, the back emf acts as if it were damping the system. It appears in the equivalent damping in the same way as the load damping B. It also is multiplied by the gear ratio squared so, in fact, may dominate the dynamics of the system. The actual time constant may then be determined more by the back emf and inertia of the motor than by the damping and inertia in the load. In many systems this is a very good thing because damping is desired to make the system more stable but load damping when applied dissipates a great deal of power since it is essentially a friction drag on the output. When damping is obtained through the back emf, it is done so without penalty of power consumption.

We shall return to this example in a later example when we study the concept of a simple servomechanism.

8.9 Sinusoidal Frequency Response of Second Order Systems

With the techniques and theory developed in Sec. 8.2, we are ready to write the frequency response function for a second order system immediately on inspection by replacing with $j\omega$'s the D's found in equations of the form of Eqs. 7.5 and 7.6. However, we shall not take this easy way out but rather compromise by solving Eqs. 7.5 and 7.6 for sinusoidal inputs assuming that the outputs may be represented as the real parts of rotating vectors. We shall not use the complex conjugate procedure presented in Sec. 8.7 in Eqs. 8.30–8.34 nor shall we use the method of Chap. 5 although these approaches are perfectly applicable in the case of second order systems.

Since we propose to solve Eqs. 7.5 and 7.6 assuming sinusoidal inputs, we ought to modify the two systems shown in Fig. 7.3 (from which the equations were derived) so that the assumption of sinusoidal inputs is more appropriate. We can do this by:

(1) adding to Fig. 7.3(a), a moving frame which oscillates sinusoidally.
(2) replacing the parallel *RLC* circuit of Fig. 7.3(b) with its series equivalent circuit.

These modifications are shown in Fig. 8.13. We shall see in some later examples that the system of Fig. 8.13(a) is representative of a wide variety of seismic instruments, or transducers.

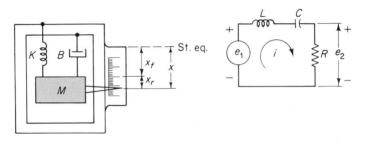

The inputs are:

$$x_f = x_{af} \cos \omega t = x_{af}\, Re\, e^{j\omega t} \qquad e_1 = E_1 \cos \omega t = E_1\, Re\, e^{j\omega t}$$

$$\ddot{x}_f = -\omega^2 x_{af} \cos \omega t = -\omega^2 x_{af}\, Re\, e^{j\omega t} \qquad \dot{e}_1 = -\omega E_1 \sin \omega t = \omega E_1\, Re j e^{j\omega t}$$

(a)   (b)

Fig. 8.13. (a) Seismic mechanical second order system. (b) Series *RLC* circuit.

We shall derive the differential equations for the two new systems shown in Fig. 8.13 in parallel. In the mechanical system note that the new variable x_r, the displacement of the mass relative to the frame, has been introduced. The figure shows this relative variable x_r and also x, the absolute position of the mass relative to fixed space, hence $x = x_r + x_f$. For a sinusoidal input, $x_f = x_{af} \cos \omega t$, the differential equations describing the systems in Fig. 8.13 may be derived using the free body diagram as shown in Fig. 8.A and the loop law in the sequence of Eqs. 8.35–8.43.

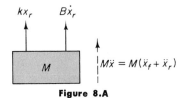

Figure 8.A

$$L\frac{di}{dt} + Ri + \frac{1}{C}\int i\,dt = e_1 = E_1 \cos \omega t = e_2 = iR \qquad (8.35)$$

$$M\ddot{x}_r + B\dot{x}_r + Kx_r = M\ddot{x}_f = M\omega^2 x_{af}\cos \omega t \qquad (8.36)$$

$$\left[LD^2 + RD + \frac{1}{C}\right]i = -\omega E_1 \sin \omega t \qquad (8.37)$$

$$\left[D^2 + \frac{B}{M}D + \frac{K}{M}\right]x_r = \omega^2 x_{af}\cos \omega t \qquad (8.38)$$

$$\left[D^2 + \frac{R}{L}D + \frac{1}{LC}\right]e_2 = -\omega\frac{RE_1}{L}\sin \omega t \qquad (8.39)$$

$$[D^2 + 2\zeta\omega_n D + \omega_n^2]x_r = \omega^2 x_{af}\cos \omega t \qquad (8.40)$$

$$[D^2 + 2\zeta\omega_n D + \omega_n^2]e_2 = -2\zeta_n\omega_n E_1 \sin \omega t \qquad (8.41)$$

where

$$\omega_n = \sqrt{\frac{K}{M}} \quad \text{and} \quad \zeta = \frac{B}{2\sqrt{KM}}$$

and

$$\omega_n = \sqrt{\frac{1}{LC}} \quad \text{and} \quad \zeta = \frac{R}{2}\sqrt{\frac{C}{L}}$$

$$[D^2 + 2\zeta\omega_n D + \omega_n^2]x_r = \omega^2 x_{af}\,\text{Re}\,e^{j\omega t} \qquad (8.42)$$

$$[D^2 + 2\zeta\omega_n D + \omega_n^2]e_2 = 2\zeta\omega_n\omega E_1\,\text{Re}\,je^{j\omega t} \qquad (8.43)$$

Equations 8.42 and 8.43 have been reduced to the simplest possible form and are as much alike as possible. We see the left-hand or charac-

---

Verify that $-\sin \omega t = \text{Re}\,je^{j\omega t}$. ☆

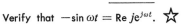

teristic sides are identical and the right-hand sides have been reduced to sinusoidally varying inputs of amplitudes as defined. We note that because of the extra differentiation required in the electrical circuit to bring it into second order form, the input cosine is differentiated once so that it may be considered as a negative input sine. This is taken care of in Eq. 8.43 by means of the j which we have seen previously results from differentiation and can be interpreted as a unit vector at 90° which advances the phase angle by 90° as required by the cosine to sine transformation.

8.9-1   MECHANICAL SYSTEM SOLUTION

We shall proceed with the analysis of Eq. 8.42 for the mechanical system. As before we shall assume a solution for the steady state response which is sinusoidal at the frequency of the input but with a different amplitude and phase angle as represented by a complex coefficient A. Thus x_r may be assumed as in Eq. 8.44.

$$x_r \equiv x_{rss} = \text{Re } \mathbf{A}e^{j\omega t} \tag{8.44}$$

As before, if the real part of the rotating complex number is to represent a solution, the complex number itself must also be a solution for a differential equation. We therefore define $x_r(j\omega)$ as in Eq. 8.45.

$$x_r(j\omega) = \mathbf{A}e^{j\omega t} \tag{8.45}$$

Substituting Eq. 8.45 into Eq. 8.42 gives the following definition for the complex coefficient A as in Eq. 8.47.

$$(j\omega)^2 \mathbf{A}e^{j\omega t} + 2\zeta\omega_n j\omega \mathbf{A}e^{j\omega t} + \omega_n^2 \mathbf{A}e^{j\omega t} = \omega^2 x_{af} e^{j\omega t} \tag{8.46}$$

$$\mathbf{A} = \left[\frac{1}{2j\zeta\omega_n\omega + \omega_n^2 - \omega^2}\right]\omega^2 x_{af} \tag{8.47}$$

Let us define a new parameter or ratio of parameters, β, the ratio of the applied frequency ω to the natural frequency ω_n of the second order system as in Eq. 8.48.

$$\beta \equiv \frac{\omega}{\omega_n} \equiv \frac{\omega}{(K/M)^{1/2}} \tag{8.48}$$

Dividing numerator and denominator of Eq. 8.47 by ω_n^2 and introducing the β notation results in Eq. 8.49.

$$\mathbf{A} = \left[\frac{1}{j2\zeta\beta + 1 - \beta^2}\right]\beta^2 x_{af} \tag{8.49}$$

The complex number in the denominator of the expression in the brackets of Eq. 8.49 may be replaced by a magnitude and phase as in Eq. 8.50.

$$\mathbf{A} = \left(\frac{1}{\sqrt{(2\zeta\beta)^2 + (1 - \beta^2)^2} \ e^{j\Phi}} \right) \beta^2 x_{af} = x_{af} \left[\frac{1}{\sqrt{(2\zeta\beta)^2 + (1 - \beta^2)^2}} \right] \beta^2 e^{-j\Phi}$$

(8.50)

where

$$j\Phi = \tan^{-1} \frac{2\zeta\beta}{1 - \beta^2}$$

The factor in the brackets in Eq. 8.50 is sometimes called the magnification factor and given the single symbol, μ, as in Eq. 8.51, since it appears so often in the frequency response analysis of second order systems.

$$\mu \equiv \frac{1}{[(2\zeta\beta)^2 + (1 - \beta^2)^2]^{1/2}}$$

(8.51)

The final steady state response equation may then be written by substituting back into Eq. 8.44 to give Eq. 8.52.

$$x_r = x_{af} \mu\beta^2 \operatorname{Re} e^{j(\omega t - \Phi)} = x_{af} \mu\beta^2 \cos(\omega t - j\Phi)$$

(8.52)

The ratio of the amplitude of x_r, x_{ar} to the exciting amplitude x_{af} is then seen from Eq. 8.52 to be as in Eq. 8.53.

$$\left| \frac{x_r}{x_f} \right| = \frac{x_{ar}}{x_{af}} = \mu\beta^2$$

(8.53)

The significance of this ratio as a measure of the performance of a seismic vibrometer will be brought out in later examples. The non-dimensional parameter $\mu\beta^2$ has been plotted in some detail in Fig. 8.14 as a function of dimensionless frequency β and damping ratio ζ.

Notice that for $\beta \gg 1$, that is for input frequencies ω above the natural frequency ω_n, the amplitude of $x_r(t)$ is nearly equal to the amplitude of $x_f(t)$. For $\beta \ll 1$, i.e., for input frequencies below the natural frequency,

$$x_{ar} = \beta^2 x_{af}$$

or since

$$x_f = x_{af} \cos \omega t$$

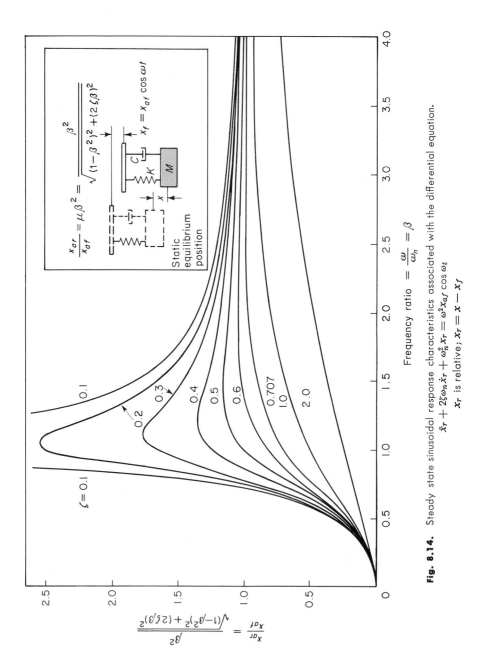

Fig. 8.14. Steady state sinusoidal response characteristics associated with the differential equation.

$$\ddot{x}_r + 2\zeta\omega_n\dot{x}_r + \omega_n^2 x_r = \omega^2 x_{af}\cos\omega t$$

$$x_r \text{ is relative; } x_r = x - x_f$$

and

$$\ddot{x}_f = -x_{af}\omega^2 \cos \omega t$$

the amplitude of $x_r(t)$ is nearly proportional to the amplitude of $\ddot{x}_f(t)$.

For $\beta \approx 1$, the relationship between the amplitude of $x_r(t)$ and the amplitude of $x_f(t)$ depends greatly on damping ratio ζ. Thus the output amplitude x_r can be a measure of the input x_f or its acceleration $\ddot{x}_f$ depending on the magnitude of β. Thus β determines the function of the system.

8.9-2 ELECTRICAL SYSTEM SOLUTION

We now return to Eq. 8.43 for the *RLC* series circuit of Fig. 8.13(b) and assume a solution of a form similar to that in Eq. 8.44 as in Eq. 8.54.

$$e_2 = e_{2ss} = \text{Re } \mathbf{A}je^{j\omega t} \tag{8.54}$$

The extra j in the assumed form in Eq. 8.54 is introduced because we know that the input function contains a j in the same place and we wish to cancel the whole form when substituted back. This is merely another way of writing that the output response will be a *sine wave* with respect to the original input *cosine* voltage.

As before the complex number itself satisfies the differential equation so we may write the input and output as frequency functions in Eq. 8.55.

$$e_2(j\omega) = \mathbf{A}je^{j\omega t} \quad \text{and} \quad e_1(j\omega) = 2\zeta\omega_n\omega E_1 je^{j\omega t} \tag{8.55}$$

Equation 8.55 substituted back into Eq. 8.43 permits a definition of the complex coefficient $\mathbf{A}$ as follows in Eq. 8.56.

$$(j\omega)^2 \mathbf{A}je^{j\omega t} + 2\zeta\omega_n j\omega \mathbf{A}je^{j\omega t} + \omega_n^2 \mathbf{A}je^{j\omega t} = 2\zeta\omega_n \omega E_1 je^{j\omega t}$$

$$\mathbf{A} = \left[\frac{1}{2j\zeta\omega_n\omega + \omega_n^2 - \omega^2}\right] 2\zeta\omega_n\omega E_1 \tag{8.56}$$

Introducing the frequency ratio β gives Eq. 8.57.

$$\mathbf{A} = \left[\frac{1}{2j\zeta\beta + 1 - \beta^2}\right] 2\zeta\beta E_1 \tag{8.57}$$

In terms of μ previously defined we can replace the complex number in the brackets of Eq. 8.57 and write Eq. 8.58 where μ and Φ are defined as before in Eqs. 8.50 and 8.51.

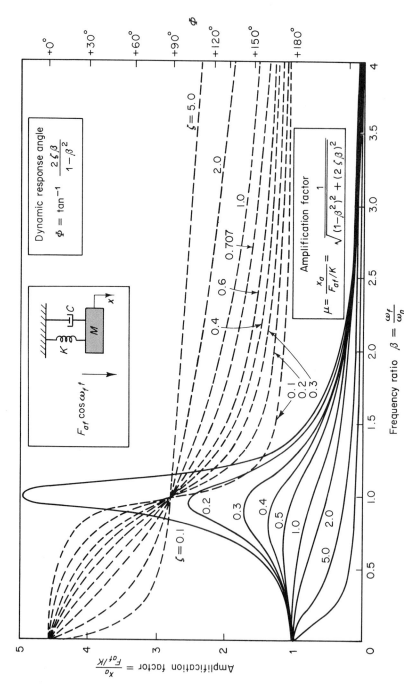

Fig. 8.15. Steady state sinusoidal response characteristics associated with differential equation

$$\ddot{x} + 2\zeta\omega_n\dot{x} + \omega_n^2 x = \frac{F_{aF}}{M}\cos\omega_f t$$

Dynamic response angle

$$\Phi = \tan^{-1}\frac{2\zeta\beta}{1-\beta^2}$$

Amplification factor

$$\mu = \frac{x_a}{F_{af}/K} = \frac{1}{\sqrt{(1-\beta^2)^2 + (2\zeta\beta)^2}}$$

Frequency ratio $\beta = \dfrac{\omega_f}{\omega_n}$

$F_{af}\cos\omega_f t$

Amplification factor $= \dfrac{x_a}{F_{af}/K}$

$$\mathbf{A} = \mu 2\zeta\beta E_1 e^{-j\Phi} \tag{8.58}$$

where

$$\Phi = \tan^{-1}\frac{2\zeta\beta}{1-\beta^2}$$

The final answer for the voltage response may then be written as in Eq. 8.59.

$$e_2 = 2\zeta\beta E_1 \mu \operatorname{Re} je^{j(\omega t - \Phi)} = -2\zeta\beta\mu E_1 \sin(\omega t - \Phi) \tag{8.59}$$

The input-output voltage ratio and phase angle of the series *RLC* circuit of Fig. 8.13(b) can then be written from Eq. 8.59 as in Eq. 8.60. Phase angle $= \pi/2 - \Phi$ where

$$\left|\frac{e_2}{e_1}\right| = \frac{E_2}{E_1} = -2\zeta\beta\mu \qquad \Phi = \tan^{-1}\frac{2\zeta\beta}{1-\beta^2} \tag{8.60}$$

The amplification factor μ has appeared in both of the response functions derived. It appears in almost every similar situation. For this reason special plots of μ as a function of β are provided. Figure 8.15 gives μ versus β on a linear scale. The angle Φ is also plotted versus β. Note that this angle Φ in terms of ζ and β is the same as defined for the mechanical system just studied. Note that Fig. 8.15 is presented as a response of a second order mechanical system to a sinusoidally varying force. Not only may this figure be interpreted as a general plot of a nondimensional ratio μ but it is also the specific amplitude ratio plot for the mechanical system indicated. The student may verify this as an exercise. Also see Ex. 8.11–1.

As in the case of the first order system it is desirable to plot μ and the angle Φ on logarithmic scales. Such plots allow multiplication of frequency response functions by means of addition of logarithms and addition or subtraction of phase angles.* They, of course, provide specific numerical data for problem solving. Figure 8.16 is the logarithmic plot for the amplification factor μ and Fig. 8.17 gives the phase angle data. Note that the first order system amplitude ratio and phase angles are also plotted on these figures as previously mentioned.

The point, $\beta = 1$, is of interest for when $\beta \ll 1$, and $\zeta < 1$, $\mu \approx 1$, and when $\beta \gg 1$ and $\zeta < 1$, $\mu \approx 1/\beta^2$. Thus two straight lines, one horizontal at $\mu = 1$ and the other of slope -0.01 per decade, intersecting at $\beta = 1$ define asymptotes that show the general shape of the log μ versus log β curve. The second order system may be said to "fall

---

*See Ex. 8.8–2

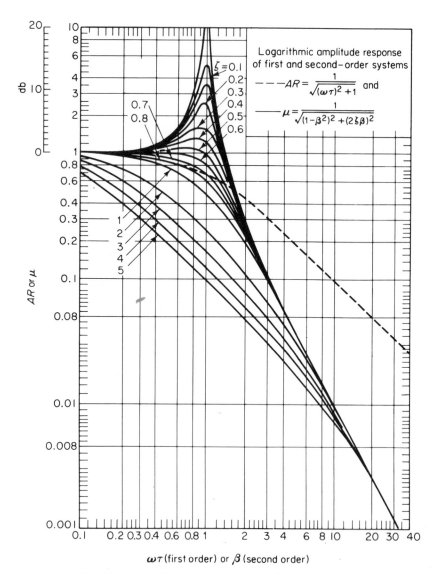

Fig. 8.16. Amplification factor, μ, versus frequency ratio, β.

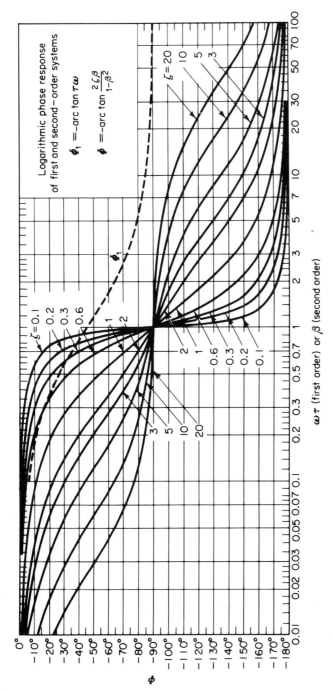

Fig. 8.17. Phase angle, Φ, for second order systems versus frequency ratio, β.

Logarithmic phase response
of first and second-order systems

$$\Phi_1 = -\arc\tan\tau\omega$$

$$\Phi = -\arc\tan\frac{2\zeta\beta}{1-\beta^2}$$

261

off" at frequencies above $\beta > 3$ or so at the rate of 40 db/decade or 12 db/octave.

8.10 Second Order System Frequency Response Function

As pointed out in the beginning, we could have obtained Eqs. 8.47 and 8.56 directly by substituting $j\omega$ for D in Eqs. 8.42 and 8.43. This will result immediately in Eqs. 8.61, 8.62, and 8.63; and in Eqs. 8.64, 8.65, and 8.66:

(1) Mechanical

$$\frac{x_r(j\omega)}{x_f(j\omega)} = \frac{x_r(j\omega)}{\omega^2 x_{af} e^{j\omega t}} = \frac{1}{(j\omega)^2 + 2\zeta\omega_n(j\omega) + \omega_n^2} = \frac{1/\omega_n^2}{j2\zeta\beta + 1 - \beta^2} \qquad (8.61)$$

$$x_r(j\omega) = \left[\frac{1}{j2\zeta\beta + 1 - \beta^2}\right] \frac{\omega^2}{\omega_n^2} x_{af} e^{j\omega t} \qquad (8.62)$$

from which

$$x_r = \mu\beta^2 x_{af} \operatorname{Re} e^{j(\omega t - \Phi)} = \mu\beta^2 x_{af} \cos(\omega t - \Phi) \qquad (8.63)$$

(2) Electrical

$$\frac{e_2(j\omega)}{e_1(j\omega)} = \frac{e_2(j\omega)}{2\zeta\omega_n \omega E_1 j e^{j\omega t}} = \frac{1}{(j\omega)^2 + 2\zeta\omega_n(j\omega) + \omega_n^2} = \frac{1/\omega_n^2}{j2\zeta\beta + 1 - \beta^2} \qquad (8.64)$$

$$e_2(j\omega) = \left[\frac{1}{j2\zeta\beta + 1 - \beta^2}\right] 2\zeta \frac{\omega}{\omega_n} E_1 j e^{j\omega t} \qquad (8.65)$$

from which

$$e_2 = \mu 2\zeta\beta E_1 \operatorname{Re} j e^{j(\omega t - \Phi)} = -2\zeta\beta\mu E_1 \sin(\omega t - \Phi) \qquad (8.66)$$

Equations 8.63 and 8.66 are the same as the solution we obtained for the mechanical and electrical systems previously by a somewhat more arduous approach. The implication of the foregoing is that for sinusoidal frequency response, all second order systems may be reduced to a form which may be represented by the simple block notation of Fig. 8.18.

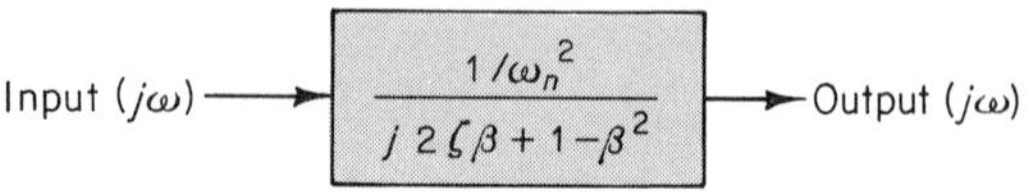

Input $(j\omega)$ ⟶ $\boxed{\dfrac{1/\omega_n^2}{j\,2\zeta\beta + 1 - \beta^2}}$ ⟶ Output $(j\omega)$

Fig. 8.18. Frequency response function of a second order system.

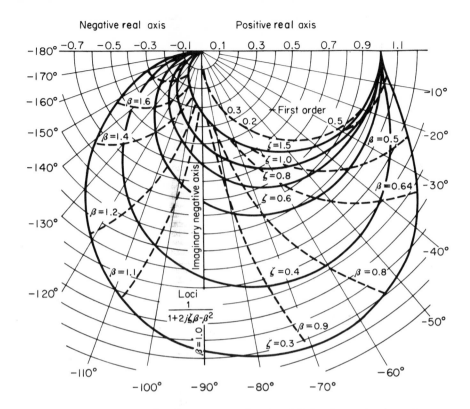

Fig. 8.19. Frequency response function of first and second order systems.

The frequency response function multiplied by ω_n^2 which is a complex number may be plotted in a complex plane. This has been done in Fig. 8.19 for the second order system where μ in its complex form is plotted as a function of β for various values of ζ. Also shown is the frequency response function for the first order system, where $\beta \equiv \tau\omega$.

8.11   Examples of Frequency Response Analysis of Second Order Systems

8.11–1   FORCED TORSIONAL OSCILLATIONS (see Fig. 8.20)

$$J\ddot{\theta} + B\dot{\theta} + K\theta = M_{af}\,\mathrm{Re}\,e^{j\omega t}$$

$$(D^2 + 2\zeta\omega_n D + \omega_n^2)\theta = \frac{M_{af}}{J}\,\mathrm{Re}\,e^{j\omega t}$$

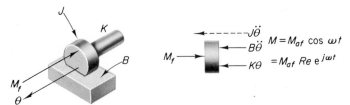

Fig. 8.20.　Forced torsional system.

where $\omega_n = \sqrt{K/J}$ and $\zeta = B/2\sqrt{KJ}$

From Eqs. 8.42 and 8.61 we may write immediately

$$\frac{\theta(j\omega)}{M_f(j\omega)} = \frac{\theta(j\omega)}{(M_{af}/J)e^{j\omega t}} = \left(\frac{1/\omega_n^2}{j2\zeta\beta + 1 - \beta^2}\right)$$

$$\theta(j\omega) = \left[\frac{1}{j2\zeta\beta + 1 - \beta^2}\right]\frac{M_{af}J}{JK}e^{j\omega t} = \mu e^{-j\Phi}\frac{M_{af}}{K}e^{j\omega t}$$

where

$$\Phi = \tan^{-1}\frac{2\zeta\beta}{1 - \beta^2} \qquad \text{(see Fig. 8.17)} \qquad (8.67)$$

$$\theta(t) = \mu\frac{M_{af}}{K}\text{Re } e^{j(\omega t - \Phi)} = \mu\frac{M_{af}}{K}\cos(\omega t - \Phi)$$

$$\left|\frac{\theta}{M_f/K}\right| = \frac{\theta_a}{M_{af}/K} = \mu \qquad \text{(see Figs. 8.15 and 8.16)} \qquad (8.68)$$

Note that this solution is identical to that for the forced linear system in Fig. 8.21 with the specified changes in variables and parameters.

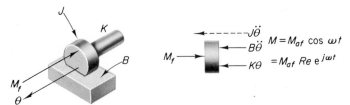

$$\theta \rightarrow x$$
$$M_f \rightarrow F_f = F_{af}\cos\omega t$$
$$J \rightarrow M$$
$$B \rightarrow B$$
$$K \rightarrow K$$

$$\frac{\theta_a}{M_{af}/K} \qquad \frac{x_a}{F_{af}/K} = \mu$$

$F_f = F_{af}\cos\omega t$

Fig. 8.21.　Forced mechanical system.

The amplitude ratio given in Eq. 8.68 above is worth special attention. Figure 8.15 shows the phenomenon of resonance. Note that the *maximum amplitude* occurs at the natural frequency ($\beta = 1$) only for values of ζ near zero. As ζ increases, the maximum amplitude shifts to frequencies (β) somewhat lower than the natural frequency. This fact raises the question "Does resonance occur at the natural frequency or at the frequency of maximum amplitude of oscillation?" A peculiar characteristic of the phase (see Fig. 8.17) is used to settle this question. Note that all phase curves intersect at 90° at $\beta = 1$. Experimentally it is often easier to detect the 90° phase shift than it is to detect a maximum amplitude. For this reason the *resonant frequency* and the *natural frequency* are defined as the same thing, and *resonance* occurs only at $\beta = 1$. The amplitude ratio at this frequency is given by

$$\mu|_{\beta=1} = AR|_{\beta=1} = \frac{1}{2\zeta}$$

The frequency at which the maximum amplitude occurs (found by setting $d\mu/d\beta = 0$) is

$$\beta|_{\mu_{\max}} = \sqrt{1 - 2\zeta^2}$$

8.11-2 TRANSMITTED FORCE IN MECHANICAL SYSTEMS

Figure 8.22 is intended to represent an unbalanced machine resting on shock mounts. We shall assume vertical motions only (even though rotating unbalance produces horizontal components of force). Rotor unbalance is given as wr which may be visualized as a weight w located a distance r from the center of rotation, since $w/g = m$ (see Fig. 8.B)

$$M\ddot{x} + B\dot{x} + Kx = m\omega^2 r \cos \omega t = m\omega^2 r \, \text{Re} \, e^{j\omega t}$$

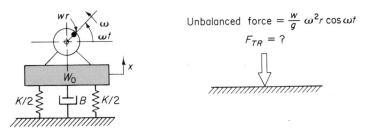

Fig. 8.22. An unbalanced machine shock mounted from the floor.

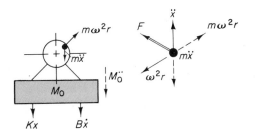

Figure 8.B.

$$[D^2 + 2\zeta\omega_n D + 1]x = \frac{m}{M}\omega^2 r \, \mathrm{Re} \, e^{j\omega t}$$

$$x(j\omega) = \left[\frac{1}{j2\zeta\beta + 1 - \beta^2}\right]\frac{1}{\omega_n^2} \cdot \frac{m}{M}\omega^2 r e^{j\omega t}$$

$$x(j\omega) = \mu\beta^2 \frac{m}{M} r e^{j(\omega t - \Phi)}$$

$$\frac{x_a}{(w/W_0)r} = \mu\beta^2 = \frac{\text{amplitude of machine vibration, } x_a}{\text{ratio of unbalance, } wr, \text{ to machine weight, } W_0}$$

Now force transmitted to ground, $F_{TR} = Kx + B\dot{x} = (K + BD)x$, and

$$F_{TR}(j\omega) = (K + Bj\omega)x(j\omega)$$

$$F_{TR}(j\omega) = (K + Bj\omega)\mu\beta^2 \frac{m}{M} r e^{j(\omega t - \Phi)}$$

$$F_{TR}(j\omega) = (1 + j2\zeta\beta)\mu \frac{\omega^2}{\omega_n^2} \cdot \frac{K}{M} \cdot mr e^{j(\omega t - \Phi)}$$

$$F_{TR}(j\omega) = \sqrt{1 + (2\zeta\beta)^2} \, e^{j\alpha} \mu\omega^2 mr e^{j(\omega t - \Phi)}$$

where $\alpha = \tan^{-1} 2\zeta\beta$.

$$F_{TR}(j\omega) = \sqrt{1 + (2\zeta\beta)^2} \, \mu\omega^2 mr \, \mathrm{Re} \, e^{j(\omega t - \Phi + \alpha)}$$

$$\left|\frac{F_{TR}}{\omega^2 mr}\right| = \mu\sqrt{1 + (2\zeta\beta)^2} \tag{8.69}$$

Equation 8.69 above shows the ratio of the amplitude of the force transmitted to the floor to the unbalanced force as a function of ζ and β. Note how working with frequency functions (rotating vectors) leads directly to amplitude ratios and phase angles.

The object in most vibration isolation problems is to make $|F_{TR}/\omega^2 mr|$ very small by selecting K and B to make β large for a given rotor speed ω.

8.11-3 VIBROMETER

Figure 8.23 shows some examples of ways that seismic instruments have been constructed. Seismic instruments are used to measure vibration when it is impossible to obtain a fixed frame of reference, for example on the wing of an airplane. Many other possibilities exist, such as the seismographs for detecting earth vibrations. They are all described by the same differential equation, Eq. 8.36 or Eq. 8.42 repeated on p. 267.

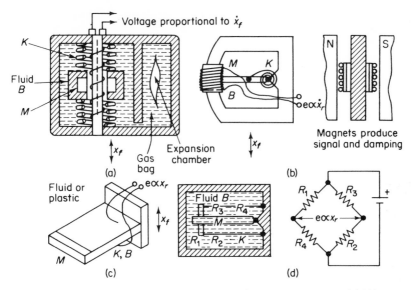

Fig. 8.23. Some examples of seismic instruments: (a) Vibrometer; magnetic mass is spring suspended around coil in damping fluid. (b) Vibrometer; mass is a horizontal pendulum with torsional spring at pivot; coil is moved between magnets. Damping is produced by eddy currents in aluminum coil form. (c) Vibrometer or accelerometer; mass on end of Rochele salt or barium titinate piezo-electric crystal. (d) Accelerometer; mass is horizontal pendulum supported by strain gage wires which act as springs and produce signal.

$$[D^2 + 2\zeta\omega_n D + \omega_n^2]\,x_r = \omega^2 x_{af}\mathrm{Re}\,e^{j\omega t}$$

We may write

$$x_r(j\omega) = \left[\frac{1}{j2\zeta\beta + 1 - \beta^2}\right]\frac{\omega^2 x_{af}}{\omega_n^2}\,e^{j\omega t}$$

and

$$x_r = \mu\frac{\omega^2 x_{af}}{\omega_n^2}\,\mathrm{Re}\,e^{j(\omega t - \phi)}$$

Many times we desire the magnitude of x_r, x_{ar} to be proportional to x_{af}. When a seismic instrument is used thus it is called a *vibrometer*. Of main interest is the ratio of x_{ar} (measured electrically in the instrument) and x_{af} (the amplitude of applied vibration) which is for system shown in Fig. 8.13,

$$\frac{x_{ar}}{x_{af}} = \mu\beta^2 \qquad \text{(see Fig. 8.14)}$$

For the widest range of use, we would like $\mu\beta^2$ to be as near unity as possible. This results if $\zeta = 0.71$ which is a design parameter in vibrometers. Inspection of Fig. 8.14 shows $\mu\beta^2$ is "near" unity for $\beta > 2.0$ if $\zeta = 0.71$ as shown in Fig. 8.C. We see that ω_n in a vibrometer should be at least $\frac{1}{2}$ of the lowest frequency to be measured.

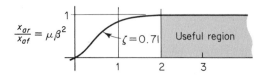

Figure 8.C

8.11-4 ACCELEROMETER

In an accelerometer we wish x_{ar} to be proportional to $\ddot{x}_{af}$ or $\omega^2 x_{af}$ for sinusoidal oscillations. The equation for x_r above can be rewritten to form this ratio.

$$\frac{x_{ar}}{\omega^2 x_{af}} = \frac{x_{ar}}{\ddot{x}_{ar}} = \mu \frac{1}{\omega_n^2}$$

For the widest range of use, an accelerometer should be designed so that μ/ω_n^2 is unity over the widest frequency range possible. This occurs for $\mu \cong 1$. Inspection of Fig. 8.15 shows this happens $\zeta = 0.71$ as before and for $\beta \leq 0.5$ as shown in Fig. 8.D. The conclusion is that for an accelerometer, $\zeta = 0.71$ and ω_n should be as high as possible or at least twice the maximum frequency to be measured. Note, however, that x_{ar} is inversely proportional to ω_n^2 which means that the higher ω_n is, the lower the signal produced. Thus the designer of an accelerometer must compromise between effective frequency range and instrument sensitivity. For this reason manufacturers usually supply a number of different accelerometers.

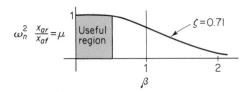

Figure 8.D

8.11-5 PHASE EFFECTS IN VIBROMETERS AND ACCELEROMETERS

The same phase angle curves apply in both the vibrometer and accelerometer but the instruments are used at different regions in the curve. The phase curve for $\zeta = 0.71$ is shown in Fig. 8.E:

The figure shows that a vibrometer essentially shifts phase by

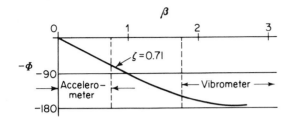

Figure 8.E

$-180°$ at all frequencies while the accelerometer has associated with it a phase angle shift which is approximately linear with frequency where $\Phi = +\pi/2\beta$.* This fact becomes very important when these instruments are used to measure periodic waves which are composed of sine waves of different frequencies. In the case of the vibrometer, each *harmonic component* will be shifted $-180°$ or so but each $-180°$ angle represents a different time ($T = \pi/\omega$). Thus the output wave will be badly distorted in shape! In the case of the accelerometer all is well, for while each component may be shifted through a different angle (proportional to ω), the time shift of each component is nearly identical since T is proportional to $1/\omega$.

8.11–6   SIMPLE POSITION SERVOMECHANISM SYSTEM

The system shown in Fig. 8.24 is a *closed-loop servomechanism* built around the *DC* motor-gear-inertia system of Fig. 8.11, Ex. 8.8–3. The output position θ_C is compared on a potentiometer with an input reference signal θ_R. A voltage, $e_p = k_p(\theta_R - \theta_C)$, is fed into an amplifier with voltage gain A. The amplifier supplies armature current i_a to the motor at a voltage $e = A e_p$. We shall study the performance of this servo system in terms of two *input* quantities: (1) θ_R, reference input angle and (2) M_L, externally applied load torque. θ_C is given in terms of M_L and e in Ex. 8.8–3 as follows:

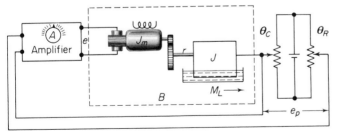

Fig. 8.24. Position servomechanism. DC motor system of Fig. 8.11 is made into a closed loop system.

*For $\beta < 1.5$

$$(\tau D + 1)\dot{\theta}_C = \left(\frac{rk_T}{B_{eq}R_a}\right)e - \frac{M_L}{B_{eq}}$$

where

$$\tau = \frac{J_{eq}}{B_{eq}}$$

$$J_{eq} = J + r^2 J_m$$

$$B_{eq} = \left(B + \frac{r^2 k_T k_m}{R_a}\right)$$

$J =$ load inertia $k_T =$ motor torque constant

$J_m =$ motor inertia $k_m =$ motor back emf constant

$r =$ gear ratio $R_a =$ armature resistance

$B =$ viscous damping of load

In terms of θ_C we may write

$$(\tau D + 1)D\theta_C = \left(\frac{rk_T}{B_{eq}R_a}\right)e - \frac{M_L}{B_{eq}}$$

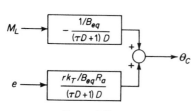

Figure 8.F

This equation may be put into a block diagram as in Fig. 8.F: We note that

$$e = Ak_p(\theta_R - \theta_C)$$

which allows us to draw a complete block diagram as in Fig. 8.G: where

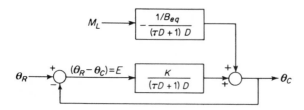

Figure 8.G

$$K = \frac{Ak_p rk_T}{B_{eq}R_a} = \text{system gain}\left[\frac{1}{\text{sec}}\right]$$

From the diagram we may write

$$\theta_C = \frac{K}{(\tau D + 1)D}(\theta_R - \theta_C) - \frac{1/B_{eq}}{(\tau D + 1)D} M_L$$

or

$$\left[1 + \frac{K}{(\tau D + 1)D}\right]\theta_C = \frac{K}{(\tau D + 1)D}\theta_R - \frac{1/B_{eq}}{(\tau D + 1)D} M_L$$

which can be written as

$$\theta_C = \left[\frac{K}{\tau D^2 + D + K}\right]\theta_R - \left[\frac{1/B_{eq}}{\tau D^2 + D + K}\right] M_L$$

or

$$\theta_C = \left[\frac{1}{(\tau/K)D^2 + (1/K)D + 1}\right]\theta_R - \left[\frac{1/B_{eq}K}{(\tau/K)D^2 + (1/K)D + 1}\right] M_L \quad (8.70)$$

Equation (8.70) is the final differential equation relating the output θ_C to the inputs θ_R and M_L. The system performance may be studied by assuming only one input acts at a time. Thus we may write two separate differential equations as follows:

$$\left(\frac{\tau}{K} D^2 + \frac{1}{K} D + 1\right)\theta_C = \theta_R \quad (8.71)$$

and

$$\left(\frac{\tau}{K} D^2 + \frac{1}{K} D + 1\right)\theta_C = \frac{1}{KB_{eq}} \cdot M_L \quad (8.72)$$

Equations 8.71 and 8.72 may be written in more familiar form if we note that

$$\omega_n^2 = \frac{K}{\tau} \quad \text{and} \quad \zeta = \frac{\sqrt{K/\tau}}{2K} = \frac{1}{2\sqrt{K\tau}}$$

The main parameter susceptible to variation in this system is the gain K. It may be varied easily by means of amplifier gain A. We see then that the natural frequency is proportional to $\sqrt{K}$ and ζ is proportional to $\sqrt{1/K}$. The final value of θ_C for a steady load torque M_{LS} is seen from Eq. 8.72 to be $\theta_{CS} = M_{LS}/KB_{eq}$ and therefore proportional to $1/K$. These facts and the dynamic performance due to step and sinusoidal inputs enable us to reach design decisions for such a simple servo.

For no load and a step change in input θ_R, the output θ_C would appear as in 8.H for various values of K.

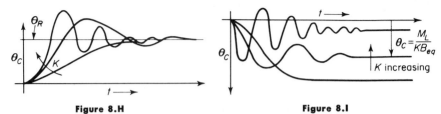

Figure 8.H   Figure 8.I

For a step change in load (from zero to M_{LS}), θ_C would appear as in 8.I.

One may conclude from Figs. 8.H and 8.I that the speed of response of the system and its accuracy under load conditions can be increased by increasing K but that the system becomes more oscillatory. A compromise must be reached. Sometimes a criterion of 20% overshoot is used.

Design decisions can also be made on the basis of frequency response. The frequency response function amplitude can be plotted for various K as in Fig. 8.J.

We see that the useful frequency range increases with increasing K but that the amplification near resonance increases. Sometimes a maximum amplitude ratio of 1.3 is used in design. The phase performance is also improved with increasing K (see Fig. 8.K).

A final design consideration is indicated when one solves for the differential equation in terms of error, $(\theta_R - \theta_C) = E$ rather than θ_C.

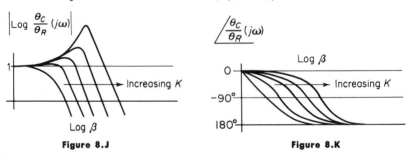

Figure 8.J   Figure 8.K

$$E = \theta_R - \left[\frac{1}{(\tau/K)D^2 + (1/K)D + 1}\right]\theta_R + \left[\frac{1/KB_{eq}}{(\tau/K)D^2 + (1/K)D + 1}\right]M_L$$

$$\left[\frac{\tau}{K}D^2 + \frac{1}{K}D + 1\right]E = \left[\frac{\tau}{K}D^2 + \frac{1}{K}D\right]\theta_R + \frac{M_L}{KB_{eq}} \qquad (8.73)$$

$$\text{i.e., } E = \frac{[(\tau/K)D^2 + (1/K)D]\theta_R + M_L/KB_{eq}}{[(\tau/K)D^2 + (1/K)D + 1]}$$

Let us consider two possible *constant* inputs:

(a) $M_L = M_{LS}$ Constant load torque
(b) $D\theta_R = \dot{\theta}_{RS}$ Constant input velocity

The solution of Eq. 8.73 is the same for each of the assumed constant inputs. We may conclude that in each case there will be a steady state error E_S given by the following:

(1) Steady torque M_{LS}, $E_S = M_{LS}/KB_{\text{eq}}$
(2) Constant velocity input, $E_S = \dot{\theta}_{RS}/K$

The reduction of these steady state errors is a design objective of optimum servo systems. In each case increasing gain K helps but with consequent more oscillatory dynamic response or reduction of stability. The point may also be made that such servomechanisms cannot operate without *load* and *velocity* errors, hence the design of control systems is a compromise between accuracy and stability.

8.12 Frequency Response and Nonsinusoidal Periodic Inputs

The utility of the frequency response function for quickly determining the output of a system whose input is a sinusoid has been demonstrated by the previous examples. In this way we can obtain the solution to a differential equation without solving it directly. The charts for first and second order systems can be used by factoring the frequency response function for a given system into first and second order factors. These charts can be combined on a log AR and phase angle Φ versus log frequency plot. We may then say that the frequency response function characterizes the system steady state response to a sinusoidal input.

We have seen how the impulse reponse of a linear system can be used to determine the system response to any input using the convolution integral as demonstrated in Chap. 7. In general it is best suited to characterize the response of a system to a nonperiodic input.

The convolution technique used the idea that in a linear system the sum of outputs to a series of input pulses acting separately is the same as the output of the sum of a series of input pulses acting together. An analogous concept for frequency responses rests on the same fundamental property of a linear system.

The frequency response function assumes the same role as the

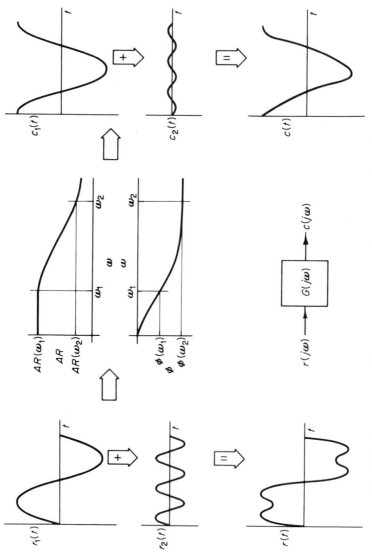

Fig. 8.25. Superposition of frequency components of nonsinusoidal periodic input-output.

impulse response in determining the response of a system to periodic inputs. This can be demonstrated as follows.

Referring to Fig. 8.25, consider a system characterized by a linear-constant-coefficient-differential equation with a corresponding frequency response function plotted as shown. Let the input to the system be represented by the sum of two sinusoids where ω_2 is $n\omega_1$ with n an integer, thus $r(t) = R_1 \sin \omega_1 t + R_2 (\sin \omega_2 t + \theta_2)$. What works here for two sinusoids will work for any number. n does not really need to be an integer but we are led more directly to the Fourier series concept (which is the point of all this) if we make this assumption here.

Since we have restricted ourselves to linear systems, superposition holds and we can consider the combined output being composed of the sum of the individual outputs due to each of the input sinusoids. Thus there is a contribution to the output due to the input $r_1(t)$.

$$r_1(t) = R_1 \sin \omega_1 t$$

The frequency response function tells us that a sinusoid at frequency ω_1 will cause the system output to be sinusoidal at frequency ω_1 with an amplitude of $R_1 AR(\omega_1) = R_1 \,|\, G(j\omega_1)\,|$ and a phase angle of $\Phi(\omega_1) = \angle\, G(j\omega_1)$. That is,

$$c_1(t) = R_1 \; AR(\omega_1) \sin \left[\omega_1 t + \Phi(\omega_1) \right]$$

There is also a contribution to the output due to an input sinusoid of frequency ω_2,

$$r_2(t) = R_2 \sin (\omega_2 t + \theta_2)$$

The frequency response function tells us that the output of the system $c_2(t)$ due to this input will be a sinusoid of frequency ω_2 and amplitude

$$R_2 \,|\, G(j\omega_2)\,| = R_2 AR(\omega_2)$$

with a phase angle of $\Phi(\omega_2) = \angle\, G(j\omega_2)$ relative to the input, thus:

$$c_2(t) = R_2 AR(\omega_2) \sin \left[\omega_2 t + \theta_2 + \Phi(\omega_2) \right]$$

Then superposition tells us that

$$c(t) = c_1(t) + c_2(t)$$

thus

$$c(t) = R_1 AR(\omega_1) \sin \left[\omega_1 t + \Phi(\omega_1) \right] + R_2 AR(\omega_2) \sin[\omega_2 t + \theta_2 + \Phi(\omega_2)]$$

Knowing the frequency response function $G(j\omega)$, we are able to obtain $AR(\omega_1)$, $\Phi(\omega_1)$, $AR(\omega_2)$, and $\Phi(\omega_2)$ so that $c(t)$ can be determined from the input, knowing R_1, R_2, θ_2, ω_1, and ω_2 which describe the nonsinusoidal input.

In general we can perform this process whenever the system input can be decomposed into a sum of sinusoids. This will lead to more general approaches which you will encounter in later courses. The general method which allows the frequency response function to characterize the system response to *any* periodic input is called the Fourier series method.

8.13 Summary

We have shown for systems characterized by linear-constant-coefficient-differential equations that the steady state response to a sinusoid can be used to describe the response to any periodic input. The frequency response function can be obtained directly from the D function which allows us quickly to write the solution. It can also be obtained from a factored form of the overall frequency response function using charts and graphical methods. Consequently, the frequency response function represents a quick and general solution to a differential equation for all periodic inputs.

In this text our goal has been to introduce the student to the process of using mathematics to describe the behavior of physical systems. This procedure, known as mathematical modeling, provides the student with very powerful methods of predicting and analyzing engineering systems. The methods presented are very basic and the strategy used can be applied to all types of physical situations.

We have also introduced the student to the solution of differential equations. These solution methods, and indeed all solution methods, involve converting an equation in unknown functions to one in unknown constants which can then be solved using simple algebra.

The solution methods we have developed have been applied to a fairly restricted set of inputs. Steps, ramps, impulses, and sinusoidal inputs have been considered to introduce solution methods. However, the mechanism for obtaining outputs for more general inputs is also presented in the convolution integral and the Fourier series method. More powerful solution methods can be introduced in later courses once the student understands the approaches which we have described. The equivalence of the D function, frequency response function, and the impulse response for linear systems will also become more evident later.

Problems

8-1. Determine the expression for $e_2(t)$
if $e_1 = \cos 2\pi ft$. Plot amplitude
and phase for e_2 versus ω. Calculate values at $\omega = 2\pi f = 10^2$, 10^3,
10^4. Write the frequency response
function $G(j\omega)$ and plot its locus
in the complex plane.

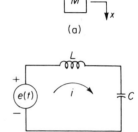

Figure P. 8.1

8-2. Plot the frequency response function
amplitude ratio (db versus $\log \omega$) and
phase angle versus $\log \omega$ for the following transfer functions:
(a) $10/D$
(b) $1/(10D + 1)$

8-3. (a) For input motion $y(t) = Y_a \sin \omega_f t$,
solve for x_{ss} of the system in Fig. P.
8.3(a).
(b) For input voltage $e(t) = E_a \sin \omega_t t$,
solve for i_{ss} of the system in Fig. P.
8.3(b).

8-4. Given the first order lead element represented in Fig. P. 8.4.
(a) Write the differential equation relating x and y.
(b) Write algebraically and sketch $y(t)$
for $x = tu(t)$.

Figure P. 8.3

(c) Derive the frequency response function and draw frequency and
phase plots of $G(j\omega)$.

Figure P. 8.4   **Figure P. 8.5**

8-5. In the circuit shown in Fig. P. 8.5, R is variable and $e_1 = E_1 \cos \omega t$.
(a) Find R for critical damping.
(b) Find ω_n of the circuit.
(c) Sketch the frequency response of e_2/e_1 for $R = 1000\Omega$.
(d) What is the maximum value for $|e_2/e_1|$ when $R = 1000\Omega$? At what
frequency does this occur? At what phase angle?
(e) Write the expression for e_2 if $e_1 = 10 \cos (377t + 30°)$ and $R =
3000\Omega$.

8-6. Find $i_1(t)$, in the steady-state, for $e(t) = E \cos \omega_f t$ in Fig. P. 8.6.

8-7. Find $v(t)$ for $e(t) = E \sin \omega_f t$ for the system in Fig. P. 8.7.

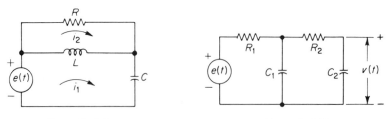

Figure P. 8.6   Figure P. 8.7

8-8. Figure P. 8.8 shows the top view of a phonograph arm. The needle (stylus) may be considered as a spring, one end of which is moved by the record groove and the other end follows the tone arm movement. What is the shape of the curve of $|x/x_f|$ (i.e., amplitude ratio) versus f, and what is the resonant frequency in cps for the arm in vertical oscillation?

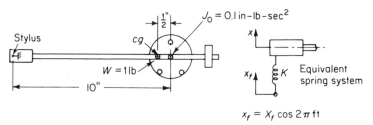

$$x_f = X_f \cos 2\pi f t$$

Figure P. 8.8

8-9. Given a conventional commercial three mode series type proportional-integral-derivative controller with the transfer function as shown in Fig. P. 8.9. Assume that $K = 1$, $T_1 = 10$ sec, and $T_2 = 1$ sec.
(a) Sketch $y(t)$ given that $x(t) =$ unit step function $u(t)$ with $y(t)$ initially at rest in a zero value state.
(b) Sketch magnitude plots of the frequency response function. Show pertinent slopes, intercepts, asymptotes, etc.

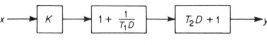

Figure P. 8.9

8-10. Given: $(D + 2)(D^2 + D + 1)x = (D + \frac{1}{2})y$, for $y = \cos \omega t$.
(a) Plot db and phase angle as a function of ω.
(b) For $\omega = 1$ rad/sec, what is x_{ss}?

8-11. Plot the roots of the characteristic equation of the system for Prob. 8-10. Write algebraically and draw a typical step transient response.

8-12. Given the differential equation

$$f(t) + \frac{1}{3}\frac{df(t)}{dt} = \frac{d^2x(t)}{dt^2} + \frac{\sqrt{3}}{3}\frac{dx(t)}{dt} + 8x(t)$$

If $f(t) = \sin 3t$, use frequency response methods to calculate $x_{ss}(t)$.

8-13. An amplifier of unity gain ($e_3 = e_2$) is used to drive the motor as shown in Fig. P. 8.13. A filter of $R = 100K$ ohms and $C = 5 \mu f$ is placed between an input voltage e_1 and the amplifier input e_2. Assuming the torque supplied by the motor is $T = K_T e_3$, plot the amplitude and phase characteristics of θ for $e_1 = 10 \cos \omega t$ volts.

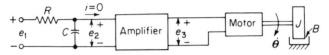

Figure P. 8.13

8-14. A hydraulic valve manufacturer sent some frequency response data for one of their valves. From the approximate response shown.
(a) Find the transfer function for the valve.
(b) Put the roots of the characteristic equation in the complex plane and sketch the possible transient response from the root locations. If more than one solution is possible, include all solutions.

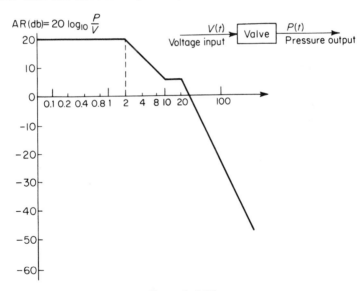

Figure P. 8.14

Appendix

Complex Numbers
for Engineers

A.1 Introduction

It was shown in Chap. 7, Sec. 7.5 that sinusoidally varying quantities could be represented as projections on a line in the plane of rotation of a line segment rotating at constant angular frequency. The geometric problem is to locate the rotating end in a plane. If we choose an axis of coordinates to coincide with the axis of rotation, we see that the other end of the line may be located at any time by its Cartesian coordinates. We know that all real numbers ranging from $-\infty$ to $+\infty$ can be represented by points on a single line running from $-\infty$ to $+\infty$. Such a line is taken for the horizontal axis of coordinates and is called the *real* axis (along which real numbers will be measured). The word *imaginary* is assigned to all numbers lying on the perpendicular axis which is called, therefore, an *imaginary* axis or axis of imaginary numbers. Figure A.1 shows a line segment of length C lying in the plane which may be termed the *plane of complex numbers* or the *complex plane*. We shall adopt the notation **C** to represent the line segment itself and the symbol C, which is not in boldface type, to designate its magnitude alone.

The complex number **C** is seen to be the simple vector sum of the horizontal component a and the vertical component b. These com-

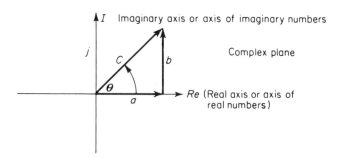

Fig. A.1.   Representation of a complex number, **C**.

ponents, *a* and *b*, which are basically Cartesian coordinates are also numbers in the number system.

Using these notations, a series of equations may be immediately written from Fig. A.1. These follow in Eqs. A.1–A.6. Equation A.6. is a defining equation in which the complex number is represented by its magnitude and angle and may be read as "a magnitude C at an angle θ." Note the symbols Re and $\mathscr{I}$ which when placed in front of a complex number mean "real part of" and "imaginary part of."

$$\mathbf{C} = a + jb \tag{A.1}$$

$$|\mathbf{C}| = C$$

$$a = C \cos \theta = \operatorname{Re} \mathbf{C} \qquad \text{means "real part of } \mathbf{C}\text{"} \tag{A.2}$$

$$b = C \sin \theta = \mathscr{I}\mathbf{C} \qquad \text{means "imaginary part of } \mathbf{C}\text{"} \tag{A.3}$$

$$C = \sqrt{a^2 + b^2} \tag{A.4}$$

$$\theta = \tan^{-1} \frac{b}{a} \tag{A.5}$$

$$\mathbf{C} = C \angle \theta \qquad \text{means "magnitude } C \text{ at angle } \theta\text{"} \tag{A.6}$$

A.2 Addition of Complex Numbers

Complex numbers are added following the simple rules of vector addition. The sum of two complex numbers can be found by graphical *parallelogram* addition as in Fig. A.2(a) or by adding components (real and imaginary parts) as in Fig. A.2(b).

From Fig. A.2(b) we obtain Eq. A.7:

$$\mathbf{C}_3 = \mathbf{C}_1 + \mathbf{C}_2 = (a_1 + a_2) + j(b_1 + b_2) = a_3 + jb_3 \tag{A.7}$$

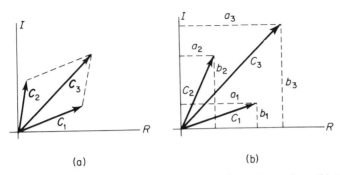

Fig. A.2. (a) Graphical addition of complex numbers. (b) Algebraic addition of complex numbers.

A.3 Multiplication of Complex Numbers

We shall state a rule for multiplication and check its validity later. *The product of two complex numbers is a third complex number whose magnitude is the product of the magnitudes of the two complex numbers being multiplied and its phase angle is the sum of the angles of the two numbers being multiplied.* Thus the product of the two complex numbers shown in Fig. A.3 may be written as in Eq. A.8

$$\mathbf{C_3} = (\mathbf{C_1})(\mathbf{C_2}) = C_1 C_2 \angle(\theta_1 + \theta_2) = C_3\theta_3 \tag{A.8}$$

An interesting consequence arises from the rule just stated for the multiplication of complex numbers. Consider the real number, 1. The square root of 1 is of course ± 1. Figure A.4 shows the complex number representation of this statement. Note that -1 may be thought of as a complex number of magnitude unity lying at $180°$ and $+1$ may be thought of as a complex number of magnitude unity at $0°$ or

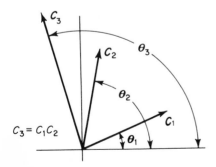

Fig. A.3. Multiplication of complex numbers.

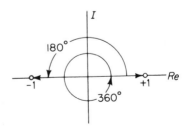

Fig. A.4. Complex representation of $+1$ and -1.

360°. The square root of 1 may be interpreted from Fig. A.4 as in Eq. A.9

$$\sqrt{1} = \pm 1 \qquad 1 = (-1)^2 = (1 \angle 180°)(1 \angle 180°) = 1 \angle 360°$$

$$1 = (+1)^2 = (1 \angle 0°)(1 \angle 0°) = 1 \angle 0° \qquad (A.9)$$

This seems a long way around to represent something which is well-known. However, one may carry this point of view to consider the square root of -1 or even higher roots of -1 with profit. It is difficult to conceive the significance of a square root of -1 in ordinary algebra of real numbers, but a meaningful representation for the square root of -1 becomes possible using complex numbers. Figure A.5 and Eq. A.10 illustrate this fact and show how the symbol j, which now may be defined as a unit length imaginary number, represents the square root of -1.

$$(1 \angle 90°)(1 \angle 90°) = 1 \angle 180° = -1 = (j1)(j1) = j^2$$

or

$$\sqrt{-1} = j$$

also

$$(1 \angle 270°)(1 \angle 270°) = 1 \angle 540° = 1 \angle 180° = -1 = (-j1)(-j1) = (-j)^2$$

or

$$\sqrt{-1} = -j \qquad (A.10)$$

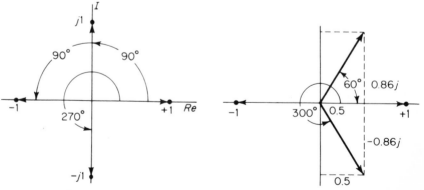

Fig. A.5.   The square roots of -1.   **Fig. A.6.**   The cube roots of -1.

The foregoing type of reasoning allows us to represent the higher roots of -1 as, for example, Fig. A.6 and Eq. A.11 show the cube roots of -1.

$$(1 \angle 60)(1 \angle 60)(1 \angle 60) = 1 \angle 180 = -1 = (0.5 + 0.86j)^3$$

or

$$\sqrt[3]{-1} = 0.5 + 0.86j$$

$$(1 \angle 300)(1 \angle 300)(1 \angle 300) = 1 \angle 900 = 1 \angle 900 - 720 = 1 \angle 180$$

$$= -1 = (0.5 - 0.86j)^3$$

or

$$\sqrt[3]{-1} = 0.5 - 0.86j \qquad (A.11)$$

The purpose of the foregoing is to make the student reasonably comfortable with the idea that j is equivalent to the square root of -1. Using this idea, the ordinary rules of algebra for the product of two binomials and the fact that $j^2 = -1$ permits ready algebraic multiplication of complex numbers. Thus the product of the two complex numbers shown in Fig. A.2(b) would appear as in Eq. A.12.

$$(C_1)(C_2) = (a_1 + jb_1)(a_2 + jb_2) = a_1a_2 + j(a_1b_2 + a_2b_1) + j^2b_1b_2$$

$$= (a_1a_2 - b_1b_2) + j(a_1b_2 + a_2b_1) \qquad (A.12)$$

Equation A.12 may now be used to check the so-called polar form of multiplication originally stated at the beginning of this section. If we note that the real and imaginary parts of the new complex numbers shown in Fig. A.2 may be represented as follows,

$$C_1 = a_1 + jb_1 = C_1 \angle \theta_1 \qquad a_1 = C_1 \cos \theta_1 \qquad b_1 = C_1 \sin \theta_1$$

$$C_2 = a_2 + jb_2 = C_2 \angle \theta_2 \qquad a_2 = C_2 \cos \theta_2 \qquad b_2 = C_2 \sin \theta_2$$

we may substitute these terms into Eq. A.12 to show that trigonometric identities are fulfilled and that multiplication of complex numbers can be accomplished through simple addition of their angles and multiplication of their magnitudes. This is shown in Eq. A.13.

$$C_3 = (C_1)(C_2) = C_1C_2(\cos \theta_1 \cos \theta_2 - \sin \theta_1 \sin \theta_2) + jC_1C_2$$

$$\times (\cos \theta_1 \sin \theta_2 + \cos \theta_2 \sin \theta_1)$$

$$C_3 = C_1 C_2 \left[\cos (\theta_1 + \theta_2) + j \sin (\theta_1 + \theta_2) \right] = C_1 C_2 (a_3 + j b_3)$$
$$= C_1 C_2 \angle (\theta_1 + \theta_2) \tag{A.13}$$

Note that multiplication by j or 1 at $90°$ is equivalent to a counterclockwise rotation of $90°$.

A.4 Division of Complex Numbers

Division of complex numbers is the inverse of multiplication wherein the quotient of two complex numbers is found by dividing the magnitudes and subtracting their angles. This must necessarily follow from the rules of multiplication of complex numbers.

Division by j is therefore equivalent to a clockwise rotation of $90°$. Note also that $1/j$ is equal to $-j$.

When dividing two complex numbers in algebraic form, it is often convenient to remove all imaginary representation from the denominator of an expression. This can easily be done by multiplying both the numerator and denominator by an appropriate complex number which will produce only real numbers in the denominator. A complex number which is appropriate is the same in all respects to the denominator complex number except that the imaginary part will have the opposite algebraic sign. Such numbers are called *complex conjugates* of each other. More will be said of these later. The rationalizing of a complex ratio is illustrated in Eq. A.14.

$$\frac{C_2}{C_1} = \frac{a_2 + j b_2}{a_1 + j b_1} = \frac{(a_2 + j b_2)(a_1 - j b_1)}{(a_1 + j b_1)(a_1 - j b_1)} = \frac{(a_1 a_2 + b_1 b_2) + j(a_1 b_2 - b_1 a_2)}{(a_1)^2 + (b_1)^2} \tag{A.14}$$

A.5 Complex Conjugates

The special complex number called the *complex conjugate*, which may be visualized as the "mirror image" (mirror placed on real axis) of a complex number, is of special importance. The complex conjugate is denoted by an asterisk and is defined as in Eq. A.15.

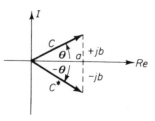

$$C = a + jb \qquad C^* = a - jb \tag{A.15}$$

This is pictured in Fig. A.7.

The complex number and its conjugate

Fig. A.7. A complex number, **C**, and its conjugate **C***.

are seen to have the same real part but their imaginary parts have opposite signs.

An important consequence of the definition of the conjugate is that the sum or product of conjugates is always a real number. We shall see that one way of representing a time varying function which is at all times real is in terms of the sum of a pair of conjugates. This will enable us to deal with real numbers using expressions which exist in the complex plane.

A.6 Exponential Representation of Complex Numbers

The student may already have observed that the rules for multiplication of complex numbers are similar to those for the multiplication of exponentials. This is no coincidence and the consideration of the possibilities of expressing the complex number in exponential form leads to the very powerful representation due to Euler. Consider the power series expansion of the complex number when written in sine and cosine terms as follows.

$$\mathbf{C} = a + jb = \mathbf{C}\,(\cos\theta + j\sin\theta)$$

$$\cos\theta = 1 - \frac{\theta^2}{2!} + \frac{\theta^4}{4!} - \frac{\theta^6}{6!} + \cdots$$

$$j\sin\theta = j\theta - j\frac{\theta^3}{3!} + j\frac{\theta^5}{5!} - j\frac{\theta^7}{7!} + \cdots$$

$$\cos\theta + j\sin\theta = 1 + j\theta - \frac{\theta^2}{2!} - j\frac{\theta^3}{3!} + \frac{\theta^4}{4!} + j\frac{\theta^5}{5!} - \frac{\theta^6}{6!} - j\frac{\theta^7}{7!} + \cdots$$

$$\text{(A.16)}$$

However,

$$e^{j\theta} = 1 + j\theta + \frac{(j\theta)^2}{2!} + \frac{(j\theta)^3}{3!} + \frac{(j\theta)^4}{4!} + \frac{(j\theta)^5}{5!} + \frac{(j\theta)^6}{6!} + \frac{(j\theta)^7}{7!} + \cdots$$

$$\text{(A.17)}$$

Equation A.16 is the power series for a unit complex number at an angle θ. Consider the power series expansion of an exponential $e^{j\theta}$ as shown in Eq. A.17. At first glance it does not seem identical to Eq. A.16 but if the j's are raised to appropriate powers, it will be seen that Eqs. A.16 and A.17 are identities. This identity may be expressed as in Eq. A.18 and is one form of Euler's equation.

$$e^{j\theta} = \cos\theta + j\sin\theta \qquad\qquad \text{(A.18)}$$

The foregoing provides a functional notation for dealing with complex numbers in polar form. The ordinary rules for algebraic manipulation of exponentials may be applied to this notation. Thus we can deal with complex numbers either in rectangular form or in polar form. Some of the resulting identities are listed below in Eqs. A.19, A.20, and A.21.

$$\mathbf{C} = a + jb = C\angle\theta = Ce^{j\theta} \tag{A.19}$$

$$(\mathbf{C}_1)(\mathbf{C}_2) = C_1 e^{j\theta_1} C_2 e^{j\theta_2} = C_1 C_2 e^{j(\theta_1 + \theta_2)} \tag{A.20}$$

$$\frac{\mathbf{C}_2}{\mathbf{C}_1} = \frac{C_2 e^{j\theta_2}}{C_1 e^{j\theta_1}} = \frac{C_2}{C_1} e^{j(\theta_2 - \theta_1)} \tag{A.21}$$

Alternate forms of the equations of Euler may be derived through considering a pair of complex conjugates in exponential form. Figure A.8 shows two such complex conjugates.

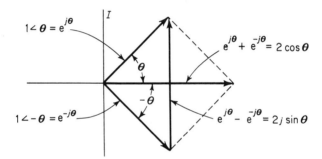

Fig. A.8. Sum and difference of complex conjugates in exponential form.

Equations A.22 and A.23 may be written from inspection of Fig. A.8.

$$\sin\theta = \frac{e^{j\theta} - e^{-j\theta}}{2j} \tag{A.22}$$

$$\cos\theta = \frac{e^{j\theta} + e^{-j\theta}}{2} \tag{A.23}$$

A.7 Representation of Sinusoids

The foregoing notations prepare us to represent sinusoidal variations in a number of different ways. Consider the time varying quantity given in Eq. A.24.

$$x = A\cos\omega t \tag{A.24}$$

It may be thought of as a projection of the real axis of a complex number as in Fig. A.9.

If a phase angle is present, the representation is only a little more complicated as shown in Fig. A.10.

The cosine function may be written in our new notations in a number of ways as follows:

$$x = \mathrm{Re}\ \mathbf{A} = \mathrm{Re}\ A e^{j(\omega t - \phi)} = \mathrm{Re}(a + jb) = A \cos(\omega t - \phi) \qquad \text{(A.25)}$$

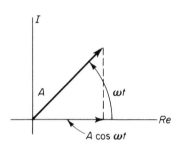

Fig. A.9. Representation of $x = A \cos \omega t$.

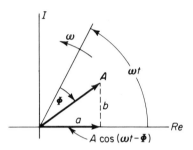

Fig A.10. Representation of $x = A \cos (\omega t - \phi)$ as Re **A**.

Equation A.25 may be read as "$x =$ the real part of (whatever complex representation is used)." It is also possible to use a projection on the imaginary axis.

The use of Re, "real part of," notation may be avoided through the use of complex conjugates. This is illustrated in Fig. A.11. The sum of the two complex conjugates may then be seen to be the real number which represents the time function desired. This is shown in Eq. A.26.

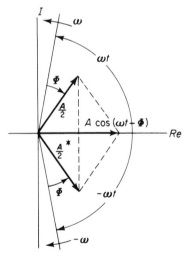

Fig. A.11. Representation of $x = A \cos (\omega t - \phi)$ as $\dfrac{A}{2} + \dfrac{A^*}{2}$.

$$\frac{A}{2} + \frac{A^*}{2} = \frac{A}{2}\, e^{j(\omega t - \phi)} + \frac{A}{2}\, e^{-j(\omega t - \phi)}$$

$$= A \cos(\omega t - \phi) = x \qquad \text{(A.26)}$$

A further check on Eq. A.26 is obtained by adding versions of Euler's equation, Eq. A.18, as follows:

$$\frac{A^*}{2} = \frac{A}{2}\, e^{-j(\omega t - \phi)} = \frac{A}{2}\,[\cos(\omega t - \phi) - j\sin(\omega t - \phi)]$$

$$\frac{A}{2} + \frac{A^*}{2} = A\cos(\omega t - \phi) = x \tag{A.27}$$

From this specific example we may note the general conclusion that the sum of complex conjugates is a real number which is twice the real part of the complex number, and the difference between complex conjugates is an imaginary number which is twice the imaginary part of the complex number. These are shown in Eqs. A.28 and A.29.

$$A + A^* = 2\operatorname{Re}A = 2\operatorname{Re}A^* \tag{A.28}$$

$$A - A^* = 2\mathscr{I}A = 2\mathscr{I}A^* \tag{A.29}$$

Index